A native of Dundee, Marion studied music with the Open University and worked for many years as a piano teacher and jobbing accompanist. A spell as a hotel lounge pianist provided rich fodder for her writing and she began experimenting with a variety of genres. Early success saw her winning first prize in the *Family Circle* Magazine short story for children national competition and she followed this up by writing short stories and articles for her local newspaper.

Life (and children) intervened and, for a few years, Marion's writing was put on hold. During this time, she worked as a college lecturer, plantswoman and candle-maker. But, as a keen reader of crime fiction, the lure of the genre was strong, and she began writing her debut crime novel. Now a full-time writer, Marion lives in North-east Fife, overlooking the River Tay. She can often be found working out plots for her novels while tussling with her jungle-like garden and walking her daughter's unruly but lovable dog.

Also by Marion Todd

Detective Clare Mackay

MARION TODD

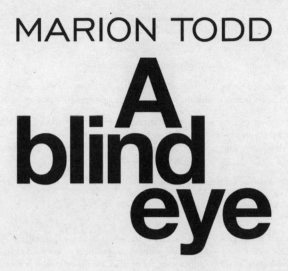

A blind eye

CANELO CRIME

First published in the United Kingdom in 2023 by

Canelo
Unit 9, 5th Floor
Cargo Works, 1-2 Hatfields
London SE1 9PG
United Kingdom

A CIP catalogue record for this book is available from the British Library.

Print ISBN 978 1 80436 213 6
Ebook ISBN 978 1 80436 212 9

Cover design by Black Sheep

Cover images © Black Sheep, Shutterstock

Look for more great books at www.canelo.co

Printed and bound in Great Britain by Clays Ltd, Elcograf S.p.A.

1

For June, my oldest and most wonderful friend

Even though she made me late for school, almost every single day!

Day 1: Tuesday, 4th April

Chapter 1

Detective Inspector Clare Mackay looked round the hall. It was an attractive room, the light oak panelling as far from her own inner-city school as she could imagine. Towards the back of the hall was an impressive honours board next to a bank of framed photos showing the senior teaching team. Immediately beneath the stage a grand piano stood, its black polished wood gleaming in the sun that streamed through the casement windows. *Yes*, she thought. *It's a lovely building.* That, of course, didn't always make for a happy, accepting environment... but it probably helped.

She drew her eyes away from the room and scanned the rows of pupils. They'd been a more attentive audience than at the last school. No fiddling with phones from this lot. Not with the head teacher's beady eye on them. But the air of disinterest was palpable. One or two cast glances at their wrists and she took the hint. They'd been sitting long enough.

'PC Stapleton and I will be here for a bit longer so if any of you are considering a career in the police...' she tailed off and turned to the head teacher who moved forward.

'Room five,' the head teacher said crisply. 'Please allow us to leave first then anyone who wishes to speak to the officers should wait outside the door.' She moved to the steps at the side of the stage, and they followed her down and out of the hall. As they left a murmur of chatter began to build.

'They were very attentive,' Clare said as the head teacher opened the door to a small room, flicking on the light. It was cheerfully decorated with two small sofas arranged either side of a light oak coffee table.

'We do insist on good manners at Melville Academy,' the head said. She turned to Clare and Sara, her hand indicating the room. 'Will this be suitable? We use it to meet with parents.'

'Perfectly.'

The head smiled. 'Lunch is in half an hour. If you think you'll be any longer...'

'Half an hour's fine,' Clare said. 'We can always follow up any interest later. And if you could just leave the door open.'

The head teacher raised an eyebrow at this then swept from the room, her black gown flying in her wake.

'I can't see any of them being interested,' Sara said. 'They'll all be off to university or having gap years at Daddy's expense.'

Clare nodded. 'You're probably right. But it's worth a shot. We need a broad spectrum these days.'

A girl of about sixteen appeared at the door. She raised her hand to knock and let it fall. Then she turned to leave, and Clare moved forward.

'Hello,' she said. 'Please – come in. We could do with seeing a friendly face.' She smiled at the girl who remained in the doorway as if deciding whether or not to enter. She was slightly built, her fine blonde hair scraped back in a tight ponytail. Her face was pallid, the only adornment a tiny pair of gold studs in her ears and Clare wondered if there was a school rule banning make-up. The girl had a ghost-like quality and seemed on the point of flight when Sara held out a hand.

'I'm Sara,' she said. 'Sara Stapleton. One of the officers at St Andrews. Please,' she indicated the low sofas, 'have a seat.'

The girl came slowly into the room and glanced over her shoulder. Sara steered her gently towards the sofas, but the girl's eyes were trained on the door.

'I'll just shut this,' Clare said, closing the door quietly. As she did so she thought she saw another girl step quickly back. 'Is your friend waiting for you?'

The girl edged towards the door. 'Maybe. I should go...'

'Are you interested in joining the police?' Sara said, trying to distract her from looking at the door.

Clare joined Sara on the sofa and gave the girl a smile. 'I'm Clare,' she said. 'I'm the DI at St Andrews. But we don't know your name.'

'Eilidh.' Her voice was little more than a whisper. 'Eilidh Campbell.'

'Nice to meet you, Eilidh. Why not sit for a moment?'

The girl hesitated then sat down, perching on the edge of the other sofa.

Clare smiled. 'If you are interested in the police as a career we can give you some leaflets, tell you a bit about the job. Maybe arrange a visit to the station.'

She shook her head. 'No,' she said. 'It's not that.'

Clare sat forward. 'Is there something worrying you?'

Eilidh looked down, fiddling with the cuff of her navy cardigan. 'I'm not sure.'

Sara opened her mouth to speak but Clare made a slight gesture with her hand and Sara took the hint. Eventually the girl spoke again.

'If I knew something – I mean something that wasn't right, and you found out—'

Clare met her eye. 'Eilidh, have you witnessed a crime?'

She hesitated. 'Not exactly. I just wondered – if I knew something and I didn't tell anyone—'

'Failing to report a crime isn't an offence,' Clare said. 'You wouldn't be charged or anything like that. If you do know something, it's best to tell us. But we'd need an appropriate adult to be with you for your statement.'

The girl rose, avoiding Clare's eye. 'No, it's nothing like that. I don't know anything. I just wondered—' And before Clare could stop her, she'd opened the door and was gone. Clare followed her out, but Eilidh was down the corridor and out of sight in seconds. She turned back to Sara.

'What was that about?'

Sara shrugged. 'Maybe friends doing drugs, bit of shoplifting.'

Clare frowned. 'I'm not sure. Stuff like that doesn't normally bother kids her age; and I think she was worried about being overheard.' There was a tap at the door and a tall red-haired girl appeared.

'Can I take one of your leaflets?' she said. 'My brother – he fancies the police.'

–

They waited another twenty minutes then Clare scooped up their leaflets. 'Come on,' she said to Sara. 'Let's get back to the station.' They made their way to the reception desk and waited while a dark-haired girl in uniform signed herself out. Clare wondered briefly if she'd been the girl hanging around when Eilidh had come into the room, but it was impossible to tell. All she'd seen was a flash of dark hair and, from what she recalled, half the sixth form had dark hair. She thanked the receptionist and they emerged into the sunshine. As they crossed the car park, they saw the girl walk smartly towards a black BMW saloon. There was something in her manner – the way she moved – that made Clare watch her. She was of average height, thick dark hair and supremely confident, as though the world and all its glories had been arranged just for her. A man in dark glasses, his hair closely cropped, sat in the driver's seat, elbow resting on the open window. He was clean shaven, his neck thick, reminding Clare more of a nightclub bouncer than a parent at this expensive school. But you couldn't tell these days. Maybe he threw all his money at his daughter's education. The car looked new, though, and the girl, while in uniform, had the air of money about her. The way her hair hung, thick and well cut, her school bag with its Dr Martens logo, the glimpse of a pink smart watch. Top of the range, she'd bet. Yes, whoever this parent was, he had money all right.

The girl walked round to the passenger door without acknowledging him. His glance strayed in Clare's direction and she had the distinct impression she'd seen him before. As she watched he moved his elbow and the window slid noiselessly up. Seconds later the car drew out of the car park. And then, for no reason she could think of, she took out a notepad and jotted down the registration.

'Boss?'

Clare tucked the pad back in her bag. 'Dunno. Something about the driver. Something familiar.' She searched her memory, but she couldn't place him. 'Never mind. Let's get back. I'm dying for a mug of tea.'

Chapter 2

'Missing person,' Sergeant Jim Douglas said, as Clare and Sara entered the station.

'Details?'

'Solicitor. Harry Richards. Went to work as usual yesterday – didn't come home last night.'

'So, he's been gone, what, twenty-four hours?' Clare considered this. 'It's a bit early to say he's missing. Anything else to suggest he's at risk?'

'Maybe. The wife thinks she was being stalked. And now he's gone she's convinced something's happened to him.'

'Hmm. Had she previously reported the stalking?'

Jim hesitated.

'Jim?'

'Robbie went round to see her. He thought maybe someone was planning a break-in so he gave the usual advice about varying their routine, leaving lights on etc.'

Clare looked at him. 'A woman reports a possible stalker and he tells her to leave the lights on? What was he thinking?'

Jim shrugged. 'I think he was chasing his tail. Too many calls.'

Clare exhaled audibly. 'I'll speak to him. Meantime, the missing man – I presume the wife's tried phoning?'

'Mobile rings out. And he's not been seen at work since yesterday afternoon.'

'Car?'

'Plugged the reg into ANPR but nothing yet.'

Clare stood thinking. 'Did she come here to report it?'

'No. She phoned first thing. Thought I'd give it until this afternoon then send someone round.' Jim sat back in his chair. 'How did it go this morning?'

'At the schools?' Clare sank down beside him and rubbed the back of her neck. 'Oh, I dunno. A few took leaflets but no one seemed that interested.'

'Ah well. They maybe didn't want to seem too keen in front of their friends. They might get in touch over the next few days.'

Clare got to her feet. 'Hope so, otherwise my shiny new youth initiative will fall flat on its face.'

She left Jim to his paperwork and wandered through to the incident room, mulling this over. The initiative had come out of a conversation with the newly appointed superintendent, Penny Meakin. It was well known Penny expected her officers to come up with new ideas and the youth initiative had been Clare's. So far she had nothing to show for it and she knew from experience Penny wouldn't let it go.

Robbie was in a corner of the room, tapping away at a laptop. He looked up as she entered and forced a smile.

'Boss?'

She sank down beside him. 'You dealt with a woman who reported a stalker.'

He nodded but didn't say anything, his eyes full of concern.

'What made you think it wasn't serious?'

He ran a tongue around his lips. 'Erm, it just seemed more like a potential housebreaking. Him hanging about outside and so on.'

'You didn't think a woman concerned about a strange man warranted a bit more attention?' Clare's tone was sharper than she intended.

The colour rose in his cheeks. 'Is something wrong? She's not—'

'No, she's not. But her husband's missing.' Clare rose from her seat. 'We'd just better hope he turns up safe and well; and next time, Robbie, see you take it a damn sight more seriously.'

He nodded and mumbled an apology, not meeting her eye, and she left him to it.

She fetched her lunch from the kitchen fridge and carried it through to her office. As she waited for her computer to come to life she bit into a sandwich, mulling over the missing person report. Was he even missing? Maybe he'd left his wife and hadn't the courage to tell her. Or maybe he'd been on a bender and…

Her office door opened and Detective Sergeant Chris West ambled into the room and drew a chair across to the desk. '*Buenos dias, Inspectora.*'

She stared at him. 'Eh?'

He rolled his eyes. 'We're learning Spanish.'

'You and Sara?'

'Yep. She says it's rude to go to a country and expect everyone to speak English.'

'You've booked the honeymoon, then?'

'We have. Mexico. Two months tomorrow! Can't wait.'

Clare regarded him. 'You do know they speak Portuguese in Mexico?'

The colour drained from Chris's face.

'Just kidding.'

'*Idiota!*'

She laughed. 'I can guess what that means. So,' her inbox began to load and she glanced at it, running her eye down the emails for anything urgent, 'what you up to today?'

'Oh, you know. Paperwork to catch up on.' He leaned back and crossed one leg over the other. 'Anyway, Sara says the school visits weren't a roaring success.'

'Not really. Except—'

'Yeah?'

She sat back in her chair, drumming a pencil on her desk. 'I'm not sure. There was one girl, at the last school – Melville Academy. She seemed a bit ill at ease. I had the feeling someone was waiting for her outside. She kept glancing at the door.'

'So?'

'I dunno, Chris. She asked if failing to report something was a crime.'

'Report what?'

'She wouldn't say. But I think—'

Jim appeared at the door. 'Just had a call about a car at Tentsmuir. Forestry lad found it parked in the trees. Engine cold. The windows are steamed up but he thinks there's someone inside.'

Clare frowned. 'Did he try knocking on the window?'

'Aye. No response. Thing is, the car – it's a blue Peugeot.'

'And?'

'Our missing solicitor drives a blue Peugeot.'

'Got the reg?'

'Checking it now.'

Clare followed Jim out to the front office and waited while Sara stood, phone clamped to her ear. Then Sara reached for a pen and began to write. She handed the paper to Jim who sat down at his keyboard. After a minute he exhaled and handed the paper to Clare. 'It's the solicitor's car, right enough.'

'Ask the forester if he'd be kind enough to stay with the car,' Clare said to Sara. 'Just until someone gets there. But tell him not to touch anything.' She looked around the station. 'Who else is in?'

'Just Gillian and Robbie,' Jim said.

'Okay. The three of you head over there, Sara. Gloves, mask and overshoes in case there is someone inside. Call me when you know.'

'You wanna head over to the wife?' Chris said.

'Let's wait to see if he's actually in the car, first.' She checked the wall clock. 'How long will it take them to get there?'

'About half an hour.'

Clare thought for a moment. 'Once it's confirmed, we'll see the wife. I take it the report's on the system?'

Jim nodded. 'Logged at nine this morning.'

Clare wandered back to her office, Chris in her wake. She shook the mouse and navigated to the missing person report.

'Harry Richards,' she read aloud. 'Aged fifty-two – reported missing this morning by Louise Richards.' She glanced up. 'Wife, I presume?'

Chris shrugged. 'Anything else?'

'Seems there was someone hanging around the house. The wife reported it – last week, I think. Robbie attended.'

'Looking for a chance to break in?'

'That's what he thought.'

'Had she seen him anywhere else?'

Clare sat back and pushed the keyboard away. 'Dunno. We'll call round once we've heard from Sara. See what the wife can tell us.'

Chapter 3

'Car was unlocked,' Sara said.

'And?'

'It's him, all right. Wallet in his jacket pocket. Money and cards still there. He's dead, boss.'

'Suicide?'

'Definitely not.'

'Tell me?'

Sara hesitated.

'Sara?'

'Throat's been cut.'

Clare closed her eyes. The half-eaten sandwich was sitting heavily on her stomach now and she swallowed, trying not to imagine the scene in the car. Chris, sitting opposite munching a Wagon Wheel, raised an eyebrow. Clare opened her mouth to explain then she heard Sara's voice again.

'Boss?'

'Sorry. Just thinking. Erm, you didn't touch anything?'

'Only the wallet – to see if it was him; and I'd gloves and a mask on. The Ranger called the paramedics so they'll be here soon. Want me to get SOCO out?'

'Please. Doesn't sound like we need the ambulance but we'd better play it by the book.' She pushed the rest of her sandwich to the side. 'Come on,' she said to Chris. 'We've a call to pay.'

–

Louise and Harry Richards lived in a detached bungalow in Drumoig village, ten miles north-west of St Andrews. Clare left the main road and reduced her speed as Chris checked the address. A gentle incline took them past a golf practice green, a row of buggies parked neatly to the side.

'You play, don't you?' she said, her eyes straying towards the Starter's Box.

He shrugged. 'Yeah. I'm pretty good.'

'Modest with it.'

'Slow down – it's just here.'

'With the red roof?'

'Yeah, that's it.'

'What's your handicap?'

'Can't remember.'

Clare clicked off her seatbelt. 'Then you're the first golfer I've met who can't. Most of them can't wait to tell you.'

He looked past her, out of the car window, studying the house. 'Not played for a while. Used to play off eighteen but I'm out of practice. Anyway – our solicitor's wife...'

'She phoned this morning. Apparently he went to work yesterday and she's not seen him since.'

'And the stalker?'

Clare climbed out of the car and began walking past the house, Chris following. 'Where does this lead?'

'Dead end.'

'Any through roads in the village?'

He shook his head. 'Nope. The only way in or out is up the road we took.'

'Shops? Businesses?'

'Just the golf club. Oh, there's a hotel too, next to the clubhouse. But it's only houses up this end.'

She took in her surroundings. Each house was a bit different from its neighbour which somehow softened the impact of a development in the middle of the countryside. 'It's so quiet.'

'Yeah,' Chris said. 'Handy for the golf too.'

She began walking back towards the car. 'You fancy a house here? I can just see you in an Argyle sweater and plus fours.'

'Very droll.'

Clare laughed. 'Seems a nice place, though. Think you could live here?'

He inclined his head. 'Sara likes it. We'd need a bigger deposit.'

'Something to aim for, maybe.' She looked towards the house with the red roof. 'Come on. Let's see what she can tell us.'

As they approached the house Clare's phone buzzed with a message. 'Jim called the man's mobile,' she said. 'Apparently it rang out in the car.' She tucked the phone back in her pocket. 'It has to be him.'

'Better get it over with, then.'

The wrought iron driveway gates were closed, secured with a top latch, but a narrower gate to the side stood open, a path beyond leading to the front door of a single storey house. A lawn cut very short wrapped round the side, bordered by mature shrubs. A collection of terracotta pots with rolled rims stood below a front window, the lemon pansies they held nodding in the gentle breeze. Beyond the window, Clare could see a figure standing; and then it was gone. Seconds later the front door was opened by a woman in a green linen dress. She was taller than Clare, her bare legs tanned, whether from the sun or a bottle Clare couldn't tell. Her blonde hair was cut in a layered bob, the highlights glinting in the afternoon light. She nodded as Clare held out her badge and stepped back to admit them, her face lined with worry.

She led them into a sunny room with a kitchen at one end and an archway to a sitting area at the other. Clare took it all in: the gleaming eau-de-nil units, the oak worktops, the cream-coloured Aga, and she decided there was money here. Taste, as well. It was an expensive kitchen but thoughtfully put together.

Louise Richards indicated a small table with four ladderback chairs. She waited until they had sat before speaking. 'Is... is there any news? Of Harry?'

Clare hated this part of the job. No matter how many times she broke bad news, it never got easier. 'We've found your husband's car,' she said, pausing to allow this to sink in.

'His car? Where was it? Was there any sign of him?' The questions came tumbling out and Clare raised her hand slightly, a gesture to tell Louise there was more.

'I'm afraid there's the body of a man in the car.'

Louise looked at them, her eyes searching their faces. 'A man?' she managed, eventually. 'What man... you don't mean Harry?' Her hand went to her mouth and Clare saw the rise and fall of her chest as panic began to seize her. She nodded to Chris and he scraped back his chair.

'I'll just make us some tea,' he said.

'What man?' Louise said again, ignoring Chris.

'A wallet was found in the car,' Clare went on, softening her tone. 'We believe it's your husband's. I'm so sorry, Mrs Richards.'

Louise's eyes flicked left and right, as she processed this. 'But that doesn't mean it's Harry, does it?' Her voice was becoming shrill. 'This man – he could have stolen the car then crashed it. Maybe he mugged Harry and took his wallet as well. Maybe Harry's lying unconscious somewhere.'

Clare let her speak for a minute, the only other sound in the room Chris opening and closing cupboard doors softly as he searched for teabags. Then she met Louise's eye. 'It is possible it's not your husband. But we do think it is him.'

Louise stared at her, as though struggling to find the right words. 'Can you take me to him, please?'

'I will,' Clare said, 'but not for a bit. There's a team at the car – gathering evidence.'

Her brow creased. 'Evidence? What do you mean?'

'Mrs Richards, I'm afraid the man in your husband's car was killed.'

She blinked a couple of times. 'Killed? You mean, someone's done this? It's not an accident?'

Chris had stopped opening cupboard doors now and he caught Clare's eye. He held out a box of Twinings tea bags but there was no sign of a kettle. He inclined his head in a gesture of apology.

Clare rose from her seat. 'I'll put the kettle on.'

Louise regarded her for a moment. 'Oh, it's a steaming tap. Over the small sink.' She pushed back her chair. 'I'll do it. You don't know where anything is.'

Clare sat down again while Louise moved about the kitchen, filling a glass teapot from the steaming tap, and taking mugs from a wall cupboard. Chris hovered, shifting his weight from side to side until she'd loaded a Liberty patterned tray. He carried this over to the table and waited until Louise had sat down before resuming his own seat.

She seemed to be struggling with what to say then she found her voice. 'How did he die?'

Clare caught Chris's eye and he gave a slight nod, indicating he understood. *Minimal details, for now.* 'We don't have a cause of death yet,' she said. 'But we will keep you informed, as things progress.' She lifted the teapot. 'Shall I?'

Louise nodded. 'Please.'

Clare filled three mugs and passed them across the table. Chris helped himself to a chocolate biscuit while Louise sat cradling a mug, her knuckles white.

'When can I see him?' she asked.

'As soon as possible,' Clare said. 'Hopefully tomorrow.' She smiled. 'Let's have the tea while it's hot. And then, if you feel up to it, perhaps we could ask you some questions.'

They sipped their tea in silence, Chris shifting awkwardly on his chair. Clare sensed his discomfort and she smiled round at the room. 'This is lovely. Is it new?'

Louise followed her gaze. 'Oh, the kitchen?' she said. 'Erm, yes. Quite new. Nearly two years now.' She indicated the archway. 'We knocked through. There were French windows, but we thought it would be nice to open it up.'

Clare smiled. 'I agree. It's lovely and light.'

They chatted on about the house for a few moments, Clare's expert eye taking it all in. Through the archway she could see photos of the couple, and she studied these while making a pretence of admiring the room. It was hard to be sure from her seat in the kitchen, but they all looked quite recent: a holiday snap on silver sands – a turquoise sea in the background, Louise looking nervously down from a camel's back, and a wedding portrait that looked no more than four or five years old. Was this a recent marriage? Second time for them both, maybe.

She turned back to Louise. 'Have you been married long?'

Her eyes brimmed. 'Almost five years,' she said. 'Five years next month.'

'Children?'

She shook her head. 'We married late. We're both divorced, you see.'

'No children from previous marriages?'

'Harry has a daughter. Melanie. She's in New Zealand. Oh God.' Her hand went to her mouth. 'I'll have to call her.' She looked at Clare, pain etched on her face. 'If it is Harry. I'll have to tell her.' She started to sob and Clare touched her lightly on the shoulder. 'We can do that,' she said. 'If it is your husband.'

Louise's head dropped and she began twisting her wedding ring between thumb and forefinger.

'If you give us Melanie's number now,' Clare said, 'it'll save doing it later.' Louise rose, woodenly, and went to retrieve her phone from the kitchen island. She tapped at the screen and held it out for Clare to copy the number.

'Was Mr Richards in touch with his first wife?' Clare said.

She seemed surprised by the question. 'Rosie? I don't think so.'

'You don't happen to know where she lives now?'

'Dundee, somewhere I think.' She narrowed her eyes at this. 'She married again. She's Rosie King now. I saw it in the paper. Big flashy wedding at some country club.'

Clare reached into her bag for a notepad and scribbled this down. 'Can you remember when?'

'Bizarrely it was two years to the day after we married.'

'So almost three years ago?'

'Yes.'

Louise was calmer now and Clare decided to press on. 'Would you feel up to a few more questions?'

She nodded and Clare smiled.

'How had Mr Richards been?' she asked, keeping her tone light. 'Recently, I mean?'

Louise was silent as if recalling. 'He'd been working a lot. Late nights, you know? I said we needed a holiday and he agreed. In fact he went out and booked one.' She reached into her pocket and took out a paper hankie, dabbing gently at the corners of her eyes. 'We were going at the end of the week. He wouldn't tell me where. It was to be a surprise.'

Clare wondered about that. Was there any connection between a hastily arranged holiday and a gruesome murder? She jotted *holiday* down on her notepad and went on.

'When did you last see Mr Richards?'

'Yesterday morning. We had breakfast together then he left for work.'

'What time was this?'

'About eight. That's when he usually went.'

'And you were expecting him home?'

She nodded again. 'He was normally home about six. When it got to half past seven I tried his mobile but there was no answer.' She shook her head. 'I tried all evening. Must have called hundreds of times. Eventually I went to bed but I left a light on in the hall.' She stopped to take a drink of tea. 'I couldn't believe it when he wasn't there in the morning. So I called the office and spoke to Kate, his receptionist, you know?'

'Was she able to help at all?'

'Not really. She said Harry had gone out to see a client. Mid-afternoon. But he hadn't come back.'

'And was she expecting him this morning?'

Louise's face was lined with worry. 'Yes. She said she'd have to cancel his appointments if he didn't show up.'

'Did she say anything else?'

'No. She just asked me to phone if I heard from Harry.'

'That's fine, Louise. We'll speak to her as well.' Clare hesitated. 'I believe you were worried someone might be stalking you.'

Louise blanched. 'I'd seen him a few times.'

'It was a man?'

'Yes.'

'Where was this?'

She indicated the front of the house. 'Out there, a couple of times. Just standing across the road.'

'What was he doing?'

'Looking at the house. I think maybe one time he was smoking a cigarette. But this other time he was just standing there. Just looking. So I went right up to the window and put my phone to my ear, thinking that would make him move on. But he stood his ground, looking right at me.' She shivered involuntarily and clasped her arms across her chest.

'Do you have CCTV?' Clare asked. 'On the house, I mean?'

Louise shook her head. 'No. I wish I had, now.'

Clare glanced towards the window. 'You saw him outside, what, twice?'

'As far as I know. There could have been other times. When I wasn't looking.'

'Can you recall the dates?'

She sat back, thinking. 'Last Wednesday,' she said, eventually. 'I'm not sure about the other time but definitely Wednesday. I was waiting for a delivery. A rug for the bedroom. I kept going to the window to look for the van and that's when I saw him.'

'Time?'

'About half past two. The delivery was due between two and three, you see.'

Clare smiled. 'That's really helpful, Louise. Thank you. Where did you buy the rug?'

'Matthews Interiors, in St Andrews.'

Clare knew the shop. She'd often stopped to admire their window display, if not the prices. 'Was it their own van or a delivery company?'

'Oh, their own,' Louise said. 'They always do their own deliveries. Such a lovely company to deal with.'

Clare noted this down. 'And was it only here, at the house, you saw him?'

'No! I saw him in St Andrews as well.'

'Where was this?'

'South Street. I'd been to the cheese shop and was heading back to the car. I'd parked on Argyle Street and I was almost at the West Port when I saw him. He came out of nowhere.'

'You're sure it was the same man?'

She nodded vigorously. 'Oh yes. Gave me such a fright, seeing him there.'

'What was he doing?'

'Leaning against the wall – outside one of the shops.'

'Did he see you?'

'Definitely. He made sure I saw him. And that's when I knew he was stalking me.'

'Did he follow you back to the car?'

'I didn't wait to see,' she said. 'I ran through the archway and across the road.' She shivered, as if recalling it. 'It's a busy road but I was so scared, you know? A car tooted at me but I just wanted to get away.' She lifted her mug and drank from it, spilling a little as she set it back down. 'When I got to the car I jumped in and locked the doors. Then I drove away as fast as I could.'

'Did you see him as you drove off?'

She shook her head. 'I went in the opposite direction. I mean I checked my mirror but I didn't see him.'

'Can you describe him?'

20

She thought for a moment. 'Pretty nondescript. A bit rough, if you know what I mean.'

'In what way?'

'His expression. Unsmiling. And the way he stood, as if he was afraid of nothing and no one.'

'What about his clothes?'

'Dark. Well, dark trousers anyway. I think his jacket was a kind of green – khaki.'

'Hood?'

'Yes. Like a parka.'

'Anything on his head?'

'Baseball cap.' Her brow furrowed as if trying to recall. 'Grey – or black, maybe. Sorry – I can't remember.'

'Any logo?'

'I really didn't notice.'

'Could you see his hair at all?'

'No. Not under the cap.'

'Any facial hair?'

Louise's brow creased with the effort of recalling. 'I don't think so. He wasn't really close enough but I don't remember a beard.'

'Okay, can you think about his height please? Would you say he was taller than you?'

She shook her head. 'An inch or two shorter, if anything.'

'About my height, then?'

She considered this. 'Maybe. I think so.'

Clare smiled. 'I know this isn't easy, Louise, but it's really helpful.'

She waved this away. 'It's fine. Go on.'

'Skin colour?'

'Oh, white,' she said. 'A bit pasty, to be honest. Like he needed a good meal, you know? He was thin, too. Wiry. Looked as if he could run fast.'

'Any mannerisms?'

Louise shivered. 'I kept as far away from him as I could.' She looked towards the front window. 'You can stand quite far back and still see who's outside.'

Clare remembered the figure she'd seen as they'd approached the front door. Was Louise the nervous type – given to imagining things?

'And you're sure it was the same man every time?'

'Oh yes. You don't forget something like that, Inspector.'

Chris sat forward. 'You told Mr Richards.' It was more a statement than a question. At the mention of her husband's name Louise swallowed.

'I did. But Harry – he seemed to think I was imagining it. He said – he said we'd both be better after we'd had a holiday.'

Clare put down her notepad and pen. 'Would you be prepared to work with one of my colleagues?' she said. 'Help us make up a photofit of the man.'

'Of course.' Louise's voice was husky now. 'Anything that helps.'

Clare asked a few more questions but they learned little more. She caught Chris's eye. 'Did your husband have a study?'

Louise frowned at this. 'Yes. I mean, he did most of his work at the office but there is a small room he used.'

'I wonder if we could have a look round, please? And if he had a laptop, we'd like to take that with us.' She saw Louise's expression cloud. 'I can assure you we won't access anything on the laptop until we have a warrant. But we'd like to have it for when the warrant comes through. It might help us find out what happened.'

Louise dabbed at her eyes again. 'You're talking as if Harry's dead. It might not be him – in the car. It might not.' Her voice was becoming shrill again, and Clare nodded.

'Of course. But if it does turn out to be Mr Richards, we wouldn't want to have wasted any time.'

Louise closed her eyes for a moment. Then she pulled herself to her feet. 'The laptop's on his desk. It's this way.'

She led them back to the hall and opened a door opposite. Clare thanked her. 'We'll let you know when we're finished.'

Louise stayed in the doorway as though she didn't want to leave then she turned and walked back to the kitchen. Clare waited until she'd gone and pulled a pair of gloves from her pocket. 'Come on,' she said. 'Let's get on with it; and don't touch any papers, for now. We'll need a warrant to look into his affairs and it's possible anything to do with his clients might be excluded.'

It was a small room. Ideal for a study, or it might have made a single bedroom. A bookcase stood against one wall, an assortment of paperbacks on the shelves. On the top were two small shields and a silver trophy. A photo on the wall above showed a smiling man holding the trophy. Another had him teeing off, a clubhouse in the background. Harry Richards, it seemed, was a golfer.

She moved to the window which gave onto the street and pictured a scruffy man in a green parka, looking towards the house. As with the other window, there were no blinds to screen the occupants and she could imagine Louise feeling threatened, cornered, even, by the presence of a man staring straight at her. But who was he? And why was he stalking this woman?

'You sure we're clear to take this?' Chris said.

'Eh?' She turned and saw him unplugging a laptop. 'Yes, we'll take it. There's no reason to suppose it's his work computer and we won't access it until the warrant comes through. I doubt the wife's involved, but I wouldn't want her touching it, maybe deleting stuff.'

'She could already have done that.'

'True. But if she has, Tech Support will find it.'

She continued scanning the room while Chris bagged the laptop and she saw a small drawer unit to the side of the desk. She began checking the drawers but found they held nothing more than an assortment of stationery items.

'Anything?' she asked as Chris went through the book-shelves.

'Nah. Surprisingly little paperwork. No bills or anything like that.'

'Probably gone paperless,' Clare said, and Chris carried on checking the shelves.

Half an hour later Clare emerged from under the desk and she stood, dusting off her knees. 'I think we're done here.' Chris nodded.

Louise was hovering near the door when they emerged and Clare pulled her gloves off as discreetly as she could.

'We'll leave you in peace, now,' she said, 'but we will be in touch.'

Louise looked at Clare, her eyes brimming. 'Harry?' she reminded them. 'I need to see him.'

'As soon as we can arrange it.'

Chapter 4

They drove slowly back down to the junction, Chris's head turning left and right as they went.

'Can't see much in the way of CCTV,' he said.

'Doesn't mean it's not there. Can you organise an eFit officer as soon as possible? Then house-to-house with the photo.' She looked round as they passed a side road. 'I can't see any bus stops.'

'Buses don't come up here,' Chris said. 'There's a couple of stops just out on the main road.'

'So if he came by bus he'd have to walk from there?'

'He would.'

'Right, then. House-to-house guys need to find anyone who might have been driving in or out of the estate last Wednesday, including that delivery van. Let's say, between one and four. Anyone with a dashcam, I want the footage. They might have driven past him.'

'I'll get onto the bus company as well. Check their CCTV.'

They were at the road end now and Clare sat at the junction as if she couldn't decide which way to go.

'Tentsmuir?' Chris said. 'Left here then left again at St Mike's.'

She pulled out to re-join the A914 and they drove on in silence, Clare taking the road that led to the forest and beach.

Chris's phone buzzed and he squinted at the screen. 'Sara says the ambulance has been and gone. Life pronounced extinct. SOCO are on the way.'

She made no response to this, glancing left and right until a brown AA sign came into view. 'This it?'

'Yeah.'

She joined a narrow road, a sign stating it was unsuitable for heavy vehicles. A dark strip of trees on the horizon grew larger and closer, until a green Forestry Commission sign told them they were entering Tentsmuir Forest. Clare slowed right down, squinting against the sunlight as it broke through the trees here and there.

'Any idea where?'

'Not a clue,' Chris said. 'But Jim'll have someone posted at the edge of the road.'

A minute later, they saw Gillian, one of the uniformed officers, standing at a clearing with a forest track beyond. Clare pulled into the edge a little back from where Gillian stood and switched off the engine. She glanced at Chris, wondering briefly what awaited them in Harry Richards' car. 'Ready for this?'

He clicked off his seat belt. 'Only one way to find out.'

—

They made their way through the trees towards Sara who stood chatting to Robbie, a little way off from the car. Clare saw the colour had drained from Robbie's cheeks and she felt a stab of conscience. She hadn't thought she'd been particularly hard on him but now that a body had been found...

He nodded at her then looked away, his eyes avoiding the blue Peugeot. She wondered at this. The identity of the deceased hadn't been confirmed yet. There was still a chance it wasn't Harry Richards. She decided not to make a fuss and turned instead to Sara for an update.

'Spoke to Raymond,' Sara said, anticipating Clare's question. 'He should be here any time.'

Clare's eyes strayed towards the car, a dark shape among the fissured trunks of the Scots pines. 'Chris said the paramedics came.'

'Yes. Nothing they could do – obviously.'

Clare's jaw tightened. 'That bad?'

'It's not pretty, boss.'

A wave of nausea swept over Clare and she took a deep breath in and out. 'You have his wallet?' her tone as brisk as she could manage.

Sara held out a clear evidence bag and Clare squinted at it.

'You did have gloves on?'

'Yeah. Barely touched it. Just to check the name.'

'Money and cards still in it, you said?'

Sara nodded. 'They are. Whatever the motive, it wasn't robbery.'

Clare began stepping into her forensic suit. 'Common approach?'

'I've just done tape for now,' Sara said. 'Until SOCO arrive. If you keep it on your right.'

Clare jerked her head towards the car. 'Come on then,' she said to Chris. 'Let's take a look.'

They made their way gingerly through the trees following the tape Sara had set up and moved towards the car. The inside of the windscreen was obscured with condensation and what seemed to be a great deal of dried blood, but the driver's door window was clear enough for them to see the figure of a man. His head had fallen to the side exposing a gaping wound in his throat. Even through the window Clare could see his clothes were heavily bloodstained. A knot was forming in her stomach. This was no ordinary mugging. Someone had lured Harry Richards here to kill him. The question was who?

A van door slammed, and she turned to see Raymond Curtice, the Scene of Crime Officer making his way through the trees, bag in hand.

'Let's not contaminate the scene any further,' she said to Chris. They retraced their steps and she went to greet

27

Raymond. 'Pretty nasty one,' she said. 'We could do with getting him over to the mortuary. Get his identity confirmed. And I'll need a photographer.'

'Gimme a chance,' Raymond said. 'I've only just arrived.'

'Sorry.' Clare forced a smile. 'I've just spoken to the wife – assuming he's who we think he is. She's convinced herself it's not him in the car. I'd like her to ID the body as soon as possible.'

'Yeah, I know,' he said. 'I'll get the lights up and we'll see what we're dealing with. I don't want him out here any longer than necessary.'

Clare looked back towards the road. 'Tricky to close this. The car park's further down; likely to be busy – folk along the beach or walking the forest.'

Raymond stood, taking in his surroundings. 'Should be fine,' he said. 'There's too much traffic up and down for us to find any meaningful tracks anyway.'

At the mention of tyre tracks Clare suddenly realised there must have been another car. Whoever had killed this man must have left the scene somehow, probably covered in blood. Not ideal if you're planning to catch a bus. But which way would the killer have gone? These quiet country roads rarely had cameras but maybe the Forestry Commission had their own.

'I supposed CCTV's too much to hope for?'

Raymond glanced towards the road. 'Not out here. There might be something further on, at the car park, but definitely not back here. Now, if you don't mind…'

Clare smiled. 'You'll call me later?'

'Soon as I have any news.'

They made their way back to the car, Clare pulling off her forensic suit as she went. She nodded to Gillian at her roadside post. 'I'll send someone over to relieve you in a few hours.'

'Thanks, boss.'

She carried on towards the car then turned back to Gillian. 'Robbie – is he okay?'

Gillian flicked a glance in Robbie's direction. 'Bit of a shock for us all, to be honest. But he did seem pretty upset.'

Clare pondered this. She was going to need every officer she could lay her hands on. There'd be no time for anyone not giving a hundred per cent. But it did look as if Robbie had taken this one particularly hard. 'Keep an eye on him, yeah?'

Gillian acknowledged this and Clare headed back to the car.

'That lad needs to toughen up,' Chris said, one hand on the car roof as he stepped out of his suit.

Clare exhaled. 'Maybe so. But now definitely isn't the time to tell him. So button it.' She clicked to unlock the car and climbed in.

'What d'you reckon, then?' Chris said, climbing in beside her.

'I reckon,' Clare began, 'we need to take a close look at Harry Richards' business affairs. I'd say someone was pretty upset with him.'

Chapter 5

'What was the address for Harry Richards' office?' Clare asked as she slowed for the thirty miles an hour sign, just outside St Andrews.

Chris fished a notepad out of her bag and squinted at it. 'Halfway along South Street. Head for the West Port.'

She drove on into town, turning up past the bus station. 'Remind me to get someone to check their CCTV,' she said as a single decker pulled out in front of them.

Chris scribbled something on the notepad and glanced to the side as they approached the West Port. 'It's a busy bit of the road here,' he said. 'She's lucky she didn't end up under the wheels of a car.'

'Louise Richards?' Clare signalled and turned carefully through the central archway of the sixteenth-century entrance to South Street. The lime trees that provided shade in the summer were just coming into leaf and the late afternoon sun warmed the sandstone buildings. The street was a busy mix of students in their red gowns, tourists with oversized cameras slung round their necks and harassed locals trying to pick their way through. Clare nosed into a diagonal parking space outside Matthews Interiors, the shop that had delivered the rug to Louise Richards.

'We'll try here first,' she said, reaching for her bag. 'Get them moving on the dashcam.'

The three-quarter length glass door dinged as they entered the shop and Clare felt a sense of calm as it closed behind them, screening out the bustle of the street. It was a bright, beautifully laid out shop with pale lemon walls. A row of light wood shelves ran from front to back along one side holding an array of candles, small vases and tableware, their colours vibrant under a bank of downlighters. A sky-blue sofa sat along the other side, the soft velvet punctuated by an assortment of cushions, the arms draped with swatches of fabric. Further down the shop there were narrow console tables, with lamps, photo frames and several pyramids of linen tablecloths and napkins.

'Napery,' Clare muttered to herself, taking in the neat pyramids.

'Eh?'

She smiled. 'Sorry – I always think of that word when I see tablecloths and napkins.'

'Never heard of it.'

'My great aunt,' she explained. 'Fancied herself as a bit posh. Always referred to her cloths as napery. Handy bit of info for a pub quiz,' she added.

Chris raised an eyebrow. 'Not the pubs I go to.'

A neatly dressed man in a dark suit and open necked shirt came forward. Clare showed her badge and got to the point.

'We'd like to see dashcam footage from the van that delivered to a Mrs Louise Richards at Drumoig, please.'

The man's face clouded. 'Might I ask why?'

'We're investigating a serious crime. It's possible your van driver might have passed someone who's involved.'

The man checked his watch. 'The van's out on deliveries. It should be back in the next couple of hours. I can ask the driver for the SD card, but I can't guarantee the footage will still be there. The card only holds a certain number of hours before it records over the oldest clips.'

Clare reached into her pocket and took out one of her cards. 'If you could call the station when you have it. Ask for Sergeant Jim Douglas.'

The man agreed and they turned to leave.

'This is Sara Heaven,' Chris whispered as Clare pulled open the door. 'Too fancy for me, though. I'm happy with IKEA.'

'Buy a house at Drumoig and you'll be lucky if you can afford IKEA.'

They emerged onto the pavement which seemed busier than ever. Clare checked her watch. 'Better get a move on. I'm guessing the solicitors will close at five.'

Chris nodded towards the zebra crossing. 'It's on the other side.'

They made their way over South Street, towards the ruined Blackfriars Chapel, once a Dominican friary. Further along Chris stopped at a brass nameplate next to a panelled outer door which stood open.

'H Richards, Solicitor,' Clare read. 'I wonder if it's just him. No partners, I mean.'

Chris put a hand on the inner door but it was locked. There was an intercom on the wall and he pressed the button. Moments later they were buzzed into a narrow hallway, painted in dove grey. A dado rail ran along the wall with tongue and groove panelling below and a set of watercolours above, hanging from a narrow picture rail. A woman in a cream blouse and dark trousers emerged from a door to the right, a professional smile fixed in place. Clare thought she might be in her early forties. Her ash blonde hair was scraped back, held in a clip and her face was set in a frown. She made an effort to smile and asked if she could help them.

Clare read the woman's name badge and saw she was Kate Campbell, Harry Richards' receptionist. She introduced herself and Chris and asked if there was somewhere they could talk. Kate indicated the room beyond the door and pulled out two chairs.

'I have to stay by reception,' she explained. 'In case someone calls. But I'm not expecting anyone.'

Clare smiled. 'That's fine. We'd just like to ask about your employer.'

At the mention of this Kate's brow furrowed. 'He's not been in today. I had to cancel all his appointments.' She met Clare's eye. 'Is he all right?'

Clare didn't answer this directly. Instead, she said, 'Can you take me through his movements yesterday please?'

Kate looked at Clare, a troubled expression in her eyes. When Clare volunteered no further information, she reached into a drawer and withdrew a large desk diary. She leafed through the pages and turned it round to let them see. 'He was in his office all morning, preparing papers for a house sale this week. Then he went out to buy a sandwich.' She stopped to think. 'Probably twelve-thirty. I take my lunch between one and two and he was back before I left.'

'And the afternoon?'

Kate angled her head so she could read the diary. 'There was a young man in at two. A whiplash compensation case.'

Clare squinted at the diary entry. 'What was his name? Sorry, I can't read your writing.'

'It's a Mr Hudson.'

'Do you have an address for him?'

She hesitated. 'I'm afraid I can't give you that. It's a matter of client confidentiality, you see. I really can't give out any information.' She glanced away, clearly unhappy at not being able to help.

Clare was quiet as she weighed this up. She remembered enough from her time living with a solicitor – her ex-boyfriend Tom – to accept what Kate was saying. She also suspected if Kate did bend the rules and allowed them access to Harry's client list it might be deemed an illegal search. Any evidence they gathered would be inadmissible and the culprit could walk away from all charges. No, she decided. They had to play this strictly by the rules.

'Ms Campbell,' she said, 'I must tell you we believe Mr Richards has come to some harm so I will be seeking a warrant to access contact details for his most recent clients.'

The colour drained from Kate's face and she blinked a couple of times. 'Harm? You mean—'

'We have found the body of a man and there is reason to believe it may be Mr Richards.' She paused for a moment. 'I'm sorry. I know it must be a shock.'

It took Kate a minute to compose herself. Finally she reached for a tissue from a box on the desk and blew her nose. 'Sorry,' she said. 'It's just such a shock. Obviously I knew there must be something wrong, with him not coming in today and Louise phoning.'

Clare gave her a moment. 'Was Mr Hudson the only appointment?'

Kate shook her head. 'Harry went out about half past three. Said he'd a client to see.' She glanced down at the diary. 'But it wasn't in the book.'

'Why might that be?' Chris asked.

'Usually it's when something comes up at short notice.'

'And you've no idea who he'd gone to see? Or where?' Clare said.

'Sorry.'

'Not to worry.' Clare looked round the office. 'It's very quiet. Who else works here?'

'Just Simon. Simon Miller. He's our paralegal. We have a cleaner as well but she comes in after we've closed.'

'Is Simon here?' Clare asked. 'I'd like to speak to him as well.'

'He left about four,' Kate said. 'He was due some time, so he went home early. I suppose you'll want his address.'

'Please.' Clare smiled. 'And your cleaner's details as well.' She waited while Kate jotted down the names and addresses. 'It must be difficult at times,' she said, 'just having the one solicitor.'

'It is,' Kate said. 'Today, for instance. I had to cancel four appointments and tomorrow's just as bad.'

'Has it always been just Mr Richards? No other solicitors?'

'We usually take on a trainee,' Kate said. 'But she left last month.'

Clare was suddenly alert. 'Why?'

'Oh, it's quite usual. They're cheap, you see, trainees. But once they've done their two years they have their practising certificate, and the salary goes up. Harry says—' She stopped herself. 'Harry said he couldn't afford the higher salary. So the trainees usually move onto larger practices and we get a new one.'

'Where did she go?'

'One of the firms in Dundee. I can give you her details as well.'

Clare waited while Kate noted this down then went on. 'Did they work well together?'

'Harry and Emma? That was her name – Emma Halliday. Yes they did. They'd a good working relationship. Harry said she was very capable. Said she'd have no problem finding a job elsewhere.'

'And you?' Clare asked. 'Did you get on with Emma?'

It was the briefest hesitation, but it didn't escape Clare's notice. 'Yes,' Kate said, her tone brisk. 'She was a very nice young woman.'

'Hardworking?'

'Of course.' Her face was a mask.

Chris leaned forward. 'It must be a lot of work for you, a new trainee every couple of years.' He glanced at Clare. 'I know what it's like when we have new staff. Takes time for them to learn how we do things.'

Clare saw what he was doing. 'It really does. But we're lucky. Our admin assistant is a great help with new folk. We'd be lost without her, wouldn't we?'

Chris nodded. 'I'm sure it's the same for you, Ms Campbell.'

The compliment had the desired effect. 'Kate, please.'

'Kate,' Chris repeated. He inclined his head as if appraising her. 'I bet you and the paralegal hold things together.'

Kate's hand went to her neck and she began fingering a slender gold chain.

'Maybe you had the odd cross word – with the trainee,' Chris said.

'No,' she said. 'It wasn't that.'

They waited and eventually she spoke again.

'We've had a few trainees over the years,' she said. 'Some are easier to work with than others. But Harry usually picks pretty well. Emma – she was conscientious enough, always pleasant to the clients. But she'd drop the odd remark. Not to me, mind. But I'd hear her talking to Simon.'

'What sort of remarks?' Clare asked.

'Oh, things like telling him he was doing too much of Harry's work – that he wasn't paid solicitor's wages so he shouldn't be doing everything.' Kate frowned. 'She didn't seem to realise that's what a paralegal does. They do the legwork, but the solicitor ensures it's done correctly. He's the one in trouble if it goes wrong. She was saying things like he was too good to be a paralegal, like there was something wrong with it.'

Clare considered this. 'How did Simon react?'

'Told her he was quite happy with his job; said he didn't need the extra worry. And then another time,' she broke off, 'I shouldn't be saying this, really.' She met Clare's eye. 'It's not like she meant anything by it.'

Clare smiled. 'The more we know about Mr Richards the better.'

'I… I overheard her saying what Harry was doing was unethical.'

Clare was suddenly alert. 'What do you think she meant by that?'

'Oh, the trainee thing – taking them on when they were cheap then getting rid of them. But she was wrong. It wasn't unethical. We're not a big firm, here. There's not really enough work to support two fully qualified solicitors. Harry gave them a good grounding, and he put the word out once the two years were up. Helped them find a good job.'

'Was that all?'

Kate nodded. 'Yes. It was just little things like that. Something and nothing. Sometimes they're like that, the trainees – snippy little madams. But mostly they're nice.'

'Always women, then?'

Kate considered this. 'The last two were women. We did have a man once, but I think it's what we do – property and the like. Seems to attract more women than men.'

'Did Mr Richards have someone lined up to take Emma's place?'

'Not yet. I think he had a few in mind but no one definite.'

Clare glanced at Chris. They weren't learning much here. She'd liked to have looked round Harry's office but she'd never investigated the death of a solicitor. There were complications. Client privilege, for one thing. No, this was a tricky one. They'd have to tread carefully. She gave Chris a nod. 'Thanks for your time, Kate. We'll leave you for now.'

Kate rose, her expression clouded. 'And you'll let me know? About Harry?'

'We will.'

They emerged from the office to find the sun had gone, the sky overcast. A breeze caught Clare's hair, and she put up a hand to sweep it out of her eyes.

'I don't suppose—' Chris began.

'No, nor do I.' She checked the traffic and stepped out into the road, walking quickly across.

'Hold on.' Chris ran to catch up with her and put a hand on her arm. 'I'm guessing you want to interview the paralegal guy. That's another hour at least and it's nearly five already.'

'So?'

'So you know me – I can't think straight on an empty stomach.'

She stopped suddenly, swearing under her breath. A man who'd been walking behind muttered something as he swerved to avoid her.

'I'm only asking for a burger,' Chris said.

'Not that. This!' She pointed to a billboard outside a news-agent's.

Gruesome Death in Popular Forest

Chris sighed. 'How the hell do they get hold of this stuff?'

'It's a busy place. Beach, too. It wouldn't take long for someone to call it in. Maybe they interviewed the Ranger.' She glanced at her watch. 'Go on, then. Get me a burger while I call Jim. We'll need some extra officers to keep the press at bay.'

Chapter 6

They ate their burgers leaning against the car, Clare absolutely refusing to allow the food inside.

'I'm not having the next person to use it complaining about the smell.'

'Suits me,' Chris said, wiping a smear of ketchup off his chin. 'God, this is a good burger.'

Clare scrunched up the greaseproof paper her burger had been wrapped in and tossed it to Chris. 'You find a bin while I start the car.' He set off up the street, wiping his hands on the paper and Clare jumped into the car. She waited, the engine idling, running over her interview with Kate Campbell. They hadn't learned much, but the trainee solicitor – Emma something – she'd clearly caused a bit of friction. Surely not enough for such a gruesome murder, though? She doubted it. Most murders were domestic: husbands killing wives, or ex-wives, even. But this – the throat slit from side to side, the car off the road in a forest – this wasn't a normal domestic murder. This was something else altogether. But what?

The passenger door opened, and Chris climbed in. 'So,' he said, tugging on his seat belt. 'Who's first?'

Clare looked down at her notepad. 'I think we'll try the paralegal.'

'Address?'

'Drumcarrow Road,' she said. 'It rings a bell.'

'I know it,' Chris said. 'Head for Canongate. It's off there.'

Clare pulled out into the traffic immediately, hitting the brakes as a woman stepped onto a zebra crossing. 'I'll never know why they put these things right at junctions.'

'To stop you screaming round corners on two wheels.'

'That's good coming from you, Verstappen!'

'Nope. I'm a new man, now. Sara says we have to be like Sunday drivers. Save the planet and all that.'

They sat while a seemingly endless stream of pedestrians ambled across until finally there was a gap. It was after five now, the streets busy with cars, and their progress was slow. Finally, they cleared the town centre and the streets became more residential. 'What's his name again?' Clare said, turning onto a side road.

Chris squinted at the notepad. 'Simon Miller.' He looked up as Clare swung the car round into Canongate. 'It's just up here,' he said. 'Go left at the mini roundabout.'

The house was set behind a hedge of neatly trimmed conifers, halfway along the road. A large part of the front garden had been given over to monoblock paving which continued down one side of the house, leading to a single garage with a red up-and-over door. The monobloc was damp in places and Clare noticed a white weed sprayer sitting by the front door. The house itself was a bungalow with Velux windows set into a tiled roof. As she stood taking it in, a man dressed in brown cords and a zip up fleece came round the side of the house. He was about fifty, Clare thought, although his clothes and haircut made him seem older. He was clean shaven and wore a worried expression. He noticed them and formed his face into a polite smile.

'Hello.'

Clare took out her ID badge and introduced herself and Chris. 'Is there somewhere we could talk?'

He stared at the badge, his brow furrowed. Then he glanced at the weed sprayer. 'I'll just get rid of this,' he said, indicating the bottle. 'Mrs Miller likes the garden kept tidy.' He picked it up and walked round the side of the house.

Chris raised an eyebrow. 'Weird,' he mouthed, and Clare shrugged.

'Takes all sorts, Sergeant.'

A minute later Simon Miller reappeared and beckoned them to follow. 'The kitchen door's open.' He ushered them in through a half-glass door which he shut and locked behind them. 'Better safe than sorry.' He led them through a narrow hallway into a sitting room with a large window overlooking the garden and street. Clare saw a woman on the pavement opposite. She was hovering over a small boy who was padding along on a tiny balance bike.

'Please,' Simon said. 'Sit down. I could make some tea.' Clare was thirsty after the burger, but his body language wasn't encouraging, and she waved this away.

'Just a short chat, Mr Miller.'

'Of course.' He waited until they had sat then he perched on a chair opposite and formed his lips into a smile. 'How can I help?'

Clare noticed his eyes stray towards the window and waited until she had his attention again. 'We'd like to ask about your employer,' she said. 'Mr Richards.'

'Harry? Yes, of course.' His brow clouded. 'He wasn't in today. I hope there's nothing wrong.'

Clare didn't answer this directly but took out her notebook and clicked on her pen. 'How long have you worked for him?'

He looked from Clare to Chris as if seeking some clarification. When none came he said, 'Fifteen years. Not all as a paralegal, of course. I started out doing general admin. Then Harry said there was this qualification – if I was interested in doing more legal stuff. I discussed it with my wife and she thought it was a good idea.' He smiled. 'I think she thought I might go on to be a solicitor but I'm quite happy as I am. It's a good job.'

'You enjoy it?'

'I do. I mean it's mostly the same stuff. Not criminal, mind you. I'm not sure I'd like that. It's helping people buy houses. Quite a nice thing to do.'

'Is Mr Richards a good employer?' Clare asked.

'Oh yes. Excellent. I'm very happy.' He nodded, as if to emphasise this then, again, his eyes strayed to the window.

Clare decided to come to the point. 'Mr Miller, I must tell you we think Mr Richards may have come to some harm.'

He stared at them. 'Harm? What kind of harm?'

Clare watched him for a moment. 'This afternoon the body of a man was found at Tentsmuir Forest. It has yet to be formally identified but we have reason to believe it may be Mr Richards.'

The colour drained from Simon's face and he seemed at a loss. 'Harry?' he said, his voice hoarse. 'Harry's dead?' He blinked.

'Maybe we should have that cup of tea,' Clare said, softening her voice. 'I can ask Sergeant West here to make it.'

He shook his head. 'No, I'm fine, thank you. It's just a bit of a shock.'

Clare gave him a moment then she went on. 'Can I ask when you last saw him?'

He frowned, as though trying to recall. 'Yesterday. About three. He brought me notes from a meeting with a client. Then he said something had come up and he'd see me in the morning.'

'He didn't say what had come up?' Clare asked. 'Or where he was going?'

'Sorry, no.'

She hesitated, choosing her words. 'I am aware of your obligations under client privilege, but can I ask if you know of any particular case or any client who was causing a problem? Anyone he might have had to see urgently?'

He was quiet for a moment. 'Not really. As I said, we don't deal with criminal cases so there's not usually any conflict.'

'No argument over a house sale?'

'Sometimes a client will be disappointed. Harry, he gives advice, you know? *Go five thousand over the asking price*, or, *put in a low bid – see what they say.* If it doesn't work and they don't get the house, they moan a bit. But usually that's when it's gone for more than the client can afford.'

'Has there been anything like that recently?'

'No,' he said. 'Harry has a good feel for the market. Clients are usually pretty happy.'

Clare glanced at Chris. There was nothing here. He took the cue and sat forward.

'What about your colleagues?' he said. 'Get on all right with them?'

'There's only Kate. She's lovely.' Then his brow clouded. 'She'll be absolutely devastated.'

'I think you had a trainee, recently?' Chris said.

There was a flicker of something in Simon's eyes. 'Emma?' he said, after a moment. 'She left a few weeks ago.'

'Did you get on okay with her?'

'Yes, I suppose.'

'We spoke to Kate,' Clare said. 'She thought Emma might have been a bit critical.'

'Of what?'

'Your workload. I think she suggested you'd make a good solicitor.'

There was the hint of a smile at this, and his cheeks flushed. 'She was always saying things like that. But I told her. *I'm happy as I am.* It's not like I do all the conveyancing work. Harry does – Harry did lots of it himself.' He looked down, the smile gone. 'He was a good boss. I don't know what I'll do now.'

Chapter 7

They left him soon afterwards.

'Nothing much there,' Chris said as they walked down the monobloc drive.

Clare fished in her pocket for the car keys. 'No...'

'You suspicious?'

She leaned against the car. 'I'm not sure. You?'

Chris considered this. 'Maybe. Did you see he kept looking towards the window, like he was worried someone would spot us?'

'He did, didn't he? Oh, I dunno, Chris. I can't put my finger on it. He seemed genuinely shocked to hear his employer had died but...'

A man with a border terrier was walking towards them and they climbed into the car.

'You don't seriously suspect him?' Chris asked, pulling the door closed.

'Probably not. But I do think he's hiding something.' She glanced at her watch. 'What time did Kate Campbell say the cleaner came in?'

'She didn't. Want to swing by the office and see if she's there?'

'Yeah. Let's do that.' She pulled away, heading back towards South Street.

The town was quieter now, most of the teatime traffic gone and Clare pulled into a space close to Harry Richards' office. The outer door was closed but there was a light in the front window. Chris jumped out and rapped sharply on the door then put his ear to it. After a few moments he shook his head.

Clare climbed out to join him and stood on tiptoe to look in the window. The glass was obscured by a voile curtain, but she could hear the sound of a vacuum cleaner and see the outline of a figure moving back and forward. She knocked on the window, but the figure obviously didn't hear. A minute later the noise stopped, and Clare took the chance to knock again. The figure came closer and the voile was pulled back. A woman in a blue tabard peered out. She was mouthing something, probably telling them the office was closed. Clare held her ID badge up to the glass and indicated the door. The woman nodded and let the curtain fall back. They heard the inner door being unlocked then the panelled outer door was opened.

'There's no one here,' the woman said.

Clare smiled. 'I know. But we'd like a word with you please.'

The woman frowned. 'What's this about?'

'If we could come inside?'

She hesitated, as if unsure they actually were police officers. Then she drew back to admit them. She led them into the reception area where they'd spoken to Kate Campbell earlier. 'Is this okay?' she said, indicating the seats at Kate's desk.

'Perfect,' Clare said. 'We won't keep you long.'

She gave her name as Lois Fielding and told them she'd worked for Harry for the past two years. 'Look, what's this about?' she said again, her eyes moving from Clare to Chris.

Clare explained the reason for their visit and the colour drained from Lois's face.

'Seriously? Mr Richards is dead?'

'It's not confirmed yet but we think so,' Clare said. 'So we're trying to find out as much as we can about him.'

Lois considered this. 'I'm not sure I can help much. I hardly ever see him. Just the odd time if he's working late. It's mostly Kate I deal with.'

'He didn't work late often, then?' Clare asked.

'Maybe three or four times recently. Sometimes he had a client who came later – after we'd closed. I'm guessing they couldn't get off work.'

'Must have been annoying for you.'

Lois shrugged. 'Not really. He'd usually tell me just to do the bins and leave the rest. Said he'd square it with Kate. I'd get finished early. Suited me.'

'Did it happen recently?'

'Last week, actually.'

'Which day?'

She thought for a minute. 'Wednesday or Thursday. I can't remember which.'

'Did you see the client?'

'No, I'd gone before they arrived. I'd only just got here. I was hanging up my coat when Mr Richards came out. He said he'd do the bins himself so I could go. I offered to stay and do a bit but he said it wasn't a problem. Said I always worked hard and everyone deserved a day off now and then.'

'So you were only in the office a short time that day?'

She nodded. 'In and out in five minutes.'

'And you didn't see the client at all? Maybe arriving as you left?'

'No. Sorry. Does that help at all?'

'It does, Lois. Thank you. Were you aware of any problems with the firm?' Clare said.

'Like what?'

'Anything, really. Arguments between staff, people complaining, that sort of thing.'

Her eyes widened. 'No. Nothing like that. It's a nice place to work. We had a meal out at Christmas,' she said. 'Nice hotel. Mr Richards paid for everything. Taxis too. It was a good night.'

Clare sat thinking. 'I wonder – is there a store room where you keep your cleaning materials?'

Chris shot her a look but she went on.

'We were here earlier,' she said, 'but I forgot to ask about that.'

'Yes,' Lois said. 'Do you want to see it?'

'If you could just show Sergeant West. It'll only take a minute or two.' She turned to Chris. 'Just check for all the usual stuff please.'

Chris said nothing but rose and followed Lois out of the room. As soon as they'd gone Clare moved quickly round the reception desk and put a hand on the drawer she'd seen Kate take the diary from. But it was locked. There was another shallow drawer at the other side of the desk, just deep enough to hold small items. She pulled this out and found what she was looking for: a set of keys. The first one she tried fitted the lock. Pulling the drawer open she picked up the diary and leafed quickly through to the previous week. Scanning the pages, she saw there were no appointments on any day after 3 p.m. None the week before either. She thought about photographing the diary pages then decided against it. They'd need a warrant to access this information, officially. Handy to know, all the same. She closed the diary and slipped it back in the drawer, locking it again. Following the sound of voices she found Chris making a pretence of looking behind buckets and bottles of bleach.

He glanced at her and raised an eyebrow.

'All okay here?' she said, and he nodded. 'We won't hold you back any further then, Lois. But if we could have a mobile number, in case we need to speak to you again?'

They emerged into the cool evening air and walked towards the car.

'*Check for all the usual stuff?*' Chris said. 'What the hell was that about?'

'Strictly off the record.'

'Go on.'

'I wanted to look at their diary again.'

'And?'

'There were no evening appointments any day last week – or the week before.'

'Maybe he forgot.'

'Maybe he did. But somehow I don't think so. I lived with a solicitor for years, remember. And I've yet to meet one who doesn't write all their appointments down. But our Mr Richards seems to have had a lot of last-minute meetings and late clients, none of which were in the diary; and I'd very much like to know why.'

Chapter 8

'Jim says the body's off to the mortuary,' Chris said, reading a phone message as Clare drove.

'SOCO?'

'Still there. He reckons they'll be most of the night.'

'Any sign of a weapon?'

'Doesn't say.'

'Okay. Let's head back to the station. Pool our thoughts.'

The station was quiet when they entered, every spare uniformed officer over at Tentsmuir.

'Grab a drink and bring it into my office.'

It had been warm earlier in the day and she'd turned her radiator off. But now the sun was low in the sky and there was a chill in the room. She bent to turn it back on and opened her notepad. 'So, what do we know?'

Chris slopped some of his coffee down the side of his mug and he put it down on a home security leaflet to mop up the spill. 'Harry Richards was murdered in his car, probably in Tentsmuir Forest.'

'Agreed. Going by blood spatter on the windscreen I'd say he was in the driver's seat when he was killed.'

'Possibly from behind?'

Clare sipped her coffee. 'Probably. But let's wait for the forensics on that. What else?'

'He had clients or appointments his staff didn't know about.'

She frowned. 'Are we making too much of that?'

'I don't think so. I could see the odd appointment arranged at the last minute. But telling the cleaner to go – why would you do that?'

'Hmm. Maybe an important client. He didn't want the sound of her hoovering.'

'Don't forget how he died,' Chris said. 'He's seriously upset someone.'

'You're thinking he might have been doing some dodgy legal work? Upset the wrong people?'

'Something like that.'

'Right then,' Clare said. She wrote *staff* on her notepad and drew a line under it. 'Kate Campbell – thoughts?'

'Seems okay to me. Pretty efficient.'

'I agree. And I'd say the cleaning lady's sound as well.'

'Which leaves our nervous paralegal.'

'Indeed.' Clare wrote *Simon Miller* on her notepad and added a question mark. 'Some folk are like that – nervous when they have to speak to the police. Maybe he's just one of those.'

'Or maybe he's a reason to be nervous,' Chris said. 'Let's request his phone records. Bank too.'

Clare considered this. 'I'll need a DCI to sanction that; and I'll tell you what else we need.'

'Yeah?'

'Access to Harry Richards' client list.'

Chris shook his head. 'You'll never get it.'

'I'll have a damn good try.' She sipped her coffee again. 'It's all in how you draw up the warrant. Anyway, family next.'

'Wife seemed genuinely shocked.'

'She did. Let's check their finances, though. See if there's anything unusual; and let's find the ex as well.' She flicked back pages in her notebook. 'Rosie King. I doubt she's involved but we'd better check.'

'Odd thing that,' Chris said, 'her getting married on the same date as her ex-husband.'

Clare considered this. 'Might just have been a popular day. You hear about these dates when there's loads of weddings.'

'*Agosto.*'

'Eh?'

'It's Spanish for August. Apparently the most popular month to get married.'

'How do you know that?'

He rolled his eyes. 'Clare, you have no idea. We are knee-deep in wedding mags at home. There is *nothing* I don't know about getting married.'

'Ach it'll be worth it when you see Sara in her dress. Anyway, it might be a coincidence.'

'Suppose. Don't forget the eFit.'

'Ah yes. The stalker – thanks, Chris.' She scribbled this down on her pad. 'I'll try to get someone tomorrow. Anyone else?'

'The last trainee – the one that left a month ago.'

'Emma Halliday. Good point. We'll need to speak to her.'

'Shouldn't be too hard to track her down.'

'I'll get Jim onto it,' Clare said. 'Hopefully get started on these interviews tomorrow once we have a few more bodies.'

'He'll have to be ID'd as well – our victim.'

Clare exhaled. 'Don't remind me. I just hope they can tidy him up so she doesn't see the gash. That's not how you want to remember your husband.'

'What about his last client?' Chris asked. 'Or the last one in the book at least?'

'Can't do anything until we get the warrant.'

There was a tap at the door and Jim looked in. 'Just had a call from…' he glanced at his notepad, '…Matthews Interiors? Apparently their van's had a puncture and they're waiting on a recovery vehicle.' He raised an eyebrow. 'Make sense?'

'Dammit,' Clare said. 'It does. The driver has an SD card I need to see.' She thought for a moment. 'Did he say where?'

'Some back road near Stirling,' Jim said. 'Didn't get the exact location. You want me to send a car out?'

Clare checked her watch. 'Probably not worth it tonight, now. Could you ask the driver to drop the card in when he gets back?'

'Aye, no bother.' He hesitated. 'I'm guessing you'll be putting a team together. Want me to drum up a few more bodies?'

She smiled. 'That would be great, Jim. Erm, when's Max back?'

'Tomorrow, I think.'

'That'll help,' she said. 'Oh and there's a laptop to go to Tech Support. But I don't have a warrant yet so I need it stored here, securely. Likewise, our victim's mobile phone, once SOCO have finished with it.'

'Leave it with me.'

He closed the door softly and Clare consulted her notepad again.

'Where were we?'

'Harry's last client.'

She nodded. 'Soon as we have the warrant. We'll need CCTV from the buses as well.'

'Maybe see what's on the SD card first,' Chris said. 'Mind you, that might be late enough.'

'Yeah. Sounds like it.' She yawned. 'Long day.'

'Not much more we can do tonight, then,' Chris said, 'unless you want to wait for the SD card.'

She shook her head. 'Let's call it a day. We've a list of actions for tomorrow; and if Jim has a few more bodies here first thing we'll make a start.'

They left the station and made for their cars. The sun had almost set and the lights came on automatically when Clare started the engine. She pulled out of the car park and headed for Daisy Cottage, her home for the past few years.

Five minutes later she turned into her drive and parked alongside DCI Alastair Gibson's old Ford Focus. The front room lights were on and she could see him through the window, moving about. A sharp bark from behind the door told her Benjy, her English bull terrier, had picked up her scent. She took out her key but before she could put it in the lock the door opened and the man she still privately thought of as *the DCI* stood there, a tea towel in his hand. He smiled and moved back to let her enter. Then he took her in his arms and the cares of the day began to recede. She smelled his cologne, felt the stubble of his face rough against her cheek. Benjy's paws dug into her leg as he jumped up for attention and she pulled away to ruffle him behind the ears. She was home.

Chapter 9

'Sounds like a really tough day,' the DCI said.

Clare twisted spaghetti on her fork. 'Just a bit.'

'Any theories?'

She shook her head. 'Too early to say. Hopefully we'll get a DCI tomorrow.'

'You'll be lucky,' he said. 'They're pretty thin on the ground just now. Lots retired at the start of the year.'

Clare tore off a piece of kitchen roll and dabbed her chin. 'You busy?'

He laughed. 'I wish I could help. But I'm leading a course at Tullieallan.'

'Dammit. I forgot about that. When are you away?'

'Day after tomorrow.'

She put down her fork and pushed her plate away. 'Hopefully they'll find us someone.'

He rose from the table and began loading the dishwasher. 'Room for dessert?'

'Sorry,' she said. 'I'm stuffed. Chris persuaded me to have a burger earlier.'

'Just coffee then.'

They washed up while the coffee brewed and took their mugs over to the sofa. Clare kicked off her shoes and flexed her feet. Benjy wandered over and jumped up beside her, resting his head on her lap. She waited for the DCI to say something about allowing the dog on the sofa but he said nothing and she leaned into him, enjoying this simple moment of calm at the end of a stressful day. He put out a hand and began stroking her hair absently but there was something stiff, something different about his manner.

She drained her mug then decided she was too tired to mess about. 'Al, what's wrong?'

'Eh?' He seemed surprised. Caught out, even.

She sighed. 'It's been a long day and we both know something's up. So, out with it.'

He smiled. 'You've a lot going on and it's nothing urgent.'

She turned to face him causing Benjy to adjust his position. 'Well, I know something's wrong. Let's have it.'

He put down his mug and took hold of her hand. 'Nothing's wrong. I was just thinking.'

She waited.

'How would you feel if I sold my house?' He glanced at her as if gauging her reaction. 'It's been rented out for the past year,' he said, 'and I've honestly not missed it.' He looked round the room. 'This feels like home now. But, if I did sell up, it would make things more permanent between us.'

She was silent for a moment. How *did* she feel about this? He rarely visited his house – even to check on his tenants – but it had always been there, ever since his divorce and the sale of the expensive Edinburgh property. He'd bought a smaller house in Aberdour, on the south coast of Fife, overlooking the river Forth; and he'd lived there for a time while their relationship had developed. Then, as he'd spent more and more time at Daisy Cottage, they'd agreed he would move in and rent out the Aberdour house. *If it doesn't work out*, she had said, *give the tenants notice and move back out again.*

But it had worked. They'd been happy together. He'd moved to a DCI's post focusing on crime policy in nearby Dundee. It was a nine-to-five job which meant he was always there in the evenings and they'd settled into a companionable lifestyle. He was an excellent cook, too, and Clare had to admit her diet had improved since he'd moved in. It worked. It really did. But did it work because Aberdour was there? Somewhere he could go back to if things went wrong? And would selling Aberdour – him throwing his lot in with her – would it change things? If it did, might she end up losing him altogether?

'You're tired,' he said. 'I'm sorry. Shouldn't have raised it.'

She took hold of his hand. 'No, you're right. It makes sense. But...'

'But?'

'My head's full of this body in the forest. Can we talk about it in a day or two? Maybe when you get back from Tullieallan?'

He smiled. 'Of course. It was just a thought.' He picked up the remote control. 'Fancy some junk telly?'

–

In spite of her weariness, Clare lay awake long into the night, turning things over in her mind. Had she put off discussing the house because of Harry Richards' body? Or was there another reason? Maybe, after ending her relationship a few years ago with Tom – her long-term solicitor boyfriend – maybe she was afraid of commitment. If so, would she ever be ready to commit to a lifetime with this man who lay sleeping beside her? This man who loved and cared for her, who made her happy just by being in the room? And, if she couldn't, would she ever find happiness? Finally, exhausted by these thoughts and the events of the day, she drifted off to sleep, one hand touching his shoulder to reassure herself he was still there.

Day 2: Wednesday, 5th April

Chapter 10

'Bad accident on the A91 last night,' Jim said as Clare made for her office. 'Car went through a fence opposite Balgove Larder.'

Clare knew the spot. The farm shop, café and steak barn were popular with locals, and she'd eaten there a couple of times herself. 'Anyone hurt?'

'Afraid so. Just the one car but the driver died at the scene.' He shook his head. 'Poor woman. Must have lost concentration. She hit a small electricity substation – one of those grey kiosk things. Airbag deployed but the impact broke her neck. Paramedics were pretty quick,' he said, 'but she was dead by the time they got there.'

'What about the substation?'

'Electricity guys were out last night. No real damage. The car took the worst of it.'

'Was there a black box in the car?'

'No idea. It's a write off. Over at the police garage now. They'll hang onto it in the meantime in case it turns out another vehicle was involved.'

'Let's put a shout out for dashcam footage,' Clare said. 'Say a window of thirty minutes either side of the accident time. Someone might have caught something if they passed her.'

Suddenly she remembered the SD card from the delivery van. 'Did the driver drop that card in?'

'Aye. I logged it last night. I'll just fetch it. Oh, and we've a good few officers coming over from Dundee; some of the Fife stations too. I've asked them to be here for eight.'

She thanked him and made for her office. The air was cool this early in the morning and she was glad of the heat from the radiator. She turned on her computer and waited for it to come to life. A minute later an officer she vaguely recognised tapped on the door.

'From the desk sergeant,' he said, handing her a labelled bag. The SD card.

She thanked the officer and spent some minutes hunting through her desk drawer until she found an adaptor to connect the card to her computer. A few minutes later the files were up on her screen. She was still flicking through, trying to work out which file might have last Wednesday's footage when her office door opened. She looked up expecting to see Chris but it was Max, the other detective sergeant, sporting a holiday suntan. Strictly speaking he belonged to the Bell Street station in Dundee but she'd borrowed him for an abduction case and, he'd proved such an asset, she kept finding reasons to hang onto him.

'Thought you'd appreciate a decent coffee,' he said, putting a mug down on her desk. 'And I've brought you some madeleines.' He handed her an exquisitely printed box with a French-sounding name written in gold letters.

Clare broke the seal and lifted the lid to reveal a tray of six beautifully decorated cakes. 'Oh these look amazing, Max. Thank you! And you're right. I've not had a filter coffee since you left.' She studied him. He had the relaxed look that came with two weeks away from work. 'And how was Paris?'

'*Très bien*,' he said with a flourish.

Clare groaned. 'Don't you start. It's bad enough with Chris learning pidgin Spanish for his honeymoon.' She turned back to her screen. 'Any idea how to find a particular day and time on these files?' She moved it so he could see and shoved the computer mouse across the desk.

'What are you looking for?'

'Last Wednesday afternoon. About two thirty.'

It took Max only a few minutes to find the footage. 'You're in luck,' he said. 'It's a good size card. Probably holds about forty hours. Even so, another day and this would have been overwritten.'

'Thanks, Max.' Clare turned the screen back and began scrolling through the film. At first she couldn't work out where the van was. It didn't look like any of the main roads around Drumoig. More like a single-track country road. Maybe he'd taken a short cut. And then she saw the van was approaching a staggered junction, the entrance to the Drumoig estate. The time on the footage showed ten to three. What time was it Louise Richards had said the man was outside her house? She checked her notepad. Half past two. He'd probably have gone by this time. Sure enough, as the van drove up the road towards the Richards' house there was no sign of anyone at all.

'Dammit,' she said, under her breath, as her office door opened.

'Charming,' Chris said. He nodded to Max. 'Good holiday?'

Max looked for a moment as if he might say *très bien* again but he caught Clare's eye. 'Great, thanks.'

'What's up?' Chris said, indicating the monitor.

'Dashcam footage,' she said. 'No sign of the stalker.'

'He might have jumped over a hedge,' Max said. 'Avoid being spotted.'

Chris shook his head. 'It's too open up there. Not many places to hide. Keep looking,' he said, as the van stopped outside the Richards' house. 'Might spot him on the way back down.'

The footage began again as the van drove back to the junction. But there was no sign of anyone walking other than a woman with a child in a pushchair. Clare sat back as the van pulled out into the main road.

'Wait,' Chris said. 'Go back.'

She handed him the mouse and he scrolled back to the point where the van pulled out. He advanced the footage slowly, pausing as it passed a bus shelter. 'There,' he said. 'I bet that's your man.' He zoomed in to the footage and they peered at a figure standing just inside the shelter, smoking a cigarette.

'Hold on,' Clare said, reaching for her notepad. She flicked back over pages until she came to the description Louise had given. 'Dark trousers, parka coat with a hood and a baseball cap,' she read.

'That's him,' Chris said. 'That's your stalker.'

Clare studied the figure. He wasn't facing the camera so they could only see part of his face. 'Ring any bells?'

'Not with me,' Max said.

Chris was frowning. 'Not sure. But we should be able to get a clearer photo from whatever bus he caught.' He squinted at the screen. 'Two minutes past three. Shouldn't be hard to find.'

Clare took the mouse back and began tapping at her keyboard. 'I'm going to send this to Diane at Tech Support. See if she can enhance it at all. Then we'll see if anyone recognises him.'

There was a tap at the door and Jim's head appeared. 'Most of the extra officers are here now.'

Clare checked her watch. Almost eight. 'Incident room in five minutes,' she said. She turned back to her keyboard and tapped a quick email to Diane, attaching the file. Then she drained her coffee mug, picked up her notepad and pushed back her chair. 'Come on,' she said. 'Time to find our killer.'

Chapter 11

The hubbub died down as Clare entered the incident room, followed by Chris and Max. She was pleased to see familiar faces, officers she'd worked with before and who she knew she could rely on. A pile of laptops had been unearthed from the store and were stacked on a desk at the back of the room. Someone had pinned a photograph of Harry Richards up on the board, probably taken from his company website. He was smiling, full of life and Clare found it hard to reconcile with the gruesome scene at Tentsmuir Forest.

'Jim and Robbie are bringing more desks in,' Sara said, and Clare nodded.

Five minutes later the room resembled a jumble sale, desks piled on top of each other round the edge of the room. Clare smiled her thanks to Jim and Robbie and moved to the front.

'Thanks, everyone. Maybe you could all help sort the room out once we've finished. And help yourselves to a laptop.' She moved to the board and studied Harry's photo then she tapped it and turned back to face them. 'You've no doubt heard we've had a pretty grim murder over at Tentsmuir Forest. Harry Richards, solicitor in the town, found in his car with his throat cut.'

A buzz went round the room at this revelation and Clare waited for it to die down. 'I know,' she said. 'Not your usual domestic; and, for now, the cause of death does not go outside this room, understood?'

There were nods and murmurs of *Yes, boss*. 'It was a pretty messy scene,' she said, one eye on Robbie whose eyes were fixed on the floor. 'Hopefully SOCO will have something for us but I gather they're still at the scene?' She looked across to Jim who nodded.

'He's yet to be formally identified,' Clare said, 'but everything points to it being him. Married for the second time, one daughter in New Zealand from his first marriage. Current wife is Louise Richards. She thinks she was being stalked in the weeks leading up to Harry's death.'

'Any idea who?'

Clare scanned the room to see who had spoken and saw Liv, a uniformed officer from Glenrothes. She wore a set of sergeant's epaulettes on her shoulders, obviously a recent addition.

'Not yet, but we hope to have some CCTV images to work with. Once we have them I'll circulate to see if anyone knows him. Congratulations on the promotion, by the way,' she added, and Liv smiled back.

'There's an ex-wife in Dundee. We'll speak to her once the wife confirms his ID.'

Jim raised a hand. 'Should be able to view the body from midday,' he said, and Clare nodded her thanks.

'Any other family?' Max asked.

'Not that we know of. Just the wife, ex-wife and daughter.'

'Work colleagues?'

'All been interviewed. There's only a receptionist, a cleaner and a paralegal. Chris and I spoke to them all last night. The paralegal seemed pretty nervous so we'll bear that in mind. I plan to request his bank and phone records but, unless we find evidence that points to him, we may not get them.'

'There's definitely something odd about him,' Chris said.

Clare shrugged. 'Being odd isn't a crime.'

'Slitting someone's throat might just qualify.'

Eyebrows shot up at this but Clare ignored the barb.

'The other significant thing is our victim had a few appointments lately that weren't in his diary, some in the office, after hours. On several occasions he sent the cleaner away early.'

Bill, a plain-clothes officer from Dundee raised his hand. 'Any chance of looking through his client list?'

'I plan to request a warrant to cover that too,' Clare said. 'Names and addresses, at least. Apparently they don't do criminal work so I can't see why we wouldn't get them.'

'Anything from the house?' Liv asked.

'Chris and I had a quick look through his study at home,' Clare said. 'We took his home laptop to avoid it being tampered with but we can't access it without a warrant. Probably shouldn't have taken it but I didn't want to risk anything being deleted. As soon as the warrant's through I'll send it to Tech Support. I believe there was also a mobile found on the body. Once SOCO are done with it we'll send that down too. Meantime I'll request phone data for the past month. There's likely to be a lot so I'll need someone to go through that. Once we have photos of the alleged stalker I'd like a house-to-house over at Drumoig. Did anyone see him, notice anything about him, suspicious vehicles, any activity late at night? You all know the drill.' She stood thinking for a minute and glanced over at Chris. 'Have I missed anything?'

'Emma Halliday.'

'Ah yes. Harry Richards was the only solicitor in his practice, but he usually took on a trainee. They'd stay two years until they were fully qualified then move on to another firm. He's currently between trainees, the last having left a few weeks ago. Emma Halliday. Seems she was privately critical of Harry to other members of staff but we're not quite sure why. So I need someone to track her down, please. She's apparently working for a large solicitors' practice in Dundee, but I don't know which one. I do have contact details, though.'

Janey, another Dundee detective who worked closely with Bill, raised her hand. 'I'll take that, boss.'

Clare looked round the room. 'I hope to have the body ID'd by lunchtime and I'll request the warrant now. Otherwise, start digging into anyone local with a conviction for stalking, harassment, sex crimes – the usual.' She turned to Chris. 'I'd like you and Max on the bus CCTV please. You know what you're looking for. I want photos of anyone who boarded a bus from that stop around three last Wednesday. Maybe go one stop either side as well. If the bus was late or cancelled he might have decided to walk on to the next stop.'

'Are you thinking the stalker's our killer?' Liv asked.

'Not necessarily,' Clare said. 'But he could be connected so we have to find him, and fast.'

She left Chris and Max checking bus timetables and went to her office to request the warrant.

–

It was just after eleven thirty when Clare and Chris set out for Louise Richards' house.

'Any luck with the buses?' she said, slowing as they neared the scene of the previous night's accident. The area was still cordoned off with blue and white tape. Beyond this a white van was parked broadside across a metal field gate. A man in a hard hat was taking a chainsaw to a tree which lay now at an awkward angle, another casualty of last night's accident. Driving past, she found it hard to see the extent of the damage to the substation box but there was no mistaking the tyre marks on the pavement and the flattened fence posts.

'Bad one,' Chris said, and they drove on for a few minutes in silence, Clare wondering vaguely what had caused the driver to leave the road and hit the box with such force. The speed limit was forty on this stretch and a lone woman driver didn't sound like the typical speed merchant. You never could tell, though.

'You were asking about buses,' Chris said.

'Yeah. Any luck?'

'Hopefully. We narrowed it down to three. Just waiting on the CCTV files.'

'You told them it was urgent?'

'Yeah. Max should have them later today.' Chris was quiet for a moment. 'Any thoughts on this one?'

'Not really,' Clare said. 'But those appointments could be significant.'

'Yeah. I reckon so. But how do we find out where he went?'

'Phone company?'

'Maybe. Depends if he was smart enough to switch off his phone.'

'That would imply he was involved in something dodgy.'

'Think we got that from the nick on his neck,' Chris said.

'Fair point.' They were nearing Drumoig now and Clare signalled to turn into the estate. As they drove up towards the Richards' house she looked left and right. 'I can't see why our parka man would be up here if it wasn't to scare the shit out of Louise.'

'Nor me. Apart from the golf and the hotel it's just houses.'

'Unless it wasn't Louise he was trying to scare.'

'Harry?'

'Could be.' She pulled up outside the house and shut off the engine. 'Ready?'

He sighed. 'I'm never ready for this, especially with such a violent death.'

'I know. Come on, then. Let's see how she is.'

Louise was more soberly dressed in a dark grey suit and a shell-pink blouse. She was pale, her face free of make-up, save for a touch of mascara on her lashes. She followed them to the car, her head down as though somehow ashamed of what was happening. Chris waited until she'd pulled on her seat belt then he closed the car door softly.

They drove to the mortuary in near silence, Clare making the odd remark which Louise barely acknowledged. As they joined the bridge, heading for Dundee, the river sparkled and danced in the April sun, lifting Clare's spirits despite the grim task that lay ahead. Leaving the bridge they were brought to a halt at traffic lights near the iconic V&A building.

66

Clare's gaze drifted left and she indicated the gallery. 'Have you been inside?'

Louise's eyes strayed towards the building. 'Many times. Harry and I.'

Clare gave her an apologetic smile. The lights changed and she pulled away making for the centre of town.

The police mortuary was a small building located next to the Bell Street station. Clare drove past the station building towards the mortuary car park and pressed a buzzer next to the barrier. As she waited she glanced across to the main car park and saw the DCI's car. For a moment she recalled the previous night's conversation about his house in Aberdour; then the barrier was raised and she put it out of her mind.

She backed into a vacant space and turned to Louise. 'Ready?' she said, her voice as gentle as she could manage.

'I doubt I'll ever be ready for this,' Louise whispered. She met Clare's eyes. 'As long as I don't look, there's still hope.' Her voice was little more than a whisper, her lip trembling and Clare's heart went out to her. She gave Louise a moment to compose herself then climbed out and went round to open the car door. Louise sat on, staring straight ahead then slowly she clicked off her seat belt and swung her legs out of the car. The sun was bright as they walked to the entrance but, inside, the light was harsh and unnatural. Clare signed them in and they were led to the mortuary viewing room. As they approached the door Louise began to cry, softly at first then gasping sobs. Clare stood with her, a hand at her back until she managed to control her breathing.

'I'm sorry,' she said, wiping furiously at her eyes. 'It's just,' she broke off and Clare nodded.

'I'll go in before you,' she said. 'Just make sure everything's in order.' Leaving Louise and Chris in a waiting room she went to check the staff were ready for them. She was relieved to see the body had been arranged to hide the wound in Harry's neck. His face, while discoloured, had been cleaned of dried blood.

Assuring herself his appearance wouldn't be too shocking she returned to the waiting area.

Louise's eyes were red rimmed, traces of mascara below them but she seemed to have her nerves under control. She eyed Clare as she came back into the room. 'Will I be able to touch him?' she asked, her voice quavering.

'I'm afraid not. You'll be viewing the body from behind a glass screen.'

She stared at Clare. 'Then how will I know? If it's him, I mean. How will I know?'

Clare touched Louise's arm lightly. 'You'll know,' she said and she gestured with her hand. 'If you're ready?'

Louise followed her mutely to the room. She stood looking at the body, her lip quivering. Silent tears rolled down her cheeks and she accepted the tissue Clare passed her. After a minute Clare said, 'Louise, is this the body of your husband, Harry Richards?'

There was a silence – an impenetrable silence and Clare waited while Louise composed herself.

'Yes,' she said, her voice hoarse. 'That's Harry.'

'You're quite certain?'

'Yes,' she said again. 'That is my husband's body.'

Clare caught Chris's eye and they drew back, leaving Louise to stand by the window. She remained there for a minute or two then she turned back to Clare.

'I'd like to go now, please.'

She said little on the way back, speaking only to tell Clare she'd be fine when they offered to come into the house with her.

'All the same,' Clare said. 'We'll come in, just for a minute. Maybe have a quick cup of tea. I'm sure we could all do with one.'

Over coffee which Louise made, Clare explained they would send over a family liaison officer. 'It'll be company for you; and she'll be on hand to answer any questions, fend off the press and so on.'

At the mention of the press Louise's eyes widened. 'Surely they won't come here?'

'I'm afraid they might. But the liaison officer will keep them at bay; and I'll post another officer at your gate for the next few days.' She looked across to the front room window. 'It might be an idea to draw those curtains. Just until the fuss dies down.'

Louise followed her gaze to the window but said nothing.

'Would you like us to contact Harry's daughter?' Clare asked.

She shook her head. 'I called her last night. Said I'd call again once... once I'd seen Harry.' She broke off for a moment then she said, 'How did he die?'

Clare flicked a glance at Chris warning him to say nothing. 'At the moment we don't have an official cause of death. The post-mortem will establish that.'

'You don't know, then?'

This was difficult. Louise would have to know eventually but Clare decided this wasn't the moment. There was something quite horrifying, quite brutal about the way Harry had died; and his wife had been through enough already, viewing the body. The details could wait. And there was another reason, too. Louise seemed devastated by her husband's death and her grief appeared raw and genuine. But it wouldn't be the first time a guilty widow had put on a convincing performance. No. Until they could rule Louise out of any involvement, they'd keep details of Harry's death to a minimum. 'We'll speak again when the post-mortem's been done.'

They finished their tea, Chris washing up the cups. Louise reluctantly gave Clare details of her GP and Clare phoned the surgery to ask a doctor to call round.

'We'll leave you now,' she said, 'but the family liaison officer will be over before the end of the day. I should warn you we'll also be issuing a statement to the press so I would expect there to be some interest from the papers and TV. Best unplug the landline.'

Louise rose and walked with Clare and Chris to the front door. 'I can't believe this is happening,' she said. 'It's like a nightmare.'

Clare nodded. 'It must be. I'm so sorry we had to put you through that. I'll keep in touch with your liaison officer. If you need anything, just let her know.'

As they emerged into the afternoon sunlight Louise said, 'There is something.'

They waited, and after a moment she spoke again.

'You can catch whoever did this. Please tell me you'll catch them?'

Chapter 12

'Got the bus footage,' Max said as they entered the incident room.

'Anyone who looks like the stalker?'

'I'm still going through it. The footage from last Wednesday's been taped over on at least one bus. But the local one – the 99 – that looks more hopeful.'

'Quick as you can, then, Max. We need it for house-to-house. That it?'

'Pretty much. Oh, I think the Super's been on the phone for you. Jim took the call.'

Clare groaned. 'That's all I need,' and she went off to find Jim.

'You've to phone her back,' Jim said. 'Soon as possible.'

Clare thanked him and went off to make the call. She was put on hold for some minutes then she heard the clipped tones of Penny Meakin, the superintendent.

'Ah, Clare. Thanks for returning my call. I'll come straight to the point. We're extremely short of DCIs at the moment but I am aware of your murder case. What I'd like to know is if you can manage without one for the next few days?'

'Of course,' Clare said. 'The other stations have been generous with staff. But I do need warrants authorised.'

'What specifically are you after?'

'The victim's a solicitor so—'

'That's tricky,' Penny said. 'His clients' confidentiality doesn't die with him, you know.'

Clare did know but she wasn't about to rub Penny up the wrong way. 'I'd like to go for minimal information. Just names, addresses, phone numbers relating to clients. I'm happy to exclude client case information. Hopefully that'll demonstrate good faith on our part.'

'Yes, I agree. Anything else?'

'Phone and bank information for the victim, his wife and their paralegal.'

'Why the paralegal?'

Clare hesitated. 'I'm not sure. He was pretty jumpy when we interviewed him. Oh, and I seized a laptop from the victim's house.'

'Hmm. He could have some work on that,' Penny said. 'Strictly speaking you should have left it where it was.'

'I know,' Clare said. 'But I was concerned it might be tampered with.'

'Okay. Send me the details. I'll action it straight away. No guarantees, mind. But I'll do my best. I'm guessing you'll need a liaison officer as well. Anyone in mind?'

'I do,' Clare said. 'I'll give her a call now.'

'Right then.' Penny's tone was brisk. 'Any other problems, get me on my direct line. And, Clare?'

She waited.

'It goes without saying this will look good on your record.'

Clare made the right noises then she pulled her keyboard across the desk and began typing up the warrant request. She was about to send it then she stopped and went to find Chris. He was with Max, the pair poring over CCTV from the bus. 'Come and check this,' she said and turned back to her office, Chris trailing after her.

'It's the warrant. Penny Meakin said she'd action it ASAP so I want to make sure I've not missed anything.' She indicated the screen. 'I've gone for Louise and Harry's phone and bank records, same for the paralegal, and names, addresses and phone numbers for Harry's clients, specifically excluding any case information.'

72

'What if he did a bit of criminal defence on the side? Those clients he saw after hours.'

'That's way above my pay grade, Chris. We'd need the Force legal team on that one. But I doubt we'd get it. Client privilege doesn't die with the solicitor. We might have to wait until a new one's appointed to represent Harry's clients.'

'Better hope we find the killer, then,' Chris muttered.

Clare finished the email and clicked to send it. 'Any luck with the photos?'

'Yeah, think so. Looks like the parka lad got on at Drumoig.'

'And off again?'

'Bus station.'

Clare looked up. 'What, here? In the town?'

He nodded. 'Think so. It's hard to be sure – there was a bit of a crowd, all getting off together. Makes it harder to pick anyone out.'

'Okay. Get the best ones up on the network and we'll see if anyone recognises him.'

'Will do.' He wandered off and Clare sat thinking for a minute. She scrolled through her phone contacts until she found the number for Wendy Briggs, a family liaison officer she'd worked with before. Clare had always found her to have a good balance of background support with sharp eyes for any unusual behaviour.

Wendy answered immediately. 'Clare,' she said. 'Good to hear from you. How's tricks?'

'You've heard about our murder?'

'Yes. Are the rumours true? His throat was slit?'

'I'm afraid so, but we've not released that yet.'

'Understood,' Wendy said. 'I'm guessing you've phoned because—'

'Any chance you're free?' Clare said. 'We need an FLO for the wife.'

'Nothing I can't rearrange. I could be with you in, say, a couple of hours?'

Clare thanked Wendy and was about to check on progress with the photos when curiosity took her to BBC news website. She didn't even have to click for the Scottish news. Harry Richards' death was on the front page.

Mystery surrounds the death of Fife solicitor at
popular beauty spot

She read on just far enough to assure herself the cause of death hadn't been leaked. 'That's something at least,' she murmured, clicking to view the Scottish news. There was no further detail on Harry's death but there was a small item on the crash near Balgove Larder with an appeal for dashcam footage. Clare read it through then went to find Chris and Max.

'Just putting the clearest ones up on the network now,' Max said.

'Can you print a few out as well, please? Hand them round the incident room.'

Minutes later the printer began to whirr as it churned out copies of the best photos. Max spread them out on the desk and the officers in the room gathered round. Clare noticed Bill staring at one of the photos, his brow creased. 'Bill?'

'Think I might know him,' he said.

'Yeah?'

He didn't reply immediately but moved to the door and shouted on Janey who was in the front office speaking to Jim. A minute later she joined them in the room.

'What was the name of that lad we jailed a couple of years ago?' Bill asked. 'A string of housebreakings in Broughty Ferry?'

'The lad Deuchars?'

'That's him.' Bill jabbed the photo with his finger. 'Kenny Deuchars.' He held the photo out for Janey to see. 'It is him, isn't it?'

Janey studied the photo for a minute then she handed it back. 'I'd say so. But I thought he was in the Bar-L.'

Bill shrugged. 'Must have got out early for good behaviour. That'll be a first. Want me to check?' he asked Clare.

'If you would, Bill. Call them now, please. And, if he is out, we need the address he was released to.' She turned back to Max. 'Could you dig out the file copy of his photo please? And maybe another five men, similar age and build. We'll see if Louise Richards picks him out. If she does, it'll save the bother of an eFit.'

'Thing is,' Chris began, 'he's not actually done anything wrong, has he, this Kenny lad. Assuming he is out of Barlinnie prison. It's not a crime to stand outside someone's house.'

'I'll do him for a breach,' Clare said, referencing the catch-all charge *Breach of the peace*. 'If he is out on licence, I'll threaten to send him back. Anyway, I'm interested in why he was stalking her and, more to the point, who paid him to do it.'

'Someone sending Harry a message? Scaring the wife to warn him?'

Clare nodded. 'Could be. Janey, do you reckon he's capable of cutting the victim's throat – our Mr Deuchars?'

Janey glanced at Bill who had ended his call and the two of them shook their heads. 'He's small-time, boss. Works mainly for other guys. Stealing to order. Could be he was feeding them information about the Richards' movements. But I can't see him killing Harry, especially like that. I think all his previous is for non-violent stuff.'

'So he's working for someone else,' Clare said. 'If it is him. Any luck with the prison, Bill?'

'Calling me back,' Bill said. 'But I'm pretty sure it's him in the photo.'

Clare stood thinking for a minute. 'Okay. Let's check Harry's car against ANPR cameras. Go back a week and if that doesn't turn anything up go back another week. See if there's any pattern and pay particular attention to those days he left the office early. In fact, Chris, give the receptionist – Kate Campbell – give her a call and ask for dates and times especially when he left unexpectedly.'

Clare went to the kitchen to make herself a drink. While she waited for the kettle to boil Janey came in, notepad in hand.

'Emma Halliday,' she said.

'You've found her?'

'Yes and no. She works for Jepson McHardy in their property office.'

'Where's that?'

'Dundee.'

'Did you speak to her?'

'No. She's on holiday this week.'

'Get her mobile?'

'I did but it's going straight to voicemail. According to the woman I spoke to, she's gone up north to do some climbing. Probably out of signal. I've left a message for her to call.'

Clare considered this. 'Can you get me an appointment with whoever's in charge over there please? I'd like to know how she got the job – if there was any contact with Harry.'

The kettle came to the boil. 'Want one?' she said.

'Nah, I've not long had one, thanks.'

Clare took her sandwich out of the fridge and suddenly realised it was after three. No wonder she felt hungry. She carried the drink and sandwich to her office and closed the door, glad of a few minutes' peace to gather her thoughts. There were so many unknowns in this case. It didn't sound like Kenny Deuchars was the killer. It had all the hallmarks of a gangland execution; and, if so, it wouldn't be worth Kenny's while to talk. Not if he didn't want to follow Harry to the police mortuary. All the same, he might give away something that could lead them to the killer.

Hopefully the warrant would be through quickly and they could start to dig deeper into Harry's life. She bit into her sandwich. That holiday Harry had booked – they'd be able to trace the transaction through his bank. She started to write herself a note to check this when an email alert pinged – Raymond, the Scene of Crime Officer. She read it quickly:

Finished at Tentsmuir.

Sorry it took a bit longer than usual.

All yours, now.

Initial findings tomorrow but give me a call if you want the main points.

R

She clicked his number.

'You got the email?' he said.

'Yes, thanks. Any surprises?'

'No. Pretty much as it looked. Definitely murder.'

'Wasn't really in doubt,' Clare said.

'You'd be surprised. It's not unheard of. Pretty rare, I'll grant you, but it has happened, so we always check.'

Clare was intrigued. 'How would you know?'

'We look for hesitation cuts. You can imagine it would take a lot of courage to cut your own throat so there could be small superficial marks, as the person works up to the fatal wound; and they might be found with the knife clenched in their hand. The sudden shock can cause a spasm. There were no hesitation marks in this case and, crucially, no weapon at the scene.'

'Anything else?'

'It was a clean wound, consistent with a right-handed assailant from the seat behind. He or she probably pulled the victim's head back with one hand and drew the knife across his throat with the other. The cut was deeper and slightly higher at the left-hand side, tapering off as it reached the right. It was a pretty bloody scene and I'd say there was someone in the front passenger seat as well.'

'How so?'

'There was blood all over the front of the car. It would have sprayed out as the arteries were severed but there's far less on the front seat.'

'As though someone was sitting there,' Clare finished.

'Precisely; and the outside of the car on the passenger side was smeared with blood, as though the passenger used a bloody hand to shut the door after getting out.'

'Any prints?'

'A few but I'd be surprised if they belong to the assailant or the one in the front. This was a pretty cold-hearted killing. My guess is they'd be gloved up. Their clothes would be heavily stained but they've probably burned them by now. That's what I'd do.'

Clare sighed. 'Me too. Anything else?'

'Only, if they did use a vehicle to leave the scene you'll likely find the victim's blood in that too. It's hard to get rid of every trace from a scene like that. We've taken blood samples from different places in the car but I couldn't see any defensive injuries. I doubt we'll find anything other than the victim's blood.'

She thanked Raymond and sat mulling over what he'd said. No real surprises. It was useful to know the killer was right-handed but so were most people. She hadn't considered there might be two of them, though. One in the front to keep him talking while the other pretended to listen in the back. She closed her eyes, picturing the scene. What terror Harry Richards must have felt in those last dreadful moments. The phone rang, and she glanced at the display. Neil Grant, the pathologist.

'Neil, what can I do for you?'

'Oh, hi, Clare. Just wondering about the post-mortem. I presume your DCI's attending.'

She swore under her breath. When she'd agreed to run the investigation on her own she hadn't bargained for attending the PM. One of the downsides of being the Senior Investigating Officer. 'It'll have to be me, Neil. There's no DCI at the moment. When do you plan to do it?'

'I'd like to start in an hour or so.'

Clare checked her watch. 'I have to wait here to brief the FLO. But I'll head over straight after.' She sat contemplating the post-mortem. It was years since she'd attended one. Not a part of the job she enjoyed, but it had to be done. She tapped out a quick message to Al letting him know she'd be home late then started to make a list of questions for the pathologist. Her appetite had deserted her now and she threw the rest of her sandwich in the bin. Best not to face the dissection room on a full stomach.

Chapter 13

Wendy arrived half an hour later and Clare quickly brought her up to speed.

'She says she was being stalked in the days leading up to her husband's death. We think we've identified a man who was hanging around outside her house.'

'Previous?'

'Yeah. Kenny Deuchars. You come across him?'

Wendy shook her head.

'No matter. Max should have a bundle of photos for her to look through, including Kenny's. I'd like to see if she picks him out.'

'No problem. Anything else? Is she in the frame for it?'

'No,' Clare said. 'Not at the moment, but she may know more than she realises. There were times he left the office for appointments that weren't in the diary. And he'd booked a holiday for next week but not told her where. Said it was a surprise.'

Wendy nodded. 'I'll see what I can find out.' She rose. 'You look busy, Clare. I'll get my own way over there.'

Clare smiled. 'Thanks, Wendy. I appreciate it. There should be an officer on the gate. Get him to take you in so she knows you're legit.'

As Wendy left, Clare stood trying to remember if she'd covered everything. Then she picked up her bag and headed out to the front office.

'I'll be at the mortuary in Dundee,' she said to Jim. 'Hopefully two or three hours at most.' As she crossed the car park a reporter she vaguely recognised rushed up, phone held out. She put up a hand, carrying on her way. 'Sorry,' she said. 'No time. There'll be a press statement in due course.' And, with that, she jumped into her car and threw it into gear.

The streets were busier now, as rush-hour approached. Ahead of her a student on a bike, red gown flapping in the wind, was making slow progress up the Bridge Street incline. At last the bike reached the roundabout and turned left and Clare was soon out of town heading towards Guardbridge. Passing the site of the accident once more she saw the tree had been cut down and a few folk had left flowers. Poor woman. Clare hoped she'd died immediately, or at least been knocked unconscious, and known nothing about it.

The sun was behind the clouds as she entered Dundee for the second time that day, hitting one red light after another, and her thoughts drifted back to Louise Richards. Wendy would be with her now. Making tea, chatting, slowly getting to know and understand her. She'd keep her safe from press intrusion but, more importantly, she would watch and listen for any sign Louise knew more than she was saying.

Clare arrived at the mortuary barrier and was buzzed through to the car park, driving into the nearest space. Grabbing her bag she walked smartly to the entrance, signed in and made her way to the dissection room viewing area. There was a glass screen but it was only head height and her stomach lurched at the familiar chemical odour she knew would soon be replaced by the more repugnant smells of a body in decay.

Neil, gloved and gowned, his back to them, was speaking into a microphone, ceiling-mounted cameras recording the event. Another figure in a gown and mask held a digital camera, taking photos as directed by Neil while a third stood ready with evidence bags to stow clothes and belongings. There were smaller bags tied round Harry's hands and Clare wondered if they might be protecting some evidence – DNA from his assailant, perhaps. Only the lab results would tell them that.

And then it began. Swabs from the hands and nails and the removal of the clothes, each item bagged. Clare took out her notepad, but Neil called her over and she quickly put on a mask and gown.

'Raymond probably gave you an indication,' he said pointing to the large gash, 'but I'm expecting this to be the fatal wound. Obviously there might be other factors but the blood loss at the site tells us he was alive when his throat was cut. There is significant damage to the arterial system,' he said. 'Death would have followed very soon after.'

Clare noted this down. 'Any defensive wounds?'

'Not that I've seen so far,' he said. 'The hands are quite bloody, as you would imagine. But I suspect the attack was swift and unexpected. He probably raised his hands to his neck instinctively. We'll clean them up but I've not seen any cuts so far.'

'What about the blade?'

'Big,' he said. 'It's gone deep. But, given where he was killed, it wouldn't have been overlong. The assailant would have had to get it round the headrest before Harry realised what was happening so I'd say twenty to thirty centimetres, end to end.'

'Type of blade?'

'Not serrated. The cuts were clean.'

'Any indication it was damaged in the attack?'

He shook his head. 'Doesn't look like it hit bone but I'll know more once I've finished.'

'Would it have needed extreme force?'

'Depends on the blade. If it was sharp it wouldn't have taken much. A strong stomach and no conscience would do it.'

Clare thanked Neil and retreated to the viewing area as he began the lengthy process of examining and weighing the internal organs.

It was almost eight o'clock by the time it was finished.

'I'll write up my report in the next few days,' he said. 'Lab results will take a bit longer but no real surprises. He was reasonably healthy for his age – no obvious sign of disease. Blood in the airways confirms he was alive when attacked and the knife wound was the cause of death.'

'Thanks, Neil. I appreciate you prioritising this.'

'No problem. Now get home for a stiff drink. You look like you could do with one.'

She escaped thankfully, drawing in deep lungfuls of air as she walked to the car. No matter how many post-mortems she attended she never got used to the smell. How did Neil and his staff stand it?

She checked her phone and saw a message from Wendy confirming Louise had identified Kenny Deuchars as her stalker. She sent this on to Chris and Max then tapped a quick text to the DCI to let him know she was on her way home.

Day 3: Thursday, 6th April

Chapter 14

'You're remembering I'm away tomorrow,' the DCI said over breakfast.

Clare nodded. 'Bit unusual, a course starting on a Friday.'

'Doesn't start till Monday,' he said, spreading honey on a piece of toast. This had not gone unnoticed by Benjy who sat by his side, face upturned in the hope of a stray bit of crust. 'But there's staff from other UK forces arriving on Saturday.'

'It's not just a Scottish course, then?'

'Far from it. We need as much cross-border co-operation as we can get.'

'What's it about, again? Sorry – I know you told me.'

'Phone apps, and how they can be used for fraud. It's big business now. Think how popular these games are – Candy Crush and the like. All it takes is someone with the knowledge. They build a fancy-looking game and throw in a bit of marketing. It doesn't even have to work that well. Even if the user ends up deleting it they've already installed a piece of spyware; and it sits there, quietly mining their phone for data.'

Clare thought about the times she'd sat playing games on her phone when she needed to relax after a tough day.

He saw her face. 'Don't look so worried. I doubt you even know how to download an app.'

She ignored the gibe and topped up her coffee, holding the cafetiere out to him. 'I didn't realise you knew about this stuff.'

He waved away the offer of coffee. 'I don't. But I know how to run courses.'

She raised an eyebrow. 'Got a clipboard?'

'Shut up. There's more to it than that. I don't know how the app developers work but I do know how people behave, the type of people who fall prey to these guys. It's my job to teach the officers how to apply the knowledge the software guys give them.'

'Yeah, okay.' She lifted her mug and drained it. 'Better get going.' She loaded her plate and mug into the dishwasher then she shivered. 'I can't get that post-mortem smell out of my nose.'

'Sit next to your farting dog,' he said, one eye on Benjy. 'That'll do it.'

—

She drove into work, Harry Richards on her mind. But she was also conscious they'd skirted round the question of the DCI's house – last night *and* at breakfast. She wanted time to think and she couldn't do that with her head full of Harry's murder. As she pulled into the car park, the reporter from the previous night was leaning against a wall opposite the station. He'd been joined by two others, one of whom spotted Clare. Before she could reach the station door a phone was thrust in her face, a barrage of questions fired at her.

'The press office will keep you updated, gents,' she said and pushed past them, escaping into the station.

She'd called a briefing for seven and the incident room was packed when she entered. The desks and laptops had been sorted out now and it was easier to move about the room. She made her way to her usual spot in front of the whiteboard and tapped it to get their attention.

'Right,' she began. 'Quick update. No surprises from the PM. Still awaiting lab results but Harry Richards died from the wound in his neck. He was otherwise in good health for his age.' She glanced down at her notepad. 'The pathologist thinks it was a smooth-bladed knife, between twenty and thirty centimetres long. No sign the blade was damaged in the attack.'

She paused to let them make notes. 'It's likely there were two people in the car with the victim. One in the passenger seat, one behind. Neil thinks the one behind pulled Harry's head back and cut his throat, drawing the blade from left to right.'

'So right-handed?' Nita asked and Clare nodded.

'Both assailants would have been bloodstained, as would any vehicle they used to leave the scene. Chances are they've burned their clothes. Might have torched the car as well, or had it cleaned. That said, it is hard to remove every trace of blood.

'Okay, next thing. Louise Richards has identified Kenny Deuchars as the man who was stalking her. So it looks like he's out of Barlinnie. It goes without saying we need to find him urgently.' Her eye fell on Bill. 'Any word on that?'

'Aye,' he said. 'The prison called back a wee while ago. He is out. Released to...' he glanced down at his notepad, 'Pitfedden Lodge. Half-way house supporting offenders on release. Apparently staying there's a condition of his licence.'

'Any reason?'

'I'd guess to keep him away from his old haunts in Dundee. Stop him falling into bad company.'

'Thanks, Bill. You been in touch with the Lodge?'

'Not yet. Thought I'd wait to see how you wanted to play it.'

Clare considered this. 'Give them a call, please. If he's there, head over. I'd like him in for interview.'

Bill nodded and Chris raised a hand. 'Do you want Kenny's name released to the press?'

'Not yet,' Clare said. 'We've more chance of finding him if he's not expecting us.' She turned back to Janey. 'Any luck with Emma Halliday?'

Janey shook her head. 'Sorry, boss. Mobile still out of signal, as far as I can tell. But I spoke to Steve McHardy, one of the partners. Very shocked about Harry, as you can imagine. He was on the panel that appointed Emma. Said to call anytime and he'll be happy to speak to you.'

'Speaking of Drumoig,' Clare said, 'I'd like uniforms to begin house-to-house on the estate this morning. Max, can you organise that, please? It's a lot of houses so focus initially on the streets closest to the Richards. I'd also like the staff at the golf club and the hotel spoken to. Take copies of Kenny's photo and see if any of them saw him hanging around.' She glanced at her notepad. 'Final thing — at least until we get the warrant — I want an address for Rosie and Gordon King. Rosie, if you remember, was Harry Richards' first wife, now remarried and living in Dundee. They need interviewed so let's find them.'

Cheryl, a detective sergeant from Dundee indicated she would take this. 'Anything special you want to know?'

'If they've heard from Harry in the last few months, what Rosie knew about his work, any suspicions he might have fallen in with the wrong people. But tactful, mind.' Clare smiled round at them. 'Thanks, folks. That's it for now but keep in touch; and any news on Kenny, I want to know about it.'

Chapter 15

Clare went back to her office and switched on the computer. As she waited for it to come to life she took out her notepad and flicked back over the last few pages to check she hadn't missed anything. There was a tap on the door and Max pushed it open with his foot, a cup of coffee in one hand, a folded green paper towel in the other.

'Zoe's made Rocky Road,' he said, putting down the coffee and handing her the green paper towel. She opened it to find a large hunk of the tray bake.

'Thanks, Max. That'll keep me going. You two still an item, then?'

Max flushed and he suppressed a smile. 'She's great, Zoe. I've never met anyone quite like her.'

Clare thought about Zoe, her mop of curls, dyed jet black this week. She'd joined them a year or so back and had unwittingly been duped in what they'd thought was an online dating scam. For a while after that, she'd been subdued, quite unlike herself. And then Max had arrived, borrowed from the Bell Street station in Dundee, and the two had struck up an unlikely partnership. Chris had been sceptical, saying Zoe would eat Max for breakfast and Clare had privately agreed. But it seemed they'd both been wrong. Maybe opposites really did attract.

'House-to-house guys are at Drumoig, now,' he said. 'I'll let you know if they turn anything up.'

The door opened again and Chris came in, coffee mug in hand, a hunk of Rocky Road between his teeth. He put his mug down on Clare's desk and kicked the door shut.

'Does Sara know you're eating that?' she said, indicating the cake.

He pulled up a chair next to Max. 'All part of a balanced diet.'

'You'll not be saying that when you're trying to get your bellies into swimming trunks.'

Chris rolled his eyes. 'Apparently we're not lying on the beach all the time. We've to traipse around monuments and stuff.'

'Oh *Chichen Itza*,' Max began.

'Yep. That's on the list. And it seems calling it Chicken Pizza isn't funny – or clever!'

'Meanwhile, back at our grisly murder,' Clare interrupted. 'The manner of Harry Richards' death worries me.'

'The knife?' Chris asked.

'Well, yes. But more his throat being cut. Most of the knife crime we deal with is stabbings – chest or back. This feels more sinister.'

'You're thinking an organised crime group?' Chris said.

She nodded. 'I don't want to think there's an OCG operating in the area but we can't ignore it.' She sat mulling this over. 'I'd like you two to look closely into Kenny Deuchars: known associates, cell mates, prison visitors. Anyone at all connected to his recent past.' She bit off a piece of Rocky Road and chewed it, running through things in her head. Had she covered everything? Then she remembered Harry and his unscheduled appointments.

'Did you get a list of dates for when Harry left the office? The appointments not in the diary?'

Chris shook his head. 'She's calling me back. Said she'd have to go through his diary and have a think.'

'Soon as you can, then.'

They finished their coffees and the two sergeants went off to begin their tasks. Clare returned to her notepad checking she'd covered everything on the list. Her eye was drawn to a car registration. Jotted down but no note beside it. She sat back and thought. It was in her notebook just before the information on Harry's murder. And then she remembered. The black BMW outside the school. The one the dark-haired girl had got into. Possibly the same girl who'd been hanging around outside the room when Eilidh had come in to ask about reporting a crime. There'd been something familiar about the driver but she still couldn't place him. She wrote the registration on a Post-it and pushed back her chair.

Jim was at his desk in the front office and he looked up as Clare approached.

'Could you check on something, please?' She held out the Post-it. 'I'd like the registered keeper for this car; and run him through the database as well. See if he has any previous.'

Jim indicated he would do this and, as she headed back to her office, her phone began to ring. Wendy.

'Just a quick call,' she said. 'Louise is out in the garden, doing a bit of weeding.'

'How is she?'

'Quiet. Calmer than yesterday. She spoke to the stepdaughter in New Zealand. She's flying back next week.'

'Any other calls?'

'No. After the stepdaughter called she switched her phone off. We did have one reporter at the door, though.'

'What?' Clare said. 'There should have been an officer on the gate.'

'It was a genuine mistake, Clare. The reporter spun him a line about being a family friend.'

'I'll give him mistake. Who was it?'

'Sandy-haired lad. Mid-twenties.'

Robbie. Another slip up. What was wrong with him? 'I'll have a word,' she said.

'I mean, it's up to you,' Wendy said. 'But I already gave him a bit of a roasting. Pretty sure he won't let anyone else through.'

Clare sighed. 'Okay. Anything else?'

'I asked about the holiday.'

'Yeah?'

'Seems it was a complete surprise. About a week, ten days ago. Harry was working all hours. Coming home late, telling her he'd eaten – but she thought he hadn't – his trousers were getting loose round the waist. He'd go straight to his study and work late into the night. She was worried about him. Said he needed a break. Oh, hold on – I think she's coming into the kitchen.' For a minute or two Clare heard a muffled conversation. Wendy must have put the phone in her pocket. Then there was the sound of a door closing and she heard Wendy's voice again.

'She's gone back out. I'd better be quick, though. She's talking about having some lunch.'

'You were saying?'

'Yeah. She told Harry he needed a break, and he said what about a holiday. Said she was quite right. He'd been working far too hard and was going to book one that day.'

'Any idea where?'

'No. He told her to pack for warm weather and to take her jewellery.'

'That's odd. Did she say why?'

'She wondered if he'd booked a cruise – the kind with swanky dinners at night. But then she thought he might be worried about burglars, with that Kenny lad hanging around.'

Clare was silent as she considered this. 'She could have a point. But there has to be more to it than that.'

'Any sign of your warrant?'

Clare ran an eye down her Inbox. 'Not yet. I'll chase it if it's not in this morning.'

'Better go,' Wendy said, her voice low. 'Looks like she's finished weeding. Speak soon.'

Clare put down her phone, thinking about this. Was there more to Harry Richards' holiday plans than an expensive cruise?

Jim appeared at the door. He put a printout on her desk. 'Car's registered to a Colin Grandison. Address in Dundee. No previous.'

Clare thought for a moment. 'Doesn't ring a bell. Do we know what he does? For a living, I mean.'

'Not sure, to be honest. Why not ask one of the Dundee lads?'

'Good idea.' Clare went to the incident room hoping to find Bill or Janey.

'Not sure where they are,' Cheryl said. 'Bill's jacket's gone. Want me to get them on the phone?'

'No,' Clare said. 'It's fine. You're from Dundee as well, aren't you?'

'Born and bred. What are you after?'

'Come across a Colin Grandison?'

Cheryl raised an eyebrow. 'Coke Grand. Yeah, I know him. You thinking he's involved in this case?'

Clare hesitated. 'No, it's not that. I saw his car recently at Melville Academy. His daughter was getting into it. At least, I presume it was his daughter.'

Cheryl reached for her laptop. 'I think he does have a daughter. I can check if you like.' She began tapping at the keyboard.

'What does he do?' Clare asked. 'I doubt the fees at Melville are cheap.'

'Good question. He used to have a building firm. Sold it for a packet and bought a big house out the Perth Road. Rumours are he's into all sorts but we've never been able to find out exactly what. He might be clean but...' She turned the laptop screen round to show Clare a photo from a news website. 'This is him. He organised some kind of charity thing last year for underprivileged kids. The council gave him the use of Camperdown – a big park at the north of Dundee. Got a lot of press attention.' She tapped the screen. 'That's him handing over the cheque.'

Clare sat down next to Cheryl and peered at the screen. A man of about fifty stood smiling, a large cardboard cheque in his hands. He was slim, average height, as far as she could tell from the photo, but his features were quite different from the man she'd seen in the BMW. He was olive skinned, his face thinner, pinched even, his features sharp. His hair was thick and dark, a lustrous quiff swept back, his stubbly beard tending to grey. Was there a resemblance to the girl who'd got into the BMW? She thought there was. 'You're sure this is him?'

'No doubt about it. I've seen him around the town. Look – his name's in the caption.'

'That's not the man I saw at Melville Academy.'

'He probably has people working for him.'

Clare frowned. 'But you don't know what he does?'

'Nope.'

She peered at the screen again. 'Sixty thousand? How the hell did he raise a sum like that?'

'Called in favours, I heard,' Cheryl said. 'Bill might know more about it but I think he leaned heavily on his local contacts. Suddenly they were falling over themselves to offer free stuff.' Her brow creased. 'There was something to do with a shop in the town but I can't remember now. Bill will definitely know.'

Clare stared at the screen again 'Ask him to give me a shout when he comes in.' She made for the door then turned back. 'Coke, you say?'

Cheryl shrugged. 'Short for Colin. Don't ask me why.'

Clare shook her head. 'Every day's a school day.'

Jim was back at his desk as she emerged from the incident room. 'Was Cheryl able to help?'

She smiled. 'A bit.' She hesitated. 'Jim, I don't really know why I'm asking this but could you check to see if this Colin Grandison has any other vehicles?'

'Aye. No bother. Just hold on and I'll do it now.'

Clare waited and a few minutes later the printer began to whirr and Jim rose to collect the printout.

'Another two cars,' he said, handing her the sheet. 'An Audi Q8 and an old Triumph Spitfire. Collector's item, that last one; both registered to Colin Grandison.' He tapped the sheet. 'There's a van as well. Registered to his business: Granco Lettings. But it was reported stolen a week ago.'

'Oh?'

Jim shrugged. 'We've had a spate of vehicle thefts. I wouldn't bet on it turning up now. Likely at the other end of the country with false plates.'

'Suppose.' Clare took the sheet and studied it. 'No shortage of money, though?'

'Clearly not. He been a bad boy, our Mr Grandison?'

She hesitated. 'That's just it. I'm not sure. It might have something to do with a schoolgirl called Eilidh.' Leaving Jim none the wiser, she wandered back to her office, wondering if she should follow up the conversation with Eilidh. And then she gave herself a shake. They had enough to do, finding Kenny Deuchars, and whoever had killed Harry Richards. She put the printout in her desk drawer and picked up her phone. Almost nine. Time to see if Jepson McHardy were open for business.

Chapter 16

Janey had given Clare Steve McHardy's direct line and he answered immediately.

She introduced herself and explained she was hoping to speak to Emma Halliday in connection with Harry's death.

He made the usual noises about how shocked they all were. 'Dreadful thing,' he said. 'I did wonder if it was, well, if he'd done something to himself.'

'What made you think that?'

'Oh, pressures of the job, you know.'

'Had you heard he was under particular pressure?'

There was a hesitation and Clare went on.

'We will speak to Emma once we get hold of her but the sooner we have the full picture the better.'

Again, he was quiet for a moment. 'This is starting to sound as if it's not a suicide.'

'We are treating Mr Richards' death as suspicious,' Clare said, choosing her words carefully.

'I see. In that case... Emma – well, she'll tell you this herself. As you probably know, Harry doesn't keep his trainees on after they have their practising certificate. He's always said the firm can't afford the higher salary.'

'Is that common practice?'

'Some would argue it's a bit unfair, using the trainees as cheap labour. I wouldn't entirely agree. They do receive a training, and any solicitors who've come to us from Harry have had a good grounding. It's not cheap running a business these days: staff, premises, overheads – it all mounts up.'

Clare waited, sensing there was more.

'When she came to us – Emma – she was quite guarded in what she said about Harry. But there were a couple of remarks that gave me concern.'

'Such as?'

'You must understand,' Steve said, 'I wouldn't be saying any of this if you hadn't told me Harry's death was suspicious.'

'Of course,' Clare assured him. 'Anything you tell me won't go any further unless I judge it's relevant to our enquiries.'

'It's not as if I actually know anything,' he said. 'But on a couple of occasions Emma made some remark like *At least things are done properly here.*'

'Did you ask what she meant by that?'

'I did but she fudged it – said something about a misunderstanding. She didn't seem keen to say any more so I left it. And another time she said something about the importance of ethics in our profession. Again, I asked if she'd something particular in mind. She said, no, but she felt she was able to do a good job here.'

'Able to?' Clare said.

'I'm fairly sure those were her exact words.'

'And you thought there was more to it?'

'Possibly. Let's put it this way, Inspector: I've had a lot of new solicitors pass through my hands but never one who made that kind of remark.'

Clare considered this. Was he making something out of nothing? There was only one person who could tell them and she was somewhere in the wilds of Scotland. 'Had you heard any other rumours? Elsewhere, I mean?'

'No,' he said. 'If there was gossip about Harry it didn't reach my ears.'

'How well did you know him?'

'Not that well. We met at the odd dinner but that's all.'

'When did you last see him?'

'Oh.' There was a pause as though Steve was trying to remember. 'Probably a year past August. We were at a fundraising event in Camperdown Park.'

Clare was suddenly alert. 'What sort of event?'

'One of these charity things – raising money for underprivileged kids. We donated a hotel voucher. For the raffle, you know?'

Silently Clare opened her desk drawer and glanced at the printout Jim had given her. Colin Grandison's cars. 'Can I ask how you came to be involved with this charity event?'

He exhaled. 'Goodness. Now you're asking. I'm not sure I remember, to be honest. A lot of local solicitors were involved. I suppose someone talked me into helping. We had a tug-o-war team, I remember that. I think the butchers beat us!'

'Might it have been a local businessman who organised it?' Clare said, choosing her words carefully.

'That's it!' he said. 'You're right. Some lad called Grantley or something like that.'

'Grandison?' Clare said.

'Yes. I think so. Keith – no, Colin I think it was.'

'And have you had any dealings with Mr Grandison since then?'

'No. We turned up, showed face for a couple of hours, did our bit then left. I was glad to help, to be honest. Some of these kids, they've next to nothing.'

'And Harry was there?'

'He was. I think he was judging some of the competitions. Goodness knows how he got roped into that.'

How indeed, Clare thought. She asked a few more questions then decided there was nothing more to be learned from Steve McHardy. She reminded him she was keen to speak to Emma and put down her phone. She stared at the printout in her drawer. Had Harry Richards known this Colin Grandison? It was beginning to look like it. But he probably knew lots of people, particularly in the business community. She was making too much of it. She knew that. All the same...

'Sorry, boss,' Bill said. 'Kenny's staying at Pitfedden, right enough. But when I phoned they said he wasn't there.'

'Do they know where he is?'

'Nope. Apparently not been seen for a few days.'

'We should have been told about that,' Clare said. 'He's out on licence, isn't he?'

Bill nodded. 'The warden wanted to give him a day or two. Said he was probably on a bender. Apparently some of the lads struggle with suddenly having access to drink and drugs. Takes them a few weeks to settle down.'

Clare's eyes narrowed. 'It still should have been reported.'

'Aye, it should,' Bill acknowledged. 'Anyway, she suggested a pub in the town so we nipped over there but no luck.'

'How long's he been at Pitfedden?'

Bill checked his notepad. 'About six weeks.'

'Any other trouble?'

'Not that she told us.'

Clare stood thinking for a minute. 'I might head over there anyway. See the place for myself.'

'Fair enough. But it sounds like she has a pretty good handle on things.'

'Okay.' Clare looked round. 'Janey?'

'Incident room.'

'Come on,' she said. 'I want to ask the two of you something.' They entered the room and she caught Janey's attention. 'Colin Grandison,' she said. 'Know him?'

Janey raised an eyebrow. 'Oh yes. We know Coke all right.'

'That sounds ominous.'

She inclined her head. 'Not really. He keeps his nose clean but there's always a suggestion he's behind some of the stuff that goes on.'

'What sort of stuff?' Clare asked.

Bill and Janey exchanged glances.

'Hard to say,' Bill said. 'Nobody ever names him. Seems they'd rather do the time themselves than put Coke in the dock.'

Clare considered this. 'How does he make his money?'

'He had a building firm,' Janey said. 'CLG Construction. Sold it for a packet. Apparently he's living off that. So he says.'

Clare frowned. 'Even if he sold it for a million, it wouldn't last forever.'

Janey nodded. 'It would not. Rumour is he's a backstreet moneylender, among other things.'

'Surely Dundee's onto that?'

'It's not for the want of trying,' Bill said. 'He doesn't deal directly with the punters himself. He has people to do that for him.'

'No one willing to speak up?'

Bill shook his head. 'Too scared.'

Clare recalled the conversation with Steve McHardy. 'Do you two remember an event he organised at Camperdown Park, year before last?'

'Aye,' Bill said. 'We took a tour round, didn't we?'

Janey nodded. 'Just keeping an eye, you know?'

'Cheryl mentioned this Coke guy leaned on his contacts to give raffle donations,' Clare said. 'But there was something with a local shop. She couldn't remember the details. Said to ask you two.'

'Toytown,' Bill said.

'Yeah. Lovely toy shop. South Tay Street,' Janey said.

'What happened?'

'Nothing was ever proved,' Bill said. 'But it sounded like Coke was asking all the local shops for donations. Toytown declined. Said times were hard. They'd had repairs to the roof and couldn't afford to give anything. Next thing we know, there's a glazier's van outside and all the stock in the window was being thrown out. Someone had put the window in.'

'And this was Coke's doing?' Clare asked.

Bill shook his head. 'We couldn't prove anything. But it seemed pretty clear to us he was behind it.'

'Then we heard Toytown had given a generous donation,' Janey said.

'Did you have the owner in for questioning?'

'We tried but he refused to give a statement. Said it was likely kids, or drunks making their way home from the clubs.'

'But you thought it was Coke?'

'Oh for sure,' Janey said. 'He even gave an interview to the press, saying how every single business approached had given generously. Mentioned Toytown; said they'd donated a load of stuff despite their *recent troubles*. We all knew he was behind it but there were no witnesses and the staff stuck to their story.'

Clare sat back considering this. 'I saw his BMW on Tuesday – at Melville Academy.'

Bill's brow furrowed. 'Think he has a daughter.' He turned to Janey. 'Can you remember?'

'Yeah. She must be about sixteen or seventeen now. I saw her once. Striking girl. Thick dark hair. Can't remember her name, though.' She studied Clare. 'Why you asking?'

Good question, Clare thought. Why was she asking when they had a gruesome murder to solve? But there was something about that car – something that had made her jot down the registration. 'The driver,' she said. 'He looked familiar but I don't think it was him – this Coke guy.'

'What did he look like?' Bill asked.

'Bit like a bouncer. Close cropped hair, thick neck, dark glasses. Sorry,' she said, 'not a great description. I only saw him through the car window.'

Bill and Janey looked at each other.

'Sounds like Albie Kennedy,' Janey said. 'He looks like the kind of guy you wouldn't mess with.'

'That name definitely sounds familiar. Got any previous?'

'Couple of assault charges. Never got to court, though. Couldn't get anyone to testify.'

'That's it. I knew I recognised him.' Clare's eyes narrowed. 'I'm starting to see a pattern here.'

Janey nodded. 'Yeah, I'd love to put Coke away. Albie too; but I can't see it happening.'

'Is there a photo of Albie on file?'

'Probably not. But I'll find one. Might have to look back at press files. I'll let you know.'

Clare went back to her office. She had to focus on finding Harry Richards' killer. It was two days now and they were no further forward. She drew her notepad across the desk to flick back through her notes. There was a tap at the door and Sara appeared, clutching a photo.

'Something you should see.' Sara put the photo down on Clare's desk.

Clare peered at a photo from a speed camera.

'It's from a mobile unit, sitting on the Dairsie to Guardbridge road. It's a sixty limit but a lot of cars boot it along there.'

'And?' Clare couldn't see why Sara was showing her the photo.

'This is the car from the accident the other night.'

'The one at Balgove?'

'Yep. And if you look at the time stamp, it's about ten minutes before it was called in.'

'Makes sense,' Clare said, 'if she was driving fast. Distracted, lost control.'

'But look,' Sara said. 'She's not alone in the car. There's someone in the passenger seat.'

'Maybe she dropped them off before the crash. Maybe the passenger lives in Guardbridge.'

'Then why hasn't that person come forward?' Sara persisted. 'The victim's been named in the papers. Her photo was on the front page of all the locals, and we appealed for dashcam footage. If you'd been in the car minutes before the driver died, wouldn't you have come forward?'

Clare nodded slowly. 'Yes,' she said. 'I would.'

Sara tapped the photo again. 'So why hasn't this person?'

Chapter 17

Clare spoke to the press office and asked them to put out an appeal for the car passenger, then she put that and Coke Grand out of her head. She had a killer to find.

'Locating Kenny Deuchars is priority,' she told Chris and Max. 'Any luck with his known associates?'

'We're working through a list,' Chris said. 'There is a brother but no address so far.'

Clare rose from her desk. 'Max, can you carry on with the list of Kenny's contacts, please?' She nodded to Chris. 'Get your jacket. I want to see that the warden at Pitfedden myself.'

Pitfedden Lodge was a substantial property finished in a white render, lying on the outskirts of town. It had been built for the wealthy Merrick family early in the twentieth century. When the last remaining member had died it had been sold and developed as an outdoor centre. But the funding, vital to keep it open, had dried up and the B-listed building had eventually been bought by the council to prevent it falling into disrepair.

Now it was home to a group of ex-offenders and Kenny Deuchars was one of them.

She slowed as they approached the Lodge gates and turned into the drive, nosing the car into a vacant space. They climbed out and Chris regarded the Lodge without enthusiasm.

'Like walking into the lion's den,' he said.

'Just be your usual charming self.' Clare started towards the entrance. As she neared the door she felt the phone buzz in her pocket. She fished it out and squinted at the screen. 'Warrant's been granted,' she said, clicking to dial Jim's number. She spoke briefly to the desk sergeant asking him to send Harry's laptop to Tech Support. 'Tell Max to get moving with the phone and bank records, please. And let's extend ANPR to the other cars as well. Louise Richards and that Simon guy – the paralegal.' Then she nodded to Chris. 'Come on, grumpy. Let's see what we can find out.'

Fiona James was the duty officer for the day. She looked to be in her mid-thirties, Clare thought, slightly built with dark hair cut in a shoulder length bob. She carried herself well, as if she'd been trained as a dancer but, looking at her shuffling papers to make some space on the desk, there was an air of resignation about her.

'Tea?' she said, in a tone suggesting she'd prefer them to decline. Clare saw this and waved the offer away.

'We won't keep you. I realise you've already spoken to one of my colleagues but, as Kenny seems to be missing, I thought I'd like to chat to you myself.'

Fiona frowned. 'I wouldn't exactly call him missing,' she said. 'Sometimes the men need a bit of time to settle down.' She tried to smile. 'I'm sure Kenny'll turn up soon, probably with a dreadful hangover.'

Clare smiled back, in an effort to put Fiona at her ease. 'Why did he come here? I thought he was from the Glasgow area, originally.'

Fiona moved the computer mouse on her desk and began scrolling and clicking. 'Looks like he's been through here for the past couple of years. But this is his first time at Pitfedden.'

'How has he settled in?'

'Pretty well,' Fiona said. 'He stuck to his room at first, probably conditioned from being in prison. Then he started going out and about. *Looking for work*, he said. We can help them with bus fares, give them some independence back. A few even manage to find casual work.'

'Is he friendly with any of the others?'

Fiona shook her head. 'Not that I've seen. He seems to get on okay with them. No friction, but I don't think he's any particular friends here.'

'And you've no idea where he might be now?' Clare asked.

Fiona's brow creased. 'I did suggest your colleague try The Harvest Moon pub. It's in South Street.'

'They checked,' Clare said, 'but there was no sign of Kenny.'

Chris leaned forward. 'I believe Kenny has a brother.'

Fiona nodded. 'He does. It's in his file. Ryan, I think.'

'Do you have an address for him?'

'I don't... Look, leave it with me. I doubt you'd get much out of the other residents but I'll see what I can find out.'

—

They emerged from the house as a young lad in jeans and a hoodie was grinding the remains of a cigarette into the path.

'Afternoon,' Clare said but he ignored them and turned to wander back towards the door.

'If I didn't know better,' Chris said, 'I'd think they don't like the police.'

'You might have something there, Sergeant.' She clicked to unlock the car and opened the door.

'It's after one,' Chris said. 'Long time since breakfast.'

He had a point. Clare suddenly realised how hungry she was. 'Go on, then. I'll treat you to lunch.'

He tugged on his seat belt. 'I know just the place. I'll direct you.'

The Coffee Stop was at the end of Greyfriars Gardens and Clare found a parking space a short walk away.

The shop front was painted in a cheerful brick red, a table in the window occupied by three women having an animated conversation. Chris pushed open the door and the sound of swing jazz reached their ears, the smell of freshly ground coffee their noses. They made for the only vacant table near the counter and sank down.

As they waited to be served Clare looked round, taking in her surroundings. It was bright and cheerful, the walls decorated with framed posters of what she thought were South American landmarks. She recognised the statue of Christ the Redeemer and Machu Picchu and was trying to work out another which seemed to be a set of huge fingertips growing out of a sandy beach when a smiling waitress approached, iPad in hand. She was small, dark-haired and wore a badge with the name Maria.

'*Hola, Maria,*' Chris began. '*Dos cafés por favor.*'

Maria grinned and replied in a torrent of Spanish. Then she stood, clearly waiting for an answer.

Chris blinked a couple of times and began again in faltering Spanish. Clare watched him for a minute then she turned to Maria.

'I don't speak Spanish,' she said.

Maria bent closer to Clare and gave her a wink. 'Nor does he,' she said. 'I'll bring you some menus.'

As she moved away Clare leaned across the table and lowered her voice. 'You knew she was Spanish, didn't you? That's why we're here. So you could show off your three phrases!'

He assumed an air of mock innocence. 'Not at all. I just overheard her speaking to another customer. In Spanish.'

Clare raised an eyebrow but said nothing. Maria reappeared with menus and they ordered their food – in English.

Over lunch they chatted about Chris and Sara's wedding plans.

'Sara's mum's doing the flowers,' he said. 'She's got a huge delivery coming the day before and we've all to help tie posies together for the pew ends.'

'Of course,' Clare said. 'It's a church wedding.'

He shook his head. 'Don't ask me why. It's not like either of us goes. But Sara's mum – well she wanted it so—'

Clare patted him on the shoulder. 'You're a good lad, sometimes.'

'Ah well. As long as Sara's happy.'

They finished their lunch and Clare paid the bill, leaving a tip for Maria.

'So, what next?' Chris said as the café door swung closed behind them.

'Next, Sergeant, I want you to take a copy of the warrant to Harry Richards' office and ask that nice receptionist to let us have contact details for all his clients. Nothing else, mind. The warrant's limited to names, addresses and phone numbers. And, while you're at it, chase up that list of dates and times Harry was out of the office – the appointments he didn't put in the diary.' She stopped, leaning on the car, lost in thought.

'Something else?'

'Actually, yes.' She opened a browser on her phone and searched for the news website Cheryl had shown her. She typed in *Colin Grandison* and took a screenshot of the image, sending it to Chris. 'I'd like you to show this photo to the receptionist. See if she's ever seen him in the office, or with Harry at any other time.'

Chris checked his phone and nodded when the photo arrived. 'Drop me off?' he said hopefully.

'It'll do you good to walk. You've a kilt to fit into in a few weeks.'

'Kilt's adjustable,' he said. 'And I'll be quicker if you drive me.'

'I must be getting soft in my old age,' she said, clicking the car key. 'Come on, then.'

Chapter 18

'Laptop's gone to Tech Support,' Jim said as Clare entered the station. 'And I've a couple of officers working on the ANPR database.'

'Thanks, Jim. Erm,' she stood thinking, 'what about phone and bank records?'

'Max has requested them. Hopefully by tomorrow.' He smiled. 'Anything else you need?'

Her mind was racing. Was there anything? She wondered about Coke Grandison. Should she check his vehicles? Then she decided against it. There was no reason to connect him with Harry's death. Not at the moment anyway. She wandered through to her office, trying to put him out of her mind. An idea was niggling away and she checked her watch. Sara's head appeared round the door.

'Might be something and nothing,' the PC began.

'Go on.'

'The car crash woman – I took a phone message about the post-mortem.'

'Surely there's no doubt about the cause of death?' Clare said. She'd seen photos of the car and would have been surprised if anyone had survived the accident.

'No, her neck was broken in the impact. They reckon she died instantly.'

'So?'

'They mentioned she'd had sex quite recently.'

Clare considered this. 'What time was the accident again?'

'About half eight.'

'And she was heading for St Andrews?'

'Yep. She lives in the town.'

'What about work, Sara? Did she have a job?'

'Yes. She worked for a recruitment consultant. Office in Largo Road. Near the fire station.'

'So,' Clare said, 'she lives and works in town. If she was driving to St Andrews from the Guardbridge direction she must have been on a date of some kind.'

Sara nodded. 'She's married, though.'

'Not our business, Sara,' Clare said, pulling her keyboard across the desk. 'It's not against the law.'

'But remember,' her PC persisted, 'there was that other figure in the speeding photo. The person who hasn't come forward.'

'Makes sense,' Clare said. 'If she was having a fling with someone they wouldn't want to admit they'd been with her. Maybe he's married too.' She smiled at the PC. 'If there had been a passenger with her when she hit that kiosk he wouldn't have walked away from it. The whole front of the car was crushed. So unless there's anything else significant in the PM we can release the body to the family.'

Sara nodded and made to leave but Clare stopped her. 'Sara, is Robbie okay?'

The PC stiffened. 'Think so. Erm, why do you ask?'

Clare frowned. 'I'm not sure. He just seems a bit distracted at the moment.'

Sara stood, as if trying to decide what to say.

'If there's something I should know...'

She shook her head. 'It's nothing to do with work. He's just been a bit down lately.'

'Girlfriend trouble?'

Sara shrugged. 'I'm not sure. I think his girlfriend finished with him a few months back. He was upset at the time but that's not surprising. They'd been together a while.'

'Nothing else?'

Sara hesitated. 'There was a bit of trouble with his bank a few weeks ago. Some transactions he didn't authorise. Like someone was dipping into his account.'

'Is it still happening?'

'No. He stopped his card and that seemed to be the end of it. But it really upset him at the time. I suppose, being a police officer, he was embarrassed.'

Clare stared at her. 'Was it a lot of money?'

'Less than fifty pounds in total. He was just a bit, well, you know?'

'I'll maybe have a word with him,' Clare said.

Sara's face fell. 'Oh please don't, boss. He told me in confidence. I don't think he'd want you to know.'

Clare assured her she wouldn't mention anything to Robbie but Sara's words ran round her head. *He wouldn't want you to know.* She'd always prided herself on being an approachable boss – door always open. If Robbie didn't feel he could come to her, what did that say about their relationship? She decided to let the dust settle then call him in for a general chat. See if there was more to it than the problems with his bank.

Her phone rang.

'Inspector,' the voice said, 'it's Fiona James at Pitfedden.'

'Oh yes,' Clare said. 'Have you found anything?'

'I think so. At least I hope so. Kenny's brother is called Ryan and it seems he's friendly with a Dundee lad.'

'Name?'

'Mullen. Francis Mullen – known as Frankie, I believe. Anyway, the lads here seem to think Ryan's staying with Frankie just now. Maybe that's where Kenny's gone.'

'I don't suppose you have an address?'

'No, sorry. But they did say it was one of the multis.'

Clare thanked Fiona and sat thinking about what she'd said. There were still a few blocks of multis in different parts of Dundee. Hundreds of houses. How easy would it be to find Frankie Mullen? She went in search of Jim.

'I need a Dundee officer, Jim. Probably a uniform. Someone with a lot of years policing the city.'

'Aye? What are you after?'

'Our stalker's rumoured to be staying with a Francis Mullen. Apparently he lives in one of the multis but I've no idea which one.'

'Quickest thing would be to check the PNC,' Jim said.

Of course. The Police National Computer. Why hadn't she thought of that? Assuming he had a record, of course. 'Could you have a look just now?'

'Give me a few minutes and I'll get onto it. And, if he's not there, I'll find someone at Bell Street. We'll track him down for you.'

She waited while Jim checked on Francis Mullen and her spirits rose when he tapped the screen. 'He's here. But from the looks of it his last known address was in Baldovan Terrace.' He looked up. 'Near Baxter Park if you remember?'

Clare did remember. They'd been hunting a missing baby, one with a medical condition. A race against time. They'd tracked a suspect to a house near Baxter Park and searched the park to try and find him. 'I won't forget that in a hurry,' she said. 'But I don't recall any multis round there.'

Jim shook his head. 'Nope. All tenements. Nearest multi's probably the Hilltown. Must be at least a mile away.'

'Dammit.'

'Leave it with me,' Jim said. 'If he's not at Baldovan there's a couple of lads I can ask.'

'I don't want him alerted,' Clare said. 'If Kenny Deuchars gets wind we're onto him he'll disappear again.'

'Don't worry. We'll find him.'

–

'It's chaos over there,' Chris said, sinking down on a chair.

Clare pushed her keyboard out of the way. 'At Harry's office?'

'Yup. Seems the paralegal's wife died.'

'What?'

'Yeah, I know. Bizarre coincidence, after Harry's death.'

'What happened?'

'Dunno. Just an accident, I think. Anyway, Kate the receptionist's fielding all sorts of problems. She's been onto the Law Society for someone to manage the existing clients. Apparently they have an intervention team who step in when something like this happens. In the meantime, the phone's ringing off the hook.'

'Must be difficult,' Clare said. 'Anyway...'

'Yeah, I got the dates and times; and there's more.'

'Grandison?'

'Got it in one. Apparently he was in the office one afternoon. Nothing in the diary but Harry didn't seem surprised to see him. Takes him into his office and shuts the door. Five minutes later they both leave and she doesn't see Harry again until the next morning.'

'Did he explain why? To Kate, I mean?'

'Just said he was an old friend who'd moved away. That he was back in the area and decided to look Harry up.'

Clare sat back, drumming a pen on the desk. 'That's a lie for a start.'

'Yup. What's more, I don't think Kate believed him.'

'Did she say so?'

'Not in as many words. More like she was just repeating what Harry said.'

Clare nodded. 'I think I'll ask Jim to check ANPR for Coke Grandison's cars. I'd like to see if his journeys coincide with Harry's. I'm convinced there's a link there.'

She went in search of Jim who was on the phone. As she waited, Robbie came into the station and she flashed him a smile. He smiled back but it seemed forced. Then he made straight for the locker room. Clare checked the time. He was about to go off duty and she made a mental note to catch him before he left. Ask him something about Drumoig – anything to get him talking.

Jim was scribbling on a notepad then he tore off the sheet. 'Frankie Mullen,' he said. 'I've got an address.' As he was speaking, Clare saw Robbie emerge from the locker room and walk quickly to the station door. He was out and gone before she could catch him. Her eye lingered on the automatic door as it slid closed behind him. There was definitely something up. Tomorrow. She'd make a point of speaking to him tomorrow.

She turned back to Jim and read the address. 'Dallfield Court. Rings a bell.'

'Bottom of the Hilltown. There's four blocks. It's one of them but don't ask me which one.'

She thanked Jim and found Chris still in her office, playing a game on his phone. 'Come on,' she said. 'Let's see if our Mr Deuchars is home.'

Chapter 19

The Hilltown was one of the oldest parts of Dundee, the steep thoroughfare built on the slopes of Dundee Law. Near the bottom, the newer Hilltown Terrace was home to four tall tower blocks, among the last to remain in the city. Dallfield Court was the furthest west and Clare managed to squeeze the car into a tight space nearby.

'Whether I get it back out again,' she said, regarding the proximity of the other cars, 'is another matter.' Then she turned to study the block before them. 'Which floor?'

Chris squinted at the note Jim had written. 'Nine.'

'Let's hope the lift's working then.'

He hesitated and Clare nudged him. 'You can walk up nine flights if you want, Detective Sergeant, but I'm taking the lift.'

'It's all right for you.'

'Look, we'll be in and out in minutes. I'll even hold your hand.'

He rolled his eyes. 'Come on, then. Let's get it over with.'

They walked towards the blue security door which Clare was relieved to see had been wedged open. 'At least he won't know we're coming,' she said, walking into the cool interior. She was hit immediately by a strong smell of disinfectant as they stepped onto what she presumed was a newly washed floor. It took a moment for her eyes to adjust after the bright sunshine and she stopped to take in her surroundings. A door to the side led to stairs with another opposite marked *No Entry*. They walked on into the main foyer which was clean and clutter-free.

Chris indicated the lift and they waited while it rattled its way down towards them. The door slid back and an elderly man hobbled out. He muttered something Clare didn't catch and made for the front entrance. She watched his awkward progress for a minute then turned and walked into the lift, Chris following uncertainly.

'You know, there are probably things you can do,' she said. 'About lifts, I mean. Sort of desensitise.'

'Yeah, whatever.'

She saw his shoulders tense as the door slid closed and the lift lurched into action. Seconds later they emerged onto the ninth floor and made their way along a corridor of paint-scratched doors, checking numbers as they went.

'It's probably a bit late to ask,' Chris said, 'but, any violent markers on his record?'

Clare shook her head. 'I did check. Mainly housebreaking, a bit of dealing. Never been caught with a knife. We should be fine.'

'If you say so.' He stopped at the second door from the end. 'This is it. How do you want to play it?'

'Dunno. Let's see if he's here, first.' She rapped loudly on the door and stood listening. There was no sound from within. Chris knocked louder then he bent and opened the letter box.

'Open up or we'll put the door in.'

There was a sound from within the flat and a voice said, 'Wha' is it?'

'Police,' Chris said. 'Don't make us force entry.'

Clare raised an eyebrow. They hadn't brought an enforcer for breaking open doors, let alone officers to manage a forced entry.

Chris put a finger to his lips and she nodded. 'C'mon,' he barked. 'Open up.'

There was a delay then they heard the sound of bolts being drawn back and keys turned in locks. They exchanged looks. Clearly there was some dealing going on at this flat. But that wasn't their concern today. The door opened a little and Chris put a foot in it to prevent it being slammed shut. A man who could have been anything from late twenties to early forties eyed them, one hand on the door as if ready to close it again. His skin was sallow, leathery, his watery blue eyes bloodshot. A whiff of stale cigarette smoke reached Clare's nostrils and she drew back, involuntarily. Studying what she could see of him she didn't think this was Kenny Deuchars. Perhaps it was Ryan, his brother – or Frankie Mullen.

'And you are?' the man said, his voice gravelly.

'DS West and DI Mackay,' Chris said. 'We'd like to come in please.'

He opened the door a little wider. 'Whaur's yer big red key?'

Clare suppressed a smile at the name for the battering ram. 'We thought we wouldn't need it this time. So, can we?'

'If it helps,' Chris added, 'we won't be looking for any… substances or stuff like that. We just want a word.'

The man looked them up and down then he stood back to let them in. The hallway was dark, the only light coming from an open door at the end. He turned and walked towards this. Clare followed and motioned to Chris to check the other doors in the hall.

'You don't mind if my colleague here has a look round?'

The man shrugged and carried on. The carpet felt sticky beneath Clare's feet and there was a strong smell of weed. But she followed him into a square room. It was dominated by a brown corduroy sofa and a flat screen TV, on a pine blanket box. A black coffee table sat in front of the sofa, an ashtray overflowing with dogends. The man indicated the only other seat in the room, a wheeled desk chair but she waved this away.

'Your name?'

'I dinnae have to give it.'

Clare smiled. 'No, you don't. But, as my colleague said, we might be willing to overlook some *things* if you are helpful. Otherwise…' She put her nose in the air and sniffed.

'Aye awright. Frankie.'

'Last name?'

He regarded her for a moment. 'Mullen. Frankie Mullen.'

Clare nodded. They were in the right house. Chris came into the room shaking his head. Frankie was alone.

'Does Ryan Deuchars stay here?'

'Never heard o' him.'

Clare regarded him. 'We might not plan on tearing this flat apart, checking for anything illegal, but it wouldn't take long for the drugs team to get up here.'

Frankie picked up his cigarettes and lighter and fished out a fag. He put this between his lips and flicked the lighter. The tip glowed orange and he inhaled, then blew out a column of smoke. Clare was about to speak when there was the sound of a key in the front door. She held out a warning finger to Frankie as voices drifted up the hall. The front door slammed and a moment later two men, so alike they had to be brothers, wandered into the room. They both resembled the photos Clare had seen of Kenny and she wondered which of the two he was. They glanced at Clare and Chris, sizing them up. One of them made as if to run from the room; but Chris was too quick and stepped into the doorway.

'Ryan and Kenny Deuchars?' Clare asked.

The two men looked at each other. They were both about Clare's height, pencil thin, jeans hanging off their backsides. One wore a dark green parka and a baseball cap, and Clare recalled the CCTV photo from the bus. Surely this one had to be Kenny? The other had on a red sweatshirt and faded jeans. She noticed he'd a scar from one eyebrow across the bridge of his nose. Not a recent one either. She couldn't recall a scar on Kenny's photo and she turned back to the parka lad, taking a chance it was him.

'You're missing from your approved address,' she said, adding, 'You are Kenny Deuchars, yeah?'

The man inclined his head. 'Just catching up with my brother.' He glanced at Ryan. 'I'll head back over there in a bit.'

'We can offer you a lift,' Clare said. 'We'd like a word anyway.'

The other man stepped forward but Chris moved forward as well. 'No need for any bother,' he said. 'We'll just take Kenny over to the station in St Andrews. Quick word about something then we'll drop him back at Pitfedden.'

The men exchanged glances and the one without the scar said, 'It's cool, Ry. It'll be fine.'

'I just need to check something.' Clare wasn't keen to leave Chris alone with the three men and she didn't want to be overheard on the phone. Keeping her phone turned away from them she tapped out a message to Jim, marking it urgent.

> Pls check ASAP with Pitfedden.
> Does Kenny D have a scar, eyebrow to nose.
> Need answer now.

Then she stood, making conversation with the men while she waited for a reply. It wouldn't be the first time someone had given them a false name. Jim replied immediately with a thumbs up. Two minutes later another message popped up confirming Kenny didn't have a scar.

She tucked the phone back in her pocket. 'We'll get going, then,' she said, indicating the door.

They emerged onto the landing and waited once more for the lift. Kenny regarded it as the door slid back.

'I dinnae really like lifts,' he said.

Clare laughed and nodded at Chris. 'Nor does he. You're a right pair!'

They put Kenny in the back of the car, Chris slipping in beside him in case he tried to jump out at traffic lights.

'What's this about, like?' he asked.

'We'll explain everything when we get to the station,' Clare said.

He accepted this with a shrug then lay back in the car and closed his eyes.

Chapter 20

They installed Kenny in an interview room and Clare went in search of Jim.

'Thanks for checking on the scar,' she said. 'Could you rustle us up a duty solicitor, please?'

Jim sighed. 'I'll try but you know we've been struggling for a few weeks now. Nobody wants to work for the Legal Aid rate. The last one we had told me it nowhere near covers the work involved.'

Clare's brow creased. They were limited in how long they could detain Kenny if he exercised his rights. Waiting for a solicitor would seriously eat into the time they could spend with him. She decided to appeal to Kenny's better nature.

He was slumped in a chair when she entered the interview room. 'I'm afraid there's a bit of a delay getting hold of a solicitor,' she said. 'We can get you some tea or coffee. Might even have some biscuits. But I can't begin the interview until we have one.'

'S'okay,' he said. 'I'm in no hurry. Two sugars.'

In the kitchen she unearthed an almost-finished pack of biscuits and asked one of the uniformed officers to take him a mug of tea. That done, she wandered through to the incident room to see what was happening.

'Nothing yet,' Bill said. 'We've got the phone records, though. Working through them now.'

'Okay,' Clare said. 'If there's no sign of the bank records by morning let me know and I'll chase it up.' She was suddenly hungry and went through to the kitchen to see if there was anything in the fridge she could pinch. Chris was there making a coffee.

'Don't suppose you've got any Wagon Wheels in your stash?'

He looked round to see if anyone else was listening.

'Don't worry,' Clare said. 'Sara's out at Drumoig helping with the house-to-house.'

'In that case,' he disappeared out of the kitchen door and reappeared a minute later with a pack of Wagon Wheel biscuits.

'Where do you hide them?'

He took one out of the pack and bit into it. 'If I told you that, *Inspectora*, I'd have to kill you.'

'Fair enough.'

'Our Kenny ready for interview?'

Clare shook her head. 'Can't get a duty solicitor. Jim's doing his best but they're like hen's teeth these days. I've sent one of the cops in with three chocolate biscuits and enough sugary tea to put him in a diabetic coma. By the way,' she added, 'I meant to ask: what happened to the paralegal's wife?'

'Oh yeah,' he said, 'Bizarre coincidence. She was the woman in the car accident.'

She stared at him. 'The one at Balgove?'

'Yeah. Lucky he wasn't with her or he'd be dead too.'

She stood processing this. 'Does he have his own car?'

Chris shrugged. 'No idea. Oh wait—'

'If they share a car,' Clare said.

'You're thinking someone caused an accident that was meant for him?'

She rubbed the back of her head. 'It makes no sense. I mean, how could you cause an accident like that?'

'Could be the car had a fault,' Chris said. 'Dodgy brakes or something.'

'I doubt it. Modern cars – and it was a newer model – they've all sorts of warning lights. She'd have known there was something wrong.'

'Maybe she did. Maybe the warning light had just come on. Be honest, if a light came on in your car would you sit half the night waiting on the AA? Or would you try and make it home?'

Clare inclined her head. 'Suppose.'

'Let's say it was the brakes,' Chris went on. 'Someone pulls out to overtake, she swerves, hits the brakes and nothing happens.'

Clare looked at him. 'Draining the brake fluid – or whatever you'd have to do – there's no guarantee that would cause an accident. But it could give the driver a hell of a fright.'

'Could be that was the idea. Someone wanted to put the wind up her.'

'Or him. Think about it, Chris. We have Kenny Deuchars scaring Louise Richards out of her wits. Then Harry's killed. Now Simon Miller's wife's dead and he works in Harry's office.'

'I mean,' Chris began, 'it could just be a coincidence.'

'I don't believe in coincidences.'

Jim came into the kitchen. 'That's the solicitor here,' he said. 'He's having a word with Kenny now. Should be ready in five minutes or so.'

Clare thanked Jim and nodded towards the door. 'Come on,' she said to Chris. 'Quick confab in my office. We've an interview strategy to work out.'

–

'Brilliant cup of tea, that,' Kenny said as they entered the room. 'Don't suppose there's any more?'

'Let's make a start,' Clare said. 'We might manage some more tea in a bit.'

Kenny inclined his head and Clare began the recording. She introduced herself and Chris then she asked Kenny if he knew the Drumoig estate.

'Nope.'

'I'll refresh your memory,' Clare said. 'It's on the Dundee bus route, about nine or ten miles from here.'

She saw a slight reaction at the mention of the Dundee bus. 'Save us all some time, here, Kenny. We've photos of you taken from CCTV on the 99 bus last Wednesday. You boarded at the stop nearest Drumoig around three in the afternoon.' Clare passed a photo across the desk. Kenny and the solicitor looked at it then Kenny pushed the photo back towards Clare.

'Aye, okay. Must have. The folk at Pitfedden give us money for buses. So we can look for work, like. Sometimes I get off somewhere different. Have a bit of a wander. Helps pass the time.'

'Did you wander around the Drumoig estate?'

'Must have done, if you say I was there.'

'Anywhere special?'

'Dunno. Had a look at the golf. There's a hotel there. Had a look at that. Some nice houses.'

'Any particular house catch your eye?' Clare asked.

'Nope.'

'We have a witness who says you were hanging about outside the house, staring in the front window.'

Kenny shook his head. 'No' me.'

'This witness picked your photo from a selection which included men of a similar appearance.'

'I'm no' saying I wasn't there. Just that I wasn't staring at anybody.'

'The same witness almost bumped into you in St Andrews and formed the impression you were a stalker.'

'Some women are like that,' Kenny said. 'Start imagining things.'

Clare smiled. 'I didn't say it was a woman.'

There was a flicker in Kenny's eyes. *He knows he's slipped up*, Clare thought. 'Let's get to the point, Kenny,' she said. 'You're out on licence, yes?' He made no reply and Clare went on. 'I suspect you were paid to intimidate a Mrs Louise Richards. I think you went to Drumoig on at least two occasions to make your presence known to her and, on another occasion, you contrived to meet her in South Street, causing her to run across a busy road to escape.'

The solicitor leaned forward. 'Is there any firm evidence of intimidation by Mr Deuchars? Might this simply be in the mind of Mrs Richards? Perhaps she's an anxious type of person.'

He had a point. But there was no getting away from Harry Richards' brutal murder. 'Mrs Richards' husband was killed a few days ago,' she said, meeting the solicitor's eye. 'So, the presence of a convicted criminal on at least three occasions prior to his death can't be overlooked.' She turned to Kenny. 'You've broken the terms of your licence by staying at an unapproved address. I could have you back in the Bar-L by lights-out.'

Kenny shifted on his seat, avoiding Clare's eye.

'Perhaps I could have a word with my client,' the solicitor said.

Clare paused the interview and they wandered out to the front office.

'You've got to send him back to prison,' Chris said. 'He's definitely been stalking Louise Richards.'

'It feels like he's the key, Chris. If we send him back to Barlinnie we'll get nothing out of him. He'll have nothing to gain by helping us.' She stood thinking for a minute. Something else was niggling at her, and then she remembered.

'Where's Max?'

Chris nodded towards the incident room and Clare turned without a word.

Max was poring over a sheaf of mobile phone printouts. He looked up as she approached. 'Nothing so far,' he said, 'in case you were wondering. But we're—'

'I need you to get onto Penny Meakin at Bell Street,' Clare said. 'She's the superintendent over there. I want the warrant we have extended to include,' she glanced at Chris. 'What's Simon Miller's wife's name?'

'Leona. Leona Miller.'

'Got it,' Max said, scribbling this down. 'Anything else?'

'Yes. I'd like the press office to do an appeal for anyone who saw her on the day she died. Check what time she left work and go from there. But I don't want it out yet. Chris and I will see Simon first. Who told him about the accident?'

Chris frowned. 'I think uniform dealt with him at the time.'

'Any idea who?'

'Not sure. No one from this station. Might have been one of the Glenrothes guys. Liv or Erin.'

'Max, get hold of Liv. Ask her to find out. I want to know everything about how he was when they broke the news – how he reacted, questions he asked.'

'You surely don't suspect him?' Chris said. 'He doesn't have it in him.'

She shook her head. 'No, but he might know more than he realises. Or, if someone did interfere with the car, he could have an idea who it was. I can't believe there's no connection between the two deaths. And, if there is one, I mean to find it.' She thought for a moment. 'Can you check with the collision investigator as well, please? I want to know if there was anything amiss with that car.'

Max noted this down. 'If the Millers were targeted by the same people who killed Harry, is the receptionist also at risk?'

The colour drained from Clare's face. 'Get a couple of uniforms over there now. In fact, tell her to shut up shop and send the cops home with her. I want her house checked and someone outside until I can get over there myself. Better stick someone on Simon Miller's door as well.'

'A vendetta against everyone who works there?' Chris said. 'Seems pretty far-fetched.'

'I'd rather be accused of that than have another dead body.'

Jim appeared at the door and indicated Kenny's solicitor was ready to resume the interview.

'Right,' Clare said. 'Let's see what story he's come up with.'

Chapter 21

Kenny was sitting forward on his chair when they entered the room. His hands, nicotine-stained, were clasped on the table in front of him, his glance darting between Clare and his solicitor.

'Mr Deuchars may have some information relating to the part he unwittingly played in harassing Mrs Louise Richards. But we are at pains to stress that anything he may have done was without malice or intent. We also feel his co-operation in this matter more than outweighs his failing to return to the approved address for one or two nights. This was due to him having to deal with family matters and he has assured me there will not be a repeat.'

Clare raised an eyebrow. 'Kenny will tell us what he knows in exchange for not being returned to prison, yes?'

'Indeed.'

Clare regarded Kenny and he stared back, his expression one of mock innocence. 'Okay,' she said. 'Providing I feel Kenny is being honest and telling us all he knows – and that means *everything*, Kenny – I will not return him to prison. However, should it come to light he has committed an offence, I'll have no option.'

The solicitor glanced at Kenny who inclined his head but said nothing.

'Right, then, Kenny. Why don't you start by telling us who asked you to harass Louise Richards.'

He cleared his throat. 'It wasnae like that. I just got a message. Said would I keep an eye on her. Check the house and that. Make sure nobody bothered her.'

Clare had to hand it to him. If there was a way to put a spin on stalking someone, Kenny certainly thought he'd found it. 'You're saying you were following Louise Richards in order to protect her?'

'Aye.'

'Who asked you to do this?'

He shrugged. 'Dunno. Just got a note one day. Few quid in an envelope. Gave me an address and said to keep an eye on the woman that lived there.'

'Who gave you the note?'

'Just a lad. Cannae remember, really.'

'Description?'

He glanced at his solicitor who took the cue and picked up his pen.

'You agree Mr Deuchars is co-operating?'

Clare raised an eyebrow. 'If we get a meaningful description of the man who handed him the note.'

The solicitor and Kenny exchanged glances then Kenny said, 'Big fella.'

'Tall? Broad?'

'Big all round. Like a bouncer, yeah?'

Something stirred in the back of Clare's mind but she went on.

'Age?'

'Hard to tell. He'd sunspecs on. Coulda been thirty. Or a bit older.'

'What was he wearing?'

'Black. Cannae remember what, really. Probably black jeans, leather jacket kind o' thing.'

Clare jotted this down. 'I'd like you to go through some photos with one of my officers,' she said. 'Once we've finished here.' She studied Kenny for a minute. 'Do you have a mobile phone?'

His eyes narrowed but he didn't reply.

'I'd like to examine your phone please, Kenny. We'll give you a replacement to use while it's with our technical team.'

The solicitor picked up his pen. 'May I ask what grounds you have for this? Do you have a warrant?'

Clare met his eye. 'I believe your client may be a material witness in a murder case, i.e. the murder of Harry Richards. Kenny has told us he was asked to *keep an eye on Mrs Richards*.' She emphasised the words, the subtext entirely clear. Kenny had been stalking Louise and everyone in the room knew it. 'It's possible,' she said, 'there may be some data on the phone to assist us in our hunt for Mr Richards' killer.'

A smile spread across Kenny's face and he reached into his pocket and took out an Alcatel mobile. He placed this on the desk. 'Dinnae be giving me one of those Mickey Mouse ones you lads have. I want a decent one till you get this back to me.'

Clare regarded him. That had been a bit too easy. 'And the other one,' she said.

'Other what?'

'Don't mess us about, Kenny. I've a killer to find. We both know that's not your only phone. If necessary, I'll arrest you which will give us the power to search you. But it will also mean you're returned to lawful custody.'

The solicitor leaned forward. 'This is starting to sound like blackmail, Inspector.'

Clare smiled. 'Not at all. It's Kenny's decision. I have reasonable grounds to suspect he's guilty of intimidating the wife of a man who was later murdered. I am simply offering to give him the benefit of the doubt – in exchange for information. That includes giving up his mobile phones.' She switched her gaze to Kenny. 'All of them.'

There was a pause while they locked eyes then Kenny exhaled audibly and dug into his other pocket. He took out a much smaller mobile and slammed it down on the table.

'If you could just stand and turn out all your pockets,' Clare said.

Kenny's eyes blazed. 'That's all of them,' he said. 'I don't have any more.'

'All the same.'

They waited and after a minute or so he scraped back his chair and stood. Chris rose as well but made no move towards Kenny. They watched as he emptied his pockets onto the table: cigarette papers, lighter, loose change and some notes, and a small plastic bag of something suspiciously like weed. 'No idea how that got there,' he said, indicating the bag.

Clare waved it away and once she was satisfied he didn't have another phone she thanked him and put both phones in an evidence bag. Then she ended the interview and told Kenny she'd have an officer go through some photos with him. 'After that, I'll have someone escort you back to Pitfedden.'

He shook his head. 'I'd rather walk.'

'Maybe so but you'll take a lift all the same. And you won't leave Pitfedden for the next few days.'

He glared at her but she paid no attention.

'That's the deal, Kenny. Take it or leave it. You stay put until you hear different from me.'

Chris followed Clare to her office and closed the door. 'I think it's a mistake letting him go.'

'It might be,' she admitted. 'But the evidence against him is thin, at best. And I'd rather have some leverage with him. Who knows – we might need it.'

'Suppose.' He indicated the mobile phones. 'You want those sent to Tech Support?'

'In a bit. First I'm going to hook them up to the Cyber Kiosk. I've no doubt he'll have deleted any calls or texts but the Kiosk will find deleted data. I want every number that's ever been on those phones. Then we'll check them against Harry's phone.'

Chris shook his head. 'If Harry and Kenny were in league with the same guys which, I reckon's pretty far-fetched, Harry would've had a burner as well. And I'd like to bet whoever killed him destroyed the burner. There wasn't one in the car, was there?'

He had a point. 'You're probably right,' she said. 'But it's worth a shot.' She checked her watch. Almost five. They'd been on duty for ten hours. She'd have to let them go home pretty soon. But she was worried about Simon Miller and Kate Campbell. 'Chris we're running out of day, here. Can you ask Max to check on Simon Miller please? I want to make sure he knows about the press appeal. And I'd like someone outside his house all night.'

'Yeah, sure. What about Kate, the receptionist?'

'Get on the radio and speak to whoever went to the office. Check she's okay and get me her home address. I think we'll call round. And we'll have someone on her house tonight as well.'

Chris went off to speak to Max, and Clare unlocked the drawer where she kept the Cyber Kiosk. They'd had it for a couple of years now and it had proved invaluable with its quick access to mobile phone data. She plugged it in and waited for the display to appear on screen. Then she selected calls, messages, contacts, photos and deleted data, and left the machine to do its job. When it had finished, she repeated the task with the other phone. Finally she replaced them in the evidence bag and went in search of Jim.

'Can you find someone to take these to Tech Support please? I've had a go with the Cyber Kiosk but they might be able to find more stuff. Then hand over to Cupar and get yourself home.'

Max had already left for Simon Miller's house and Clare signalled to Chris she was ready to go. 'Do you have Kate Campbell's address?'

'Yep. I'll drive.'

Kate Campbell lived in a terraced house on St Mary Street at the south end of town. The road was marked with double yellow lines and Chris turned into a side road coming to a sudden halt in the first available space.

'I remember now why I don't let you drive,' Clare said, climbing out of the car.

'Got you here in one piece, didn't I?'

She ignored this and began walking back towards St Mary Street. She was pleased to see an officer standing outside the house and nodded to him. 'She inside?'

'Yes, boss. I went through the house with her and it's all fine.'

Clare thanked him and walked up the short path, taking in the house. The dark red door was freshly painted and the windows looked to be in good condition. The front room blinds were closed and she could hear no sound from within. She rang the doorbell and heard a muffled voice calling something. But when the door opened a few seconds later it wasn't Kate Campbell who stood there.

It took Clare a moment to realise who it was. And then she remembered. Eilidh, the schoolgirl she and Sara had spoken to at Melville Academy – was it just two days ago? It seemed so much longer now. She was aware of Chris beside her, sensing something and she studied the girl's face to check she wasn't mistaken.

But there was no mistake. This was definitely Eilidh. So, what was she doing in Kate Campbell's house?

Chapter 22

'Hello,' Clare said. 'It's Eilidh, isn't it?'

The girl blinked a few times and opened her mouth but she seemed lost for words. Then Kate appeared in the hallway and took over.

'This is Inspector Mackay,' she told the girl. She smiled at Clare. 'This is my daughter Eilidh.'

Clare returned the smile. 'Eilidh and I have met already.' But something in the girl's expression prevented her from saying more.

'Oh, that thing at school?' Kate said, 'Yes I heard about it. Look, do you mind coming through? I've got something on the cooker.'

They followed her through to a cheerful kitchen with patio doors leading to a small back garden. Through the glass Clare could see a paved area flanked by tubs filled with spring bulbs. Kate moved to an electric hob and turned the heat down on a pot that was starting to spit. She picked up a wooden spoon and stirred the pot then she smiled at them.

'Please, sit down.' She indicated a small table and chairs. 'I can make us some coffee if you like. Or tea?'

Clare waved this away. 'I just wanted to have a word with you about what's happened recently.'

A worried expression crossed her face. 'First Harry, and now Simon's wife,' she said. 'It's awful. Poor man. He must be in bits.'

'Did you know his wife?'

'Leona? Not really. I met her a couple of times. Christmas drinks and so on. But I hardly spoke to her.'

'Did she come to the office at all?'

'No,' Kate said. 'She was always busy, according to Simon, anyway.' Her face softened. 'Poor man,' she said again. 'He'll be lost without her.'

'Did Simon have his own car?'

Kate's brow creased at the question. 'Oh, I don't know,' she said. 'I think he walked to work. It's not far, you know. I walk, myself. Can't afford a car these days.'

'So Simon and his wife shared their car?'

'I suppose so. I don't really know, to be honest. Why are you asking?'

Clare smiled. 'No reason.'

Kate sank down opposite them. 'Look,' she began, 'about the office – there's simply loads to do. I can't leave it closed.'

'Have you managed to arrange for a solicitor to cover?'

She sighed. 'I've tried but it looks like it'll be a day or two. At least if I was there I could take calls, explain the situation.'

Clare watched her carefully. She seemed completely unaware of a possible connection between the two deaths. 'Kate, until we can be sure Leona's crash was entirely accidental, I can't rule out the possibility someone has a grudge against the firm.'

Kate's eyes widened. 'You're not serious? I mean, Leona – she just careered off the road, didn't she? Just bad luck. Surely you're not suggesting—'

'I just want to be absolutely sure there was no more to her death than a freak accident.'

Kate was silent for a moment. 'I have two clients who take ownership of their houses next week. I have to be in the office to see it's all done properly. It's not like Simon's going to be in.'

Clare thought about this. It was such an unusual situation and the clients would have to be taken care of. 'Do you have a work mobile?'

She nodded and patted her trouser pocket. 'I'm keeping it on me in case the Law Society calls.'

'Okay. Can you hold off until Monday? If they've not appointed anyone to take over Harry's clients by then we'll arrange for you to go in. But, for now, I'd really rather you stayed put.'

'I suppose; but what about Eilidh? She has school tomorrow.'

Clare considered this. 'How does she get to and from school?'

'They send a minibus round. She's picked up at the door.'

'And dropped off again?'

'Yes. Just after four.'

'Then I'd send Eilidh to school as normal. Make her aware of the situation without alarming her. She needs to know not to do anything out of the ordinary. Stay on the premises at lunchtime, that sort of thing. And only the school minibus home. No lifts from anyone else.'

Kate stared at them. 'You're scaring me with all this.'

Chris smiled. 'Honestly, Kate, it's just routine. Standard advice. There's absolutely nothing to suggest either of you's in any danger. We like to warn folk. That's all.'

'Okay. What about Eilidh's dad? He does come to see her most weekends. I mean, we're divorced, but we're on good terms. He even pays her school fees.'

Clare smiled. 'That should be fine. But I wouldn't let her out with her friends. Not without one of you being there.'

'She won't like that,' Kate said. 'She's seventeen, you know. It's a long time since she's had me or her dad trailing along.'

'As I say, just for the next few days.' Clare glanced round. Eilidh hadn't followed them into the kitchen. 'Do you think I could have a word with her?'

'You won't say anything to scare her?' Kate said and Clare waved this away.

'No, she was asking some questions at the school event on Tuesday. I just wanted to follow it up.'

Kate seemed happy with this and went to call Eilidh. A few minutes later the girl appeared. She'd changed out of her school uniform and was in dark grey leggings and a pale pink sweatshirt which drained the colour from her face. She looked tired, Clare thought.

'Maybe we could find a comfier seat?' she said, hoping Kate wouldn't object.

'Take the officers into the sitting room,' Kate said. 'But this'll be ready in five minutes.' She indicated the pot which had begun to bubble again, and Clare smiled.

'Won't be long.'

The sitting room was darker with the blinds closed and Eilidh moved to switch on a lamp. It was cool too and she knelt and clicked on a gas fire which came to life with a pop. Then she stood and motioned towards a brown leather sofa.

'Sit down,' she said. 'I mean, if you like.'

They sat and Clare gave her what she hoped was an encouraging smile. 'You remember coming to see me on Tuesday? After I spoke to the school.'

Eilidh nodded but didn't say anything.

'You were wondering if it was a crime to withhold information,' Clare said and, again, Eilidh nodded.

'Now that makes me think you know something, Eilidh. And I think it's worrying you. Can I ask – have you spoken to anyone about this? Your mum? Or a friend, maybe?'

Eilidh shook her head. 'No,' she said, her voice small.

'Do you think it would help if you spoke to us? Chris here's a good listener.'

'I am,' he said. 'I don't interrupt all the time like Clare.'

Eilidh laughed but still regarded them, her eyes wary.

Chris indicated a seat. 'Why not sit down? Save me looking up your nose.'

She laughed again and sat, perching on the edge of the seat.

'So,' Chris said, 'is it some problem at school?'

She looked down at her hands and began to worry the cuff on her sweatshirt.

'Someone stealing?' Chris said but she made no reply, her eyes still focused on the cuff.

Chris glanced at Clare and she took the hint.

'Let me help you out,' she said, keeping her tone light. 'Is the problem something to do with the girl who was outside the room when you came to see us?'

Eilidh shot her a glance but said nothing.

'Maybe start by telling us her name. We can get it from the school,' she said. 'But it's better if we sort it out between us.'

Eilidh smoothed down the cuff then she met Clare's eye. 'Marina,' she said.

'That's her name? The girl who was outside the room?'

Eilidh nodded.

'Is she a friend?'

She inclined her head. 'Not really. She's pretty popular. Everyone likes her.'

'But you don't?'

Eilidh frowned as though trying to find the right words. 'She's like one of those *golden* girls, you know? She's pretty, they have money. Always got boys asking her out. She's clever too. It's like there's nothing she can't do.' Eilidh seemed to have found her voice now and she went on. 'You should see the car she gets picked up in. I'm waiting on the crappy school minibus and she goes home in this fancy car.'

Clare was suddenly alert. 'What kind of car? Did you notice?'

'Beamer.'

'A BMW?'

'Yeah.'

'What colour is it?'

'Oh black, of course. Couldn't be any other colour 'cause black is cool, apparently. Her dad even has this driver guy to pick her up.'

Clare felt her mouth dry and she swallowed. 'What's Marina's last name?'

Eilidh's mouth turned down, as though she hated even saying it. 'Grandison,' she said. 'She's Marina Grandison.'

—

Clare stepped out of the room to call Janey. 'I need that photo of Albie Kennedy. The lad we think drives for Coke Grandison. Did you get one?'

'Yeah. It's not great but I'll send it now.'

A minute later the photo pinged into her phone and she returned to the room.

'Does this look like the man who collects Marina?' she said.

Eilidh studied the phone for a few moments then she handed it back to Clare. 'I think so. It's hard to be sure 'cause he's usually in sunglasses. Even when it's raining. What a tosser!'

The door opened and Kate's head appeared. 'That's our meal ready.'

'If you could give us another couple of minutes,' Clare said.

Kate came further into the room. 'Is there a problem?'

Clare smiled. 'I just need to ask Eilidh a few more questions. Then I promise we'll leave you in peace.'

Kate looked doubtful. 'Do you want me to stay, Eilidh?'

The girl shook her head. 'It's fine, Mum. I'll tell you about it after.'

Kate withdrew, leaving the door ajar. Chris rose and closed it softly. Clare waited until he'd resumed his seat and turned back to the girl.

'Eilidh, is Marina involved in something you think might be against the law?'

'Not her.'

'Someone she knows?'

Eilidh began fiddling with her cuff again. 'I think… maybe her dad.'

'Mr Grandison's doing something illegal?'

She hesitated. 'Well, it might not be illegal. But—'

Chris leaned forward. 'We're good at sorting stuff like that out,' he said, giving her a smile. 'Why not tell us what you know and we'll work out if it's against the law.'

Eilidh nodded. She was quiet for a minute. 'It's money. He lends people money.'

'He's a moneylender?' Chris said.

'Yes. I think so.'

'It is possible he's doing it legally,' Chris said. 'If he was properly registered that would be fine. But some people who lend money aren't registered. They're known as loan sharks.'

'Yeah, that's it. I heard Marina boasting about it one day. She didn't know I was there. She was saying about them having loads of money and how sometimes her dad lent money to people. Then another girl, she said, what if they don't pay him back; and Marina said *Oh they always pay. Dad makes sure they do.*'

'Did you think she meant he threatens people?' Chris asked. 'Intimidates them?'

She regarded him. 'I know he does.'

'How do you know?' Chris asked, his tone gentle.

She was quiet as though trying to come to a decision. 'I have this friend. Dayna. We were friends at primary school. Then mum decided to send me to Melville and Dayna went to Albany High – the other school in town. Anyway, Dayna's brother, he's a lot older than her. Twenty-six, I think. He had this car. Dead proud of it, he was. He bought it on some kind of credit thing where you pay for four years then you can buy it at the end if you want to. And that was okay until he had an accident. Completely wrecked it and the insurance company wrote it off. I mean he got some money but nowhere near enough.'

'He was still paying for a car he didn't have?' Clare said, and Eilidh nodded.

'Then he lost his job, and he couldn't make the payments. The car company threatened him with court. Dayna said he was desperate.'

'So he borrowed from Mr Grandison?'

'Yeah. Marina's dad said the payments would be easy and it was okay at first; but the interest kept getting added on, and he ended up owing twice what he'd borrowed.'

Clare's lips tightened. So that was how Coke Grandison got his money. Taking advantage of young lads who didn't know any better. He was fast rising to the top of a list of people she'd like to nail. 'Does he still owe him money?' she asked.

Eilidh shook her head. 'No. According to Dayna, Marina's dad said Aleks – that's her brother – that Aleks could work for him to pay off the debt. Aleks said what would he have to do, and Marina's dad said he'd be collecting money from people. People like Aleks. But Aleks said he didn't want to and Marina's dad said he didn't have a choice. He could come and work for him or have his legs broken.'

Clare stared. 'He actually said that?'

Eilidh nodded. 'In the end Aleks told his mum everything and she got a bank loan. He took the money to Marina's dad and it's all paid now. But I heard Marina a few days later. Going on about how her dad was taking them all to Florida 'cause someone who owed him money had paid up.' Eilidh's face darkened. 'He doesn't even need the money. They're loaded. And now poor Dayna's mum's struggling with this bank loan.' She met Clare's eye. 'I hate people like that. I really hate them.'

Chapter 23

It was growing dark by the time Clare left the station to drive home. She was tired out and longing for a soak in the bath. Normally she tried to detach on the journey home. But tonight her mind was filled with Harry Richards and his colleagues. Was someone targeting them? And, if so, why? And where did Coke Grandison fit in?

She pulled into the drive, drawing alongside the DCI's Ford Focus. The security light came on and, somewhere within the house, Benjy began to bark.

Inside she found a leather holdall standing in the hall to the side of the stairs and she remembered. He was going away in the morning. All at once the events of the day threatened to overwhelm her. The horror of Harry Richards' death, Coke Grandison's moneylending, Leona Miller's accident – it was all going round in her head and none of it made sense; and now the DCI – her rock – he was going away in the middle of her investigation. She'd got used to him being there in the evenings, pottering in the kitchen, humming to himself. Only, now he wouldn't be. Not until his course was finished. She could ask him to put it off. Find someone else to run the course. Surely there would be someone? And then she gave herself a shake. It was nothing more than tiredness. She knew that. She was more than capable of running a major inquiry. It was time to stop relying on him so much.

The door to the sitting room opened and Benjy shot out, barrelling up the hall towards her. The DCI looked out, a tea towel in his hand.

'Cottage pie keeping warm,' he said and, in spite of her weariness, she smiled at this.

'Perfect. I'm so tired I can't face cooking.'

'Like you normally do!'

She laughed. 'I can't even be bothered to defend myself.'

'You *are* tired, then.' He took hold of her hand and led her into the sitting room. 'Go on,' he said. 'Feet up on the sofa. I'll bring you a tray. Then I must get to bed. I've an early start.'

She eased herself down on the sofa and kicked off her shoes. Benjy jumped up beside her and she put out a hand to stroke him.

'You're remembering about Tom?' the DCI called from the kitchen.

'Eh?'

He appeared in the doorway, bearing a tray and a delicious smell reached her nose. She sat up and swung her legs round, holding her hands out for the tray.

'What about him?'

He shook his head. 'You're hopeless. Remember he said he had some business up this way tomorrow and asked if he could stay the night.' He handed her the tray. 'I knew you'd forgotten.'

'Rubbish,' she said. 'It just temporarily slipped my mind.'

'Look on the bright side. He might cook you a meal.'

She considered this. Tom, her former boyfriend, now happily married, seemed keen to stay in touch. She didn't mind. He was good company and, as the DCI had observed, was an excellent cook. But she could do without him coming to stay, right in the middle of a murder investigation. She picked up her fork and dug into the cottage pie.

He saw her face. 'Want to put him off? You've a perfect excuse, with this murder.'

She held out her fork, watching steam rise from the pie. 'Nah. It's fine. He's pretty self-sufficient.'

'He'll have to be,' the DCI said and wandered back to the kitchen to finish the dishes.

Half an hour later, the pie eaten, she lay on the sofa, Benjy curled up beside her. She could hear the DCI moving about upstairs, first in the bathroom then in the bedroom. As Benjy's breathing became rhythmical and the movements upstairs ceased, a quiet descended on the house. Clare allowed her mind to empty as she stretched out, enjoying the warmth of the little dog beside her.

Day 4: Friday, 7th April

Chapter 24

'Got an address for Aleks Petrova,' Bill said as Clare entered the incident room the following morning.

She squinted at the paper he held out. 'Braid Crescent — rings a bell.'

'Apparently out by the swimming pool.'

Clare nodded. 'Yeah, I've got it now. Anyone else live there?'

'The mother and a sister.'

She took the paper. 'Thanks, Bill. I'll head over there after the briefing.' She glanced at her watch. 'Ten minutes — pass the word round please.'

She went through to her office, feeling the morning chill and bent to turn up her radiator. Then she sank down behind her desk and stifled a yawn. She'd woken just before midnight, her neck stiff from sleeping on the sofa. The heating had gone off and she'd hurried upstairs, climbing in beside the sleeping DCI. He'd stirred and put out an arm pulling her towards him and she'd lain there, stiff and uncomfortable, afraid of waking him. It seemed she'd only just fallen asleep when her alarm sounded. She'd reached out to turn it off and was suddenly aware of the space where he'd been. He'd be back in a week. She knew that but, with a major investigation on her hands, it felt like it would be a very long week.

Her computer came to life with a hum and she pulled the keyboard towards her. The emails began dropping into her Inbox and she regarded them without enthusiasm. She ran an eye down the messages and clicked to open one from Penny Meakin, headed *Touching Base*. She read it briefly and typed a

quick reply. There was nothing else that needed urgent attention so she locked her computer and went to the kitchen to
make a strong coffee.

The incident room was warming up as she entered, thanks
largely to the twenty or so officers crammed in, and to the April
sunshine which was peeping through gaps in the blinds. Chris
and Sara were perched on a desk, deep in conversation, Max
standing a little way off. The room fell silent as Clare threaded
her way through to the front, beside the whiteboard.

'Thanks, everyone,' she began. 'Quite a lot to get through
so let's make a start.' She paused to make sure they were all
attending. 'I've had an email from the Super, asking us to carry
on without a DCI. She's trying to rejig a couple of enquiries
but, for now, there's no one to spare.' This was met with silence.
'She's at the end of a phone if we need her but let's just get on
as best we can.' Heads nodded and she glanced down at her
notepad. 'Okay, we'll start with phone and bank records. Who
was looking into that?'

Liv raised a hand. 'I've been through Louise Richards' bank
records. Nothing much there – just the usual shopping.'

'What about Harry?'

'Again, nothing out of the ordinary. His holiday booking
checks out. Well, flights, at least.'

'No accommodation?'

'Not that I can see. It may be an airline package, though.'

'How much was it for?'

'Just over eight thousand.'

There was a low whistle from someone.

'Quite,' Clare said. 'Can you check what he booked please?'

Liv nodded at this, and Clare said, 'Chris and I interviewed
Kenny Deuchars yesterday. For those who don't know him
he's a small-time offender, out on licence, staying at Pitfedden
Lodge. Kenny is the man Louise Richards thought was stalking
her. He admits hanging around her house and other locations
but claims a man he didn't know paid him to keep an eye on

147

her. He's playing the innocent; maintains he was protecting her. Frankly, I don't believe it but he's sticking to his story.'

'Who paid him?' Max asked.

Clare frowned. 'Who went through the file photos with Kenny?'

Erin raised a hand. 'Sorry, boss. He didn't ID anyone. But I did show him the photo Janey had of Albie Kennedy.'

'And?'

She inclined her head. 'Hard to say. I thought there was a reaction but he denied knowing him.'

Clare stood thinking. 'Can we find out if their names have been linked in the past? Maybe questioned in the same inquiry?'

Chris raised his hand. 'Albie's not been charged with anything. Apparently there were never any witnesses prepared to give a statement.'

'All the same, let's go through Kenny's convictions. See if Albie was ever a co-accused or connected in some other way.' She checked her notepad again. 'Let's get back to the bank statements. What about the paralegal?'

Liv shook her head. 'Nothing there. Direct debits for bills and the odd cash withdrawal.'

'And the wife? Leona?'

Liv hesitated. 'Might be nothing.'

'Go on.'

'She took out seventy pounds every Tuesday. Lunchtime, usually.'

'Maybe she preferred using cash.'

'I don't think so. There are loads of small transactions. Sometimes several in a day: Tesco, the cheese shop, sandwich bar – she pays for everything by card.'

'I take your point,' Clare said. She looked round the room. 'Why would Leona Miller need seventy pounds in cash on a Tuesday night?'

'Remember that speed camera photo,' Sara said.

'Good point. Leona was flashed by a mobile camera on the Dairsie to Guardbridge stretch and there was another person in the car. We know she was alone when she had the accident so who was the other passenger and why haven't they come forward? Maybe she met a friend for a meal so let's look for restaurants west of the camera location. In fact, let's look for hotels. The post-mortem showed she'd had sex in the hours before the accident so maybe she booked a room in a hotel. Could be the other passenger was her sexual partner.' She looked round and spotted Max. 'Can you ask the press office to renew the appeal for dashcam footage please? Then I want uniforms checking on restaurants and hotels anywhere west of Dairsie. Pull a few off the house-to-house at Drumoig. See if we can find where she spent the hours before she died – and who she spent them with.'

Chris shook his head. 'Sorry, Clare, but it sounds to me like she was just having an affair. She takes the money out to pay her share of a hotel room, maybe a meal as well. They eat, have sex then drive back. She drops him off, somewhere between the speed camera and Balgove and she drives home. They most likely do it every Tuesday.'

Clare nodded. 'You're probably right, Chris, but let's be sure. Don't forget the husband works with our murder victim; and someone paid Kenny Deuchars to stalk the victim's wife. Maybe Kenny interfered with Leona's car as well.'

There was no response to this and Clare went on. 'I'll check with the vehicle examiner. They may have found something. In the meantime, get the dashcam appeal out again.' Speaking of the accident victim, she said, 'who saw the husband last night?'

Max raised his hand. 'He wasn't too bad, considering. I warned him about the press appeal and he was fine with it. Said *anything that helps.*'

'Any luck with Harry Richards' ex-wife?' Clare said, directing her question to Janey. 'Rosie… something?'

Janey nodded. 'Rosie King. Husband's Gordon. Don't think there's much there. She seemed pretty shocked. Said he was a nice man.'

'What about Gordon – the husband?'

'He didn't say much. Apparently he never met Harry. They'd separated before Rosie and he met. He made the right noises but didn't seem that interested, to be honest.'

'That it?'

'I asked Rosie why she and Harry divorced. She said they grew apart. Wanted different things. He was all for a quiet life. She's more of a livewire.'

'Okay, thanks Janey. Em… I'd like you guys from Dundee to look into Coke Grandison.'

Bill had been doodling on his notepad and he looked up. 'Anything special?'

'Moneylending. I've reason to believe he's lending on impossible terms. When the debtors can't pay he has them work for him to pay it off. My guess is he gets them doing stuff that's borderline illegal. Then he threatens to drop them in it if they try to walk away.'

'Anyone speaking to it?' Cheryl asked.

'Not yet. But I hope to interview someone this morning.'

Bill, Janey and Cheryl exchanged looks.

'I think we'd all like to nail Coke,' Janey said. 'Leave it with us.'

'You might want to look into Albie Kennedy as well,' Clare added. 'I'm pretty sure he's been driving our Mr Grandison's Beamer. Oh, and Chris has a list of dates when Harry left the office for unscheduled appointments. I'd like ANPR cameras checked for Harry's car on these dates. Then, cross reference with Coke Grandison's cars. He'd a van registered to the company as well and he reported it stolen so keep an eye out for that too. There's definitely something linking those two and I want to know what it is.' Her eye fell on Gillian, one of the uniformed officers. 'If you, Sara and Robbie, oh, where's Robbie?'

'Off sick,' Sara said.

Aware that every eye in the room was on her, Clare did her best not to react. 'Sara and Gill, then. Look for anything linking Harry and Coke. Get onto the phone company. We need historical location data for Harry on those dates.'

She waited for a moment while they scribbled down notes. 'Last thing: we've been given a warrant to access Harry's clients contact details. But that's as far as it goes. Liv and Erin, I'd like you on that. Everyone who had an appointment with Harry in the last two weeks is to be spoken to. Just the usual – how long had he been their solicitor, any problems, any red flags. But nothing – absolutely nothing – about their business with him.' She smiled round at them. 'Sorry, guys. This is a big investigation and we're under-manned as it is but it can't be helped. Keep in touch.'

She stepped away from the board, indicating the briefing was over. Sara was avoiding her eye, but Clare moved across to where she stood talking to Chris and tapped her on the shoulder. 'Spare me a minute?'

Chapter 25

'I don't know what's wrong,' Sara said, her face pink. 'He's been a bit down, as you know. He texted me this morning to say he was calling in sick.'

Clare was silent for a moment. 'I can't ask, officially, Sara. He's perfectly entitled to self-cert for seven days. But if there's anything I should know...'

The PC avoided Clare's eye. 'Like I said. He's a bit down. Maybe depressed.'

'We have a counselling service. I could refer him.'

Sara sat down and let her shoulders sag. 'I think he's embarrassed. Like he should be stronger, you know? If he went for counselling he'd have to admit he has a problem.'

Clare spread her hands. 'But he does have a problem. He's not fit for work and if he ignores that he could end up a lot worse than he is now.'

Sara shook her head. 'I don't know what to tell you, boss. He won't speak about it.'

'Okay, Sara. But will you tell him – please – tell him I'm here if he needs to talk.'

Sara nodded and escaped with obvious relief. Clare sat on thinking, after she'd gone. She really should have caught up with Robbie before now. Looking back she could see he hadn't been his usual cheery self. The slip up with Louise's stalker was proof of that. Dammit, it was her job to manage the team and she'd missed this completely. She clicked the calendar on her computer and counted forward five days. If Robbie wasn't back by then she'd go round to see him.

But for now there was work to do and Robbie being off only increased the pressure. She'd told Penny Meakin they'd manage without a DCI, but would they? She sent a quick text to Tom giving him the combination for her key box in case she was late home and was tapping out a message to the vehicle examiner when Chris opened the door.

'Two minutes,' she muttered. He pulled out a chair and sat down, drumming his fingers on the desk while she finished the email.

'What's first?' he said when the message had gone.

'First, *Sargento*, we are going to call on the Petrova family. See if they'll finger Coke Grandison.'

'Get you with the *español*!'

Clare laughed. 'I keep up.' She scraped back her chair. 'Come on. We might just catch them before they leave for work.'

It was clouding over as they emerged from the station, the sun gone now.

'Hope it doesn't rain,' Chris said, casting a glance at the sky. 'Got my washing out.'

Clare laughed. 'Slowly but surely, Sara's making a new man of you.'

'I like to do my bit,' he said, jumping to the car. 'Besides, if I'm out with the washing, I'm not discussing wedding favours – whatever they are – or which song we'll have for our first dance.' He tugged on his seat belt. 'Apparently Metallica's out.'

Clare pulled out of the car park and headed down Pipeland Road. 'So what's favourite?'

'Dunno. I point blank refused to have Beyonce. No way I'm having my mates seeing me jigging to that crap. It's been a sore point since then.' He put a hand on the door sill as the car jolted over the speed bumps. 'I have no idea why you persist in driving along Lamond Road.'

'It's the most direct route. And anyway, it's a lot quieter since the school shifted to the new site.'

'Suppose. So, what do you know about this Petrova lad?'

'Aleks? Not much. You heard what Eilidh said about the car loan and Coke bailing him out.'

Chris's lips tightened. 'Easy meat for a guy like Coke, these young lads. Turn here,' he added and Clare pulled into Albany Crescent. 'It's just along here to the right.'

The Petrovas lived in a mid-terraced house near the top of Braid Crescent. The front garden was paved in monobloc, a darker patch in the centre that looked as if it might have been from an oil leak. Clare wondered if this was where Aleks's car had stood. A narrow strip of grass separated the house from the neighbouring property and there was a border of heathers under the front window. There didn't seem to be a doorbell so Clare rattled the letterbox and stood, taking in the house. A movement at the window caught her eye and then it was gone. She turned back to the front door which had two long strips of frosted glass. A figure loomed up behind the glass and a voice from inside asked who it was.

'Detective Inspector Clare Mackay and Detective Sergeant Chris West,' she said.

There was a pause then the door was unlocked and opened as far as a security chain would allow. Clare held out her warrant card and nudged Chris to do likewise. Clearly Aleks Petrova was wary of callers. She explained they would like a quiet word and he released the door chain, standing back to admit them.

He was tall and slim, with thick dark hair and a short stubble beard. He was dressed casually in jeans and a light grey sweat-shirt, a fitness tracker-type watch on one wrist. His expression was wary but he said nothing, closing and locking the door behind them.

They followed him along a short hall into a room painted in magnolia. A dark blue sofa sat in front of a low coffee table with a modest TV in the corner. On the opposite side of the room there was a square dining table, a laptop open, its cable trailing to a socket on the skirting board. It was simply furnished but clean and tidy. Clare looked round, smiling in an effort to put Aleks at his ease.

'It's a nice room,' she said. 'Do you live here with your family?'

He seemed reluctant to answer, shifting from one foot to the other. 'My mother and sister,' he said eventually.

Clare nodded. 'Are they at home?'

He shook his head. 'My sister's at school and my mother's at work.' He gestured at the laptop. 'I'm studying. College.'

'Oh,' Clare said, seeing a way in. 'What's your subject?'

'Computing.' He smiled. 'I like computers. And maybe it'll help me get a job.' He looked from Clare to Chris. 'What's this about?'

Clare indicated the sofa. 'Maybe we could sit down for a few minutes?'

Aleks waited until they had sat then he pulled the chair from in front of the laptop and sat opposite.

Clare decided to get straight to the point. 'I understand you borrowed some money.'

He held her gaze briefly then looked away, shaking his head. He muttered something Clare didn't catch.

'Is that true, Aleks? Did you borrow money?'

'There's nothing wrong with that,' Chris put in. 'We all need a bit of help now and then.'

'I had this car,' he said finally. 'Nice car. Honda,' he added. 'I had a good job when I bought it. Then one night I drove it into a wall. Black ice, you know.' He shook his head again. 'There was a lot of damage and the insurance company wrote it off. The money they gave me...'

'It wasn't enough to pay off the car?'

'No. And then I lost my job. Made redundant. Only I hadn't been there long enough so I didn't get any money. And I have to help my mother with the bills. So I asked around. For work, I mean. Asked in the pubs. There wasn't anything, of course. But one of the barmen said he knew someone who might lend me some money. Tide me over while I found another job.'

'Can you remember the barman's name?'

'No. I never saw him again. Think he was just casual. Anyway, he said this guy was a good person. Liked to help people out. The interest wouldn't be too much.' He shrugged. 'It felt like a solution.'

'Who was this man?'

Aleks hesitated. 'I don't know his name,' he said, avoiding Clare's eye.

She studied him. 'Sure about that?'

He was silent for a moment. 'These people – they're not the sort of folk you cross. And they have other people. They're everywhere. Sometimes I go to college and I think I see them. Watching me. Making sure I see them so I know not to tell anyone.'

Clare sat forward. 'Aleks, if someone's threatened you—'

He laughed. 'Oh they're so clever. Never any witnesses. No texts or anything to incriminate them. It's someone brushing past you in Tesco, following your mother home.' He shook his head. 'You won't find any of their customers talking, Inspector. It's not worth our while.'

Clare's heart sank. It was always the same with these gangsters, preying on the vulnerable, silencing them with threats. 'Okay, then,' she said. 'How about this. You tell us as much as you can about how these people operate. It won't be on record. But if we have enough to charge them, maybe you'd think again about giving us a statement?'

'I'd like to help,' he said, 'but I won't give a formal statement. I have a mother and a sister.' He looked from Clare to Chris. 'I won't take chances with their safety. But, if you ask me questions I will tell you what I can.'

Clare smiled. 'I appreciate that, Aleks. Maybe you could start by telling us about the money. How was it paid to you?'

'Cash. In a Jiffy bag.'

'You met this man?'

He shook his head. 'I don't think it was him. The man said he was acting for the other one.'

'Can you describe him?'

'Better not.'

Clare looked at him for a moment. 'Go on.'

'He handed me the money and said he'd see me at the same place every week.'

'Which was?'

'Gents toilet. Down by the harbour.'

Chris noted this down and Clare went on.

'And the repayments?'

Aleks's shoulders sagged. 'They were okay at first. For a few weeks. Then this man, he said the interest rate had gone up. So I paid a bit more. And then it went up again. One day I asked him how much I owed and it was still way more than I'd borrowed, even with all the payments I'd made. I said how could I ever pay it off and he said there were other ways...'

Clare waited and when he didn't continue she said, 'What did he mean?'

Aleks met her eye. 'I won't say any of this in court,' he said. 'If you call me as a witness I'll deny it all.'

She gave him what she hoped was a reassuring smile. 'I understand. But I'd like to know, all the same.'

'He said I could go and work for them. So I said what would I be doing and he said maybe collecting debts – like mine. Or doing deliveries.'

'What sort of deliveries?' Clare asked.

'That's what I wanted to know but he said it didn't matter. I would just be taking parcels from one place to another.' He shook his head. 'I knew what he meant.'

'What did you think would be in the parcels?' Chris said.

He laughed. A harsh laugh and he met Chris's eye. 'What do you think, Sergeant? Drugs of course. Or stolen stuff. Either way, I knew it was time for me to get out. I said I'd get the money for him and I went home – told my mother everything. Next day she went to the bank. Asked for a loan. I knew by the time I went back the amount I owed would have gone up

157

again so she asked for a bit extra. Anyway, I met him as usual and of course it had gone up. Fortunately, the loan covered it and off he went. With our money.' His face darkened. 'There's a special place in hell for these people.'

Clare could feel the anger rising within her. But what could they do without statements from people like Aleks? 'I know you don't want to tell us the man's name, but it really would help if you could give us a description. Anything at all.'

He held her gaze as though trying to come to a decision, then he exhaled. 'Big. Like a bouncer, you know? Very short hair, sunglasses.'

She glanced at Chris and from his expression she guessed he was thinking the same as her. Albie Kennedy. The same man she thought had picked up Marina Grandison in the black BMW. She took a card from her pocket and handed it to Aleks. 'We may come back to see you but, if you do remember anything else or if you change your mind about giving a statement, this is my number.'

Aleks took the card and studied it then he raised his head and nodded.

They left him to his studies and climbed back into the car, Clare lost in thought. Then she gave herself a shake and put the key in the ignition. 'I'll tell you this,' she said, pulling out into the road. 'I'll nail Coke Grandison and his lunkhead driver if it's the last thing I do.'

Chapter 26

Chris's phone was ringing as they entered the station. He stopped to take the call then followed Clare to her office.

'That was Harry's receptionist,' he said. 'The Law Society's sending a solicitor along this morning.'

'So she's going in?'

'Yep. Jim's asked a woolly suit to keep an eye on the office.'

She smiled at the reference to uniformed officers. 'You do know it's decades since they wore those suits?'

He shrugged. 'Old habits…'

'Can you get on with finding a link between Albie Kennedy and Kenny Deuchars?'

'If there is one.'

'Well, yes.'

'What're you going to do?'

Clare picked up her phone. 'I'm going to speak to the vehicle examiner. Find out if anyone interfered with Leona Miller's car.'

'Just looking at it now,' the examiner said when Clare called. 'It's a right old mess but we're picking it apart. Anything special you're after?'

'Any sign the car's been interfered with,' Clare said. 'Something that could have caused an accident.'

'It'll take a while. We're working through the electronic control modules just now. There might be something there.'

'If there's anything remotely suspicious—'

'We'll call you. Don't worry.'

And with that she had to be content. She put down her phone and was checking her notepad when the door opened and Chris came in again.

'Looks like Sara has something.'

Clare rose from her seat and made for the incident room. Sara and Gillian were sitting over a laptop making notes and they looked up as Clare approached.

'You have something?'

Sara angled the laptop so Clare could see the screen. 'Okay, first of all,' she said, 'Coke Grandison's BMW crosses the Tay Road Bridge twice a day during the week – morning and afternoon. Well, most afternoons.'

'Which direction?'

'Both. It leaves Dundee around eight fifteen in the morning, heading for Fife. Comes back an hour later. Then it does the same journey around three in the afternoon.'

'And back about four?'

'Yep.'

'So he's running the daughter to and from school?'

'Looks like it.' Sara clicked and brought up an image from an ANPR camera. 'But this photo,' she jabbed the screen with her finger. 'I don't think this is Coke.'

'No,' Clare said. 'I reckon that's Albie Kennedy.' An image of the man in dark glasses waiting outside Melville Academy flashed across her mind. 'What about lunchtimes?'

Sara scanned her notepad for a moment. 'Couple of times. Once, about a month ago and last Tuesday.' She looked up. 'The day we saw him at the school.'

'What about Monday?' Chris said. 'The day Harry died?'

'Usual journey in the morning but not the afternoon. So I went back a few weeks and it looks like he never does Monday afternoons – or Wednesday.'

'Maybe she goes to an after school thing,' Gillian said. 'School probably runs a late bus.'

'Dammit,' Clare muttered. 'That means he wasn't in Fife when Harry died. Unless… What about Coke's other cars?'

Gillian indicated her notepad. 'Nothing for the Triumph. But the Audi crossed the bridge on Monday afternoon about three.'

'Is there a photo?'

Sara clicked to change the image and another still from the ANPR camera filled the screen. 'I'd say that's Coke, boss,' she said.

Clare peered at the image. It was hard to be sure through a car windscreen but the quiff and pinched features certainly looked like Coke. Heading for Fife the afternoon Harry Richards had died. Then a thought struck her. 'He's alone in the car.'

Sara nodded. 'He is. Unless there's someone in the back but that doesn't seem likely.'

Clare shook her head. 'There had to be two of them. Raymond said Harry was attacked from behind but there was definitely someone in the passenger seat. If Coke did kill Harry, where's the other person?' She pondered this. 'There must have been another vehicle. A van.'

'They could have gone in convoy,' Chris said, and Clare nodded.

'Good point. Back to the cameras,' she said to Sara. 'Check all vehicles that crossed the bridge from ten minutes before to ten minutes after the Audi. Go through the registered keepers. Anyone with previous, I want to know about it.'

'Burned out vehicles,' Chris said. 'Any reports since Monday?'

'I'll take that,' Gillian said.

Chris glanced at Clare to see if there was anything else but she was standing, lost in thought.

'I'd like to be sure Albie Kennedy didn't collect Marina on Monday,' she said eventually. 'He might have had another vehicle.' And then she remembered Eilidh Campbell and she checked her watch. Ten thirty. It might be near the morning break – but she didn't have Eilidh's mobile number.

'Do you have Kate Campbell's number?' she said to Chris who had settled himself at a desk next to Gillian.

He took out his phone and held it for Clare to see. She tapped the number into her own phone and started walking back to her office. Kate answered within a few rings.

'Nothing to worry about,' Clare said, 'but I'd like to check something quickly with Eilidh. Would she have a mobile at school?'

'She would,' Kate said. 'But it'll be switched off. School rule. She might put it on over break time, though. I think it's ten forty.'

'Perfect,' Clare said. 'If you could just give me the number.'

At ten forty Clare dialled the number but it went straight to voicemail. She left a message asking Eilidh to call and a few minutes later the number flashed up.

'Can you be overheard?' Clare asked.

'Hold on.'

She could hear voices in the background then the sound of the wind buffeting Eilidh's phone. After a minute she spoke again. 'It's fine now. No one can hear.'

'I need to be honest, Eilidh. This isn't official. I'm just interested to know something.'

'Okay.'

'We spoke about a classmate of yours yesterday. Don't say her name, but I'm keen to know if she attends any after school activities.'

'Yeah, I think so,' Eilidh said. 'We all have to. Everyone chooses one sport and one non-sporting activity a week. I do hockey and craft.'

'And the other girl?'

'Tennis, for sure. She's on the school team. I'm not sure about the other one. Might be the computer coding class. Yes, I think it is. We both get the late bus home on Wednesdays so it must be. Craft and coding are on the same days.'

'And tennis?'

Eilidh was quiet for a minute, only the sound of distant laughing in the background. 'Monday,' she said. 'I had to count back to be sure. Tennis is on a Monday.'

'And she'd definitely have to get the late bus home? She wouldn't get picked up?'

'I'm pretty sure she gets the late bus. She definitely catches it on Wednesdays. Never stops moaning about it. Not fancy enough for her.'

Clare thanked Eilidh and went back to the incident room.

'The search for the other vehicles,' she told Sara and Gillian, 'soon as you can, please. And I'd like you to compare ANPR images with the one of Albie Kennedy in the Beamer. I need to know if he crossed the bridge that afternoon – even if he was driving a milk float.'

Chapter 27

The data for Harry's mobile came through just after lunchtime.

'We need to check this against the days he left the office early,' Clare said. 'Do you have the list of dates?'

Chris leafed back through his notebook then put it down on the desk. 'There you go.'

'Right. Let's work backwards from Monday – the day he died.' She scanned her monitor, scrolling through the data until she came to Monday. 'There's a call from an unlisted number around two forty-five.' She sat back thinking. 'What time did Kate Campbell say he'd left the office?'

'Three thirty.'

Clare turned back to the screen. 'He's pinged a few masts on his way. Leuchars, Tayport. That fits with him heading for Tentsmuir.'

'Anything else?'

'Just missed calls from his wife and the office.' She frowned. 'I'm not sure that helps us. Let's try the previous date.'

Chris read out the date and Clare scrolled back through the phone data. 'Ah now,' she said. 'There's nothing at all for two hours after the time Kate said he left the office.'

'Phone off?'

'Must be. What about the one before that?'

Again, it looked as if Harry had switched his phone off after leaving the office.

'Only one reason I know for switching a phone off,' Chris said.

'You don't want anyone to know where you've been.'

'Exactly.'

Clare tapped her fingers on the desk. 'Let's put ourselves in Harry's shoes. Suppose he's doing some business with Coke Grandison – or whoever it was. Stuff he doesn't want anyone to know about.'

'I'd bet Coke's way more streetwise than Harry was,' Chris said. 'He probably told Harry to switch his phone off. Take the SIM card out as well.'

'So why was it not turned off on Monday?' Clare said, rubbing her chin. 'Unless—'

'He had reason to be worried?' Chris said.

'Yep. My guess is he knew something was up and he wanted quick access to his phone. Unfortunately, if we're right, he had absolutely no idea the kind of people he was dealing with.'

'Problem is proving it,' Chris said.

Clare's phone began to ring and she glanced at the display, clicking to take the call. 'Hi, Liv.'

'Hi, boss. I'm with Erin. We're working our way through Harry's clients.'

'Anything?'

'With the clients? No. All straightforward so far. But I've just heard back from the company Harry booked the flights with.'

'And?'

'Two business class tickets to Costa Rica plus three nights' accommodation.'

'That it?'

'The tickets were singles.'

'As in one way?'

'Yup. Looks like they planned to fly out there, spend three nights in San Jose and take it from there.'

'They were doing a flit?'

'I'd say so.'

Clare ended the call and said nothing for a few moments.

'You want to catch me up?' Chris said, eventually.

'Harry booked two one-way tickets to Costa Rica.'

'He wasn't coming back?'

'Nope. And, unless she's a bloody good actor, I'd say the wife didn't know.' Clare's brow creased as she thought back to the actions allocated at the previous day's briefing. 'Who was going through his finances?'

'Max.' He glanced towards the door. 'I think he's out.'

'Get him back please. I want to know exactly what was going on there.'

Chris went to track down Max, and Clare turned back to her computer, closing the mobile phone data. She sighed when there was a tap at the door. It was turning into one of those days. The door opened and Gillian came in.

'There's a woman out front, boss. Thinks she saw Leona Miller's car just before the accident. Jim thought you should speak to her.'

Clare rose and went to the front office. A young woman in cargo trousers and a striped hoodie stood there, a backpack slung casually over her shoulder. Her dark hair was tied back in a low ponytail, a pair of aviator shades on her head. She was fiddling with a set of car keys and glancing round when she saw Gillian and Clare walking towards her. She lifted her head slightly as a sign she'd seen them.

Clare introduced herself then asked Gillian to find Chris and led the woman to an interview room.

The woman stood regarding the chair Clare offered. 'I don't have long.'

'We'll keep you as short a time as possible,' Clare said. 'But it might be easier if you sit. Just for a minute or two.'

The woman perched on the edge of the chair and Clare took the opportunity to study her. She struck Clare as the outdoorsy type, probably rather be dashing up a hill somewhere than sitting in this claustrophobic room. The door opened and Chris entered. He raised an eyebrow and Clare explained the woman had some information relating to the accident at Balgove. Then she turned back to her. 'Perhaps you could start by giving us your name.'

'Joy,' the woman said. 'Joy Mackintosh.'

Clare noted this down. 'And you saw the accident?'

'I didn't actually see it, but I'm pretty sure I saw the car just before it crashed.'

'Where was this?'

'Just after the Kincaple turnoff. Maybe a bit further along. Near the Strathkinness junction.'

'Can you describe the car?'

'It was red. Quite a bright red. Some kind of SUV but not one of the huge ones.'

'You didn't see the make or model?'

Joy shook her head. 'Sorry, no.'

Clare smiled. 'No problem. Please – go on.'

'I saw it from quite a bit back because of the lights. It had full beam on. So I flashed it, you know? Thinking maybe the driver didn't realise. But it just kept on coming. The signals were going on and off as well. Then the hazard warning lights. As it got closer I saw the windscreen wipers were going too. Fast speed, you know? It was like the electrics had gone bonkers.' Her brow creased at the memory. 'I was worried the driver might have had a heart attack or something, so I slowed right down and put my hazards on to alert other drivers. I did wonder if it was a new car and the driver didn't know where all the controls were. You know how they're always in different places?'

'Could you see the driver? How she was behaving?'

'When I got closer, yes. Like I say, I'd slowed right down in case I had to swerve and it looked like she was struggling with the car – maybe not paying attention to the road.'

'Just to be clear,' Clare said, 'you formed the impression the driver wasn't fully in control of the car?'

'That's it exactly.'

Clare considered this. 'Would you say she was distracted enough for this to have caused an accident a few moments later?'

Joy hesitated. 'I'm not sure,' she said. 'Maybe. When I read about the accident I wasn't that surprised.' She nodded.

'Actually, yes. Now I think about it, I was relieved she hadn't swerved into my car.'

Clare asked Joy a few more questions but learned nothing further and, noting her contact details, she ended the interview. 'Come on,' she said to Chris. 'Let's talk this through in my office.' But Max was waiting in the public enquiry area.

'Some interesting stuff,' he said.

She stopped in her tracks and exhaled. This case was growing more complicated by the minute. 'Max, could you work your usual miracle with the coffee please? I think we're going to need it. And you,' she turned to Chris, 'some of your Wagon Wheel stash would go down a treat.'

Chris glanced over his shoulder and lowered his voice. 'I daren't,' he said, 'with Sara in the incident room. I'll never hear the end of it.'

Clare frowned. If ever there was a day she needed a sugary snack. 'Tell you what, get over to the shop across the way. Get us some KitKats. You can blame me if she catches you.'

Ten minutes later the three of them sat round Clare's desk, coffees and KitKats in front of them.

'Right,' Clare began. 'Sara and Gill are looking into Coke Grandison's vehicles. Seems Coke crossed the bridge on Monday in his Audi at a time that would fit with him meeting Harry at Tentsmuir.'

'But we think he had help,' Chris added.

'We do. Even if Coke got into Harry's car to discuss whatever business they had, there must have been someone in the back to cut Harry's throat. And I doubt Coke would want to get back in his fancy Audi if he was dripping in Harry's O Positive.'

'You're thinking another vehicle?' Max said. 'A van maybe?'

Clare slapped herself on the head. 'Of course! Coke reported a van stolen a week ago.'

Max smiled. 'Oh, I get it. He reports it stolen so he can deny any involvement if it's found, covered in Harry's blood.'

'Exactly.' Clare glanced towards her office door. 'No point in speculating until we see what Sara and Gill turn up.' Then she remembered Max had been waiting for them when they came out of the interview room. 'You were looking into Harry's finances.'

'I was. And it makes very interesting reading.'

'Go on.'

'Okay – going back a year or so, everything was direct debits or debit card payments. He rarely withdrew cash and never paid in. He drew a salary from the practice and the odd expense payment.'

'So?'

'Then it all changed – about ten months ago. He started paying large sums into his account. Cash, I mean. Then he'd transfer it to an offshore account.'

Chris sat forward. 'Dodgy money?'

'Could be,' Max said. 'If he was taking bribes from the likes of Coke Grandison it would definitely be cash. Guys like Coke don't leave a paper trail.'

'But why not keep it as cash?' Chris persisted. 'Why pay it in? If he was planning to flee the country, why not stuff it in a suitcase?'

'Cash dogs,' Clare said. 'They have them at the airport some-times. It's a huge risk these days. Even the scanners can pick up money.'

'Eh?' Chris said. 'How?'

'Bundles of notes show up like thick wads of paper. But they're usually not the right size for a paperback so if the security staff spot it, they can open the suitcase to check.'

Chris stared at her. 'I didn't know that. How would the likes of Harry Richards know?'

'He probably didn't. But Coke would. Maybe Harry asked him about it and Coke advised putting it through the bank.'

Max was nodding. 'And, if he did ask Coke—'

'Coke would know Harry was planning to go abroad,' Chris finished. 'You reckon that's why Coke killed him?'

Clare shook her head. 'We're getting ahead of ourselves. There's no firm evidence linking Coke and Harry.'

'Except Coke turning up at Harry's office,' Chris said. 'Don't forget that.'

'Yeah, it's a good point,' Clare said. 'Okay. I'd like a warrant to look into Coke's business but I think we need something more to justify our suspicions. I can't see it being granted purely on guesswork. Hopefully Sara and Gill will turn something up.'

Clare picked up one of the KitKats and peeled off the wrapper. She was about to bite into the two fingers when Chris stopped her.

'Whoah,' he said, a hand on her arm. 'What are you *doing*?'

Clare indicated the KitKat. 'About to take a bite of this. What's your problem?'

Even Max was shaking his head. 'You can't eat a KitKat like that.'

'Definitely not,' Chris added. 'We're not savages, for God's sake.' He took the biscuit from her and broke the two fingers apart. Then he handed one back. 'One finger at a time.'

Clare stared at the two sergeants in disbelief. 'I'm sorry but who made you two the Biscuit Police?' She bit into the single KitKat finger and picked up her coffee. 'Anyway,' she said, 'what about Leona's accident?'

Max looked at them and she hastened to explain.

'A witness came forward this morning. She saw Leona driving erratically moments before her crash. Full beam on, hazards going, windscreen wipers, the lot; and she seemed to be distracted.'

'Something wrong with the electrics?' Max asked.

'Could be. I'm waiting on a call back from the vehicle examiner. He doesn't know about the witness, though. I'll update him shortly.'

The door opened and Gillian came in. She spotted Chris biting into his KitKat and raised an eyebrow. Then she turned to Clare. 'Think we've found your van, boss.'

Clare drew a notepad across the desk and picked up a pen. 'Tell me?'

'White Transit. Crossed the bridge three cars behind Coke's Audi. The Audi returned just before six with the Transit half an hour after.'

'Who's the registered keeper?'

A smile spread across Gillian's face. 'It's Granco Lettings. The van he reported stolen.'

'Yes!' Clare said. 'Now we're getting somewhere.'

Gillian nodded. 'And there's more.'

'Go on.'

'We zoomed in on the camera footage. Two men in front. Neither of us recognised the driver but we both think the other could be Albie Kennedy.'

'Right,' Clare said. 'Put an alert out. Finding that van is top priority. I want SOCO all over it. If there's so much as a drop of Harry's blood, they'll find it.'

Chapter 28

An alert was put out for the Transit van and Clare called SOCO to warn them. Then she put down her phone and began running over what they now knew. Coke had been to Harry's office at least once; and she was increasingly convinced he'd had a hand in Harry's death. The question was could she prove it?

And then there was Leona Miller's accident. Had someone interfered with her car? They hadn't checked Harry's car for electrical faults but maybe it was something they should look at. Louise Richards. She had her own car. Was she too in danger? She picked up her phone again and dialled Wendy's number. The phone rang out a few times and Clare guessed Wendy was moving somewhere she wouldn't be overheard by Louise.

'Is she in?'

'Yes. She's upstairs changing the bed.'

'Good. Listen, Wendy. I don't want her driving her car, okay? In fact, I'd like someone to have a look at it. But not yet.'

'Very cryptic. Care to explain?'

Clare relayed Joy Mackintosh's statement. 'I can't take the risk someone's targeting the people who work in Harry's office,' she said. 'If I find Leona's car was interfered with I'll have Louise's checked for the same thing. But, in the meantime, don't let her drive it.'

Wendy assured her she'd keep Leona away from her car then Clare phoned the vehicle examiner again.

'We've reason to believe there was a problem with the electrics.' She went on to explain what Joy Mackintosh had reported.

'That's helpful,' the examiner said. 'We'll look at that next.'

'And, if you do find something, there's another two cars I'd like you to check for the same thing: our murder victim's and his wife's car.'

'You're certainly keeping us busy,' the examiner laughed, and Clare thanked him.

Phone calls done, she sat down, wondering if there was anything else she could do. She'd requested a warrant to seize Coke Grandison's Transit van and had sent a couple of plain-clothes officers round to his premises to see if there was any sign of it. Unlikely, given he'd reported it stolen. But they had to check. No doubt he'd have had it scrubbed clean, wherever it was. But, as she'd told Chris and Max, it was very difficult to remove every trace of evidence.

By five o'clock they were no further forward. There was no sign of the van and nothing further from the vehicle examiner. Mindful the DCI was away on his course she decided to head home. Moira, her nearest neighbour and dog walker had agreed to give Benjy an extra walk in the afternoon but she didn't like to leave him too long. She was just closing up her bag when her mobile began ringing again. Glancing at the display she saw it was a withheld number.

'Inspector Mackay?' the voice asked.

'Yes. Can I help?'

'My name is Derek Peterson. I'm the solicitor appointed to take over the late Harry Richards' clients.'

'Ah yes, Mr Peterson. I gather you've had contact with two of my officers today. No problems, I hope?'

'Not at all,' he said. 'They've been careful to keep to the terms of the warrant.'

Why was he calling if it wasn't a problem with Liv and Erin? Was it just a courtesy call?

'I have found something which may interest you,' he said. 'From what I can see there's no reason not to tell you.'

Clare was intrigued. 'Go on.'

'It's rather an unusual situation,' he began. 'It seems Mr Richards sold his house at Drumoig quite recently. I wouldn't normally have known this but he did his own conveyancing. It's not common practice but perfectly legal.'

It was all starting to fall into place. Harry's plan to skip the country. It made complete sense. But was Derek Peterson suggesting there was something odd about it? 'You said it was unusual?'

'It is, yes. The house was in Harry's sole name. His wife was not joint owner. That in itself isn't remarkable – perhaps less common these days – but it wasn't that which caught my attention.' He paused for a moment. 'There was a note on file stating Mrs Richards was not to be informed of the sale.'

Clare's mind was whirling. Had Harry planned to leave the country without Louise? If so, who was the other ticket for? And how could he possibly sell the house without his wife knowing? 'But surely Mrs Richards would have been aware the house was on the market? They must have had viewers.'

'She wouldn't have known because the house didn't go on the open market. It appears Harry approached a company who deal in high-end holiday lets. Reading the correspondence, I gather he offered them the house, fully furnished and kitted out, for 10 per cent below market value. The condition was that he be allowed to remain in it for up to two months, rent-free. It was also stipulated the house should not appear on the agency website until Harry and his wife had vacated the property. That agreement still had five weeks to run.'

Clare wished Chris was there to hear the conversation. She was desperately trying to gather her thoughts. 'Just to be clear, Mr Peterson, Harry Richards sold his house to a holiday rental company without his wife's knowledge? And it was sold with most of the contents, on the understanding the couple could remain in it for two months?'

'Yes, that's it.'

'And you believe Mrs Richards knew nothing of this?'

'So it seems.'

'And the money? For the house?'

'It rested briefly in an account I suspect his wife knows nothing about. Then he used a money transfer service, probably to an offshore account.'

Clare hesitated, trying to process what she'd heard. 'Is any of what Harry's done illegal?'

'Not that I can see – so far,' he added. 'I've only just started going through his files. It's not particularly fair on his wife but he does have the right to sell the home without her consent.'

Clare was starting to wonder if Harry had been having an affair. Maybe the days he'd left the office without warning he'd been meeting another woman. If so, were they wrong in trying to connect him with Coke Grand? Was it a woman who was behind Harry's gruesome death?

'I'll be in touch again if anything else comes to light,' Derek Peterson said.

Clare thanked him. Then she remembered Benjy and logged off her computer. She picked up her work bag again and headed out to the front office. Calling to Jim that her mobile would be on, she emerged into the early evening air. The clouds were gathering, an inky sky out to the west and she felt a pressure headache beginning at the base of her skull. She climbed into her car and switched on the aircon, hoping it would help clear her head – and her thinking.

The first spots of rain fell on the windscreen as she pulled out of the car park. By the time she drew up in front of Daisy Cottage the rain was teeming down. She grabbed her bag and dashed for the front door, missing the warm glow from the lamps Al usually lit to welcome her home. Benjy was behind the door and as she turned her key in the lock and leaned against it he struggled out, one of her socks in his mouth. She ought to scold him but instead she stepped inside, kicked the door closed behind her and dropped to her knees. She threw her arms around him, letting him nuzzle her neck. She was home, albeit without Al, but home all the same.

The first peal of thunder rumbled in the distance and she got to her feet, kicking off her shoes. She went round the sitting room, switching on lamps then she wandered wearily through to the kitchen. She took a lasagne from the fridge and put it in the oven to heat, uncorking a bottle of Brunello. Benjy fussed round her ankles and she bent to take his dog food from the cupboard. She filled his bowl then filled her glass. Carrying it through to the sitting room she decided to put thoughts of Harry Richards and Leona Miller out of her mind until tomorrow. Tonight was strictly a night off.

It was only when the doorbell rang that she remembered Tom and rose from her seat to let him in.

Chapter 29

Tom stood dripping on the doorstep and Clare moved back to let him come in.

Tom who she had lived with in Glasgow for several years. Tom who had wanted to marry her but who she had declined. And now he was married and she was happily settled with the DCI. They'd kept in touch but Clare had thought the contact would wane now they both had new partners. And yet here he was. Again.

'Come in,' she urged him, forcing Benjy back from the door. 'You're letting the rain in.'

He stepped into the hall, shrugged off his dripping coat and ran a hand through his hair, soaked in the short run between car and cottage. She led him through to the sitting room and bent to put a match to the wood burner, her latest toy installed after relentless nagging by Al, and anyone else he could persuade to plead his cause. He'd set it before leaving that morning and already the flames were licking round the carefully arranged kindling. She'd say this much for him – he knew how to set a fire.

She took Tom's coat and draped it over a chair to dry and turned to survey him. He hadn't changed at all since they'd first met. Maybe the odd grey hair threaded here and there but he still had the boyish good looks that had first attracted her. For a brief moment, she remembered what it was like to be his other half then she gave herself a shake. 'You're soaked,' she said. 'Shall I get you a towel?'

'No, it's fine. I'll soon dry off.' He rubbed his hands on his trousers and held them out towards the fire which was spitting and sparking as the sticks caught. 'This is a good idea,' he said, indicating the stove. 'Yours?'

'When did I ever have a good idea?' she said, and he laughed in reply. 'Hot drink? Or something stronger? You're staying, aren't you?'

'If it's no trouble.'

'None at all. The spare room's pretty comfy – as long as you don't mind toy elephants.'

He smiled, his usual wide smile, perfect teeth, his eyes crinkling at the corners. 'For your nephew?'

'Well, they're not for me!'

'Thanks, Clare,' he said, smiling again. 'It's kind of you.'

She went to fetch another glass from the kitchen. 'Have you eaten?'

'Just a sandwich.'

'I've a lasagne in the oven if you fancy? Plenty for both of us.' When he didn't answer she added, 'I didn't make it, in case you're worried.'

'Sounds lovely,' he called back. 'Sorry, the fire was sparking.'

Clare reappeared with another glass of red. 'Yeah, I believe you.' She handed it to him. 'Cheers!'

They sat companionably sipping the wine while the lasagne heated. 'So,' she said after a bit. 'You're up here seeing a client?'

He nodded. 'That, and something else.'

'Oh yes?'

'Gilly and I – we're thinking of investing in property.'

Clare raised an eyebrow. 'In St Andrews? I hope you have deep pockets.'

'You'd think, wouldn't you? But I checked sale prices on the Land Registry the other day. There's a few that went for so little they caught my eye. I couldn't find any marketing info online so they must have been private sales. I was up here anyway so

I thought I'd check one of them out. See why it went for so little.'

'Where was it?'

Tom reached for his phone and swiped to his Notes page. Then he held it out for Clare to see. 'South side of town,' she said. 'That *is* a good price. There's a real shortage of student accommodation here. Whoever bought that would have no problem letting it.'

'That's what I thought,' he said. 'So I went round by it today. Stopped and had a look outside. It's in pretty good nick. Frankly, I can't see why it sold so cheaply.'

'Could be a family thing,' Clare said. 'Parents selling to kids.'

'Yeah, maybe.'

She studied him as he sipped his wine. He didn't look his usual relaxed self. He looked, she thought, like a man who was trying to say something but didn't know where to start. Was there more to this visit than recceing cheap property sales?

'You and Gillian okay?'

'Oh yes,' he said quickly. A little too quickly.

'Come on, then. Out with it. We both know there's more to this than viewing some cheap flat so save us some time.'

He shot her a look. 'I never could get anything past you.'

'So?'

'Gilly and I, we're fine. We really are; and we are thinking about buying some property. But something's come up and I honestly don't know what to do.'

Might Gillian be pregnant? Surely that wasn't the problem. Tom would be thrilled. He'd always talked about having children *one day*. Maybe Gillian was pregnant but there was a problem. 'Tom, you're worrying me.'

'She's down in Brighton just now,' he said. 'Job interview.'

Clare put down her glass. 'Brighton? As in south of England?'

'It's the only Brighton I know.'

'And she's gone after a job?'

He nodded. 'You've heard of Roedean?'

Clare gaped. 'That mega-posh school? Like – Eton for girls? Tom! That's incredible.'

'That's the one. Anyway... she phoned this afternoon. They've offered it to her.'

She stared at him. 'Will she take it?'

He shrugged. 'It's very prestigious. It'll look good on her CV. Good money, too.'

She studied him. His face was lined with worry. 'You'd have to move.'

'Yup.'

'But your job, Tom – it's Scots law you practise.'

'I can do a conversion course. Let me practise in England. Not sure how onerous it would be but it is doable.'

Clare didn't know what to say. Every bit of him was saying he didn't want to go but the last thing she wanted was to get between Tom and his wife. 'Do you want to go?'

He didn't speak for a few moments. 'That's what marriage is about, isn't it? Compromise.' He took a slug of wine then he met her eyes, his own troubled. 'What am I going to do?'

The oven timer began to beep and Clare rose from her seat. 'I'll get the food. Then we can talk it through.'

She spooned lasagne onto plates and Tom, now mostly dried out, came to sit at the table. His glass was empty and Clare filled it, draining the bottle. 'I can open another,' she said, hoping he'd sense the tone. She'd an early start again in the morning and needed a clear head. Tom was halfway down his second glass and, reluctantly, she reached across to the wine rack. She uncorked another bottle and topped him up, leaving her own glass empty. He drank on and she rose to fill the kettle.

'We need coffee,' she said but he didn't seem to hear. The lasagne was half eaten and he put down his fork. His hair had fallen into his eyes and he brushed it back, making it stick up in front. She reached over to pat it down and he took her hand, holding it for a moment.

'Where did we go wrong?' he slurred. 'We were pretty happy.'

She let him hold her hand for a few seconds, enjoying the sensation and then, slowly, gently, she withdrew it. 'You know what went wrong,' she said. 'And you're married now.'

He nodded vigorously. 'Yes. Married now.'

'And you love Gillian.'

More nodding. Then he met her eyes. 'What am I going to do?' he said again. 'You're always so decisive, Clare. Tell me what to do.'

Day 5: Saturday 8th April

Chapter 30

Clare appraised Tom over the breakfast table. 'You'd better leave it a few hours before driving,' she said. 'You might still be over the limit.'

He nodded, rubbing his forehead.

'Paracetamol in the kitchen cupboard,' she added.

'I'll take Benjy for a walk before I leave,' he said. 'Clear my head.'

She studied him. 'You never could hold your drink, Tom.' She hesitated. 'Have you decided?'

'About Brighton?' He exhaled. 'I don't know.'

Clare rose from the table and began loading the dishwasher. 'How about this then,' she said. 'Forget about buying a flat for now. Keep your house in Glasgow and rent somewhere in Brighton. You can work flexibly these days. Meet clients by Zoom. Spend part of your time up here going into the office and the rest of the time in Brighton, working from home. Tell Gillian you'll try it for a couple of years.'

He considered this. 'I suppose it could work.'

'You both need to make it work. And it'll mean a lot of travelling up and down. But if Gillian's prepared to come back to Scotland after a bit, maybe for a promotion, it'd be worth keeping your house and job up here.'

A smile spread across his face. 'Thanks, Clare. You always know what to do.'

'Hah,' she said. 'I wish all my problems were so easily solved. Speaking of which,' she checked her watch, 'I have to go. I'll give you the spare key. Just pop it in the key box as you leave.'

He didn't reply and Clare had the impression there was something else on his mind. She didn't have time for this.

'Come on then. Out with it.'

He hesitated. 'It's just that, you said Al was away, and I thought, you're busy with this investigation. Gilly's not back until Sunday night. I could stay on. Give your dog walker a break. Do you some food.'

She looked at him, wondering if there was something else he wasn't telling her. And then she gave herself a shake. He was married now and they were old friends. Nothing more. 'It's up to you, Tom. I'll be out most of the weekend. But, if you want to look after Benjy...'

The little dog trotted up at the mention of his name, tail wagging.

'Great!' A smile spread across his face. 'I'll walk Benjy, tidy up your garden and do something lovely for tea.'

She nodded. 'Now I really must go.'

He caught hold of her hand as she headed for the door. 'I don't know if I ever really said sorry – for not supporting you properly when...'

Gently she withdrew her hand. 'It's fine,' she said. 'All in the past now.'

—

She mulled over her words as she drove along the tree lined road towards the town. Was it all in the past? They'd been together for so long that everyone, including Clare, had thought it was for life. She signalled right at the roundabout, her mind back at the time it had all gone wrong.

If she hadn't shot and killed that boy all those years ago – the boy whose replica weapon was so real she'd thought she was about to die – would she and Tom still be together? Perhaps married now and living in a huge house in one of Glasgow's leafy suburbs. Or was the subsequent inquiry – with her on one side and Tom's employers on the other – was it the excuse she'd been seeking? Would marriage to Tom have condemned her to a life on his arm, making polite conversation at Law Society dinners and helping with charity fundraisers? Perhaps she'd have bumped into Harry Richards or, worse still, Coke Grandison. With that sobering thought she pulled into the car park and backed into her usual space.

Chris was in the station kitchen, making toast when she entered, lunchbox in hand.

'You miss breakfast?'

He nodded, scraping butter onto the toast. 'Sara's got this new milk. I say *milk* but it tastes...' He stopped and thought for a moment. 'It's a bit sickly, to be honest. Anyway, I couldn't face it this morning so said I'd stuff to get on with.'

'You know she can read you like a book,' Clare said, flicking the switch on the kettle.

He shrugged. 'It's a kind of unspoken agreement. We do the healthy stuff for a bit then I have a blow-out. She turns a blind eye and we go healthy again.'

'If it works for you two.' She poured boiling water into a mug. 'Want one?'

'Yeah, go on. Anyway, what about you two? You and the DCI?'

'What about us?'

'You ever gonna put a ring on him?'

Clare laughed. 'You *sure* you don't want Beyoncé for your first dance?'

'Oh, progress there. We've actually decided.'

'Really? Spill!'

'I'm not meant to say.'

'Then I won't tell her about your Wagon Wheels.'

'You'll never find them.'

She regarded him. 'I could have a forensic team go through this station like the wrath of God. So, come on. Out with it.'

'*What a Wonderful World.*'

Clare's face broke into a smile. 'Louis Armstrong – how lovely.'

'Think so. Old dude with a trumpet.'

'That's him.' She patted him on the back. 'Great choice. So…'

'Yeah?'

'That stuff you told Sara you were getting on with.'

'Perfectly true.'

'And?'

'Albie Kennedy and Kenny Deuchars.'

'You've found a connection.'

He beamed. 'Certainly have.'

'Tell me?'

They carried their mugs through to Clare's office, Chris with the remains of a slice of toast in his teeth.

'So,' she said, setting her mug down on the desk. 'What have you found?'

'Remember that warehouse job in Dundee about five years ago?'

She frowned. 'The copper piping?'

'Yeah. Shedload of it disappeared. Well, Kenny was the driver. The CCTV had been disabled but there was a camera on the building next door. Kenny was clearly ID'd from the footage. But they never got the other one. Big fella. Hoodie and sunspecs.'

'Albie Kennedy?'

Chris shrugged. 'The Dundee lads were pretty sure it was him. Had him in for questioning but he had an alibi.'

'Legit?'

'Not a chance. But Kenny wouldn't finger him. Said he was paid to drive a van. Denied knowing the other man. There was nothing else to place Albie at the warehouse so they had to let him go.'

'And Kenny went down for it?'

'Yep. Apparently there was a tidy sum waiting for him when he got out. Reward for taking the rap.'

Clare sipped her coffee, her hands wrapped round the mug. 'So Albie and Kenny know each other.'

'Definitely. The Dundee lads reckon Kenny's done a few jobs for Albie. Kenny and some others. But they're all too scared to name him.'

Clare put down her mug and drew her notepad across the desk. 'Let's talk it through, then.'

'Right,' Chris said. 'Start with Harry.'

'Ah yes. Harry.'

Chris raised an eyebrow. 'What?'

'Seems he's sold his house.'

'Eh?'

'Quite. And there's a note on file stating Louise Richards wasn't to be told anything about it.'

'She didn't know?'

'Don't think so.'

'Any idea why?'

Clare shook her head. 'No, but I think it's connected to Harry's murder.' She sipped from her mug again, cradling her hands around it. 'Try this: I reckon Harry did a bit of work for Coke Grand. Somehow Coke persuaded him it was legit and when it turned out it wasn't he threatened to drop Harry in it.'

Chris looked doubtful. 'I dunno. He was a solicitor, remember. He must have been bright enough to know something wasn't right.'

'Maybe Coke spun him a yarn. Sob story – who knows? But let's assume they were involved in something illegal together.'

'Okay.'

'Harry gets cold feet. Tells Coke he wants out. Coke can't have that. Either he needs Harry for whatever he's doing, or he's worried Harry'll come to us. Confess all and name Coke in the process.'

Chris was nodding. 'So Coke asks Albie to put the frighteners on Louise and Albie gives Kenny a few quid to do it.'

'Yeah, that fits. Louise tells Harry about Kenny and Harry realises Coke isn't going to let him go. He starts making plans to get out. Sells his house on the quiet, transfers the money abroad and buys two plane tickets.'

'But how would Coke know that?'

Clare shook her head. 'I dunno. Maybe he'd someone watching Harry – looking for any unusual behaviour. Guys like him have a lot of folk in their pockets.'

'Go on.'

'Coke realises Harry's planning to skip the country. He can't risk Harry leaving a letter for us, confessing all.'

'So he shuts Harry up for good?'

'I think so. Let's say Coke asked to meet Harry at Tentsmuir. He pulls in beside Harry's car. Then the white Transit turns up...'

'The one that crossed the bridge behind Coke's Audi?'

'Yep. Coke spins some yarn about two of his lads needing legal advice.'

'The ones in the Transit?'

'Yeah. Albie and the other one. They probably ask if they can talk in Harry's car – so they can't be overheard. Harry goes along with it and the three of them get in. One in the front, one behind. Seconds later it's all over. Harry's bleeding out and they get back out of the car.'

Chris nodded. 'Sounds plausible. They probably changed out of the bloodstained clothes there and then, bagged them and threw the bag in the Transit. Drove to a secluded spot to burn the clothes then bleached the van.'

Clare sat thinking. 'Pity the van wasn't picked up as it passed the bridge camera. A stolen van should have triggered an alert.'

'Apparently Roads Policing were alerted but the intel on the database didn't indicate any links to crime; plus there was a bad collision up on the Kingsway.'

'Guys like Coke always seem to be lucky.' Clare shook her head. 'I'll give him this, he's a cunning bastard.'

'You reckon?'

'Oh yes. Think about it, Chris. Coke hides the van – likely in some lock-up – then he reports it stolen. He keeps it out of sight until Monday when Albie and the other one drive it to Tentsmuir.'

'Bit of a risk,' Chris said.

'Not really. He knows we don't have the resources to go after every stolen vehicle. If some of our guys stop them they just say they borrowed the van and forgot to tell Coke. They drive to Tentsmuir, kill Harry, then they either torch the van, hide it, or leave it somewhere for us to find.'

'So Coke claims whoever stole it killed Harry,' Chris said.

'Exactly. They don't even have to worry about their prints and DNA being in the van...'

'...because they work for Coke,' Chris finished. 'Jeez it's pretty near perfect.'

Clare sat back, drumming her fingers on the desk. 'What about burned-out vehicles?'

'Nothing for the past month. Not round here, at least. But they could have driven it anywhere and set it alight.'

'Then it's in a lock-up,' she said.

'Any idea how many lock-ups there are in Dundee? Even if you're right?'

'Nope. But at some point Coke must have built, bought or rented one.'

Chris stared at her. 'Oh, Clare, no. You're not serious?'

'Want me to quote the old cliché about police work being 99 per cent perspiration?'

'Don't you dare.'

'Companies House opens at nine. Go right back to when he formed his first company. Then get onto the Planning Department and see if he's ever lodged plans to build a lock-up. Check if he's bought one or if he rents one. I'm afraid it means getting on to every letting and estate agency you can find. We'll need a warrant as well. I want to investigate every single property Coke Grand has purchased.'

'I'd add Albie Kennedy as well,' Chris said. 'Could be Coke's put the lock-up in Albie's name?'

Clare nodded and picked up her phone. 'Penny Meakin's bending over backwards to help, given she can't find us a DCI. With a bit of luck she'll rush this through. And, while we're at it, let's put a tail on Coke and Albie. Covert, mind. I don't want them warned off.'

Chapter 31

Penny Meakin agreed to action the warrant and Clare ticked it off her list. She was wondering if it was still too early to call the vehicle examiner when she saw his number flash up on her phone.

'We've found something,' he said. 'Might not be significant but it's definitely something you should know about.'

'Go on.'

'There's a software program in the car that shouldn't be there.'

'What kind of software?'

'Malware.'

Clare thought of the security programs on her laptop at home. Supposed to protect against hackers and the like. 'What sort of malware?' she asked. 'What does it do?'

'Have you ever had to call Tech Support and allow them to take control of your computer? If it developed a fault?'

Clare recalled the time her laptop had been playing up. She'd allowed the technician to take over and had watched in amazement as the pointer moved about the screen, typing instructions and executing commands. 'Yes, I've had that.'

'It's a similar thing. A program's been embedded in the car's electronics. It would allow the person who installed it to take over some of the operations.'

Clare sat back, trying to take this in. 'That's *possible*?'

'It is. Obviously the important stuff like acceleration, braking, steering – that's pretty secure. But other things like the infotainment screen, lights, wipers – they're easier to interfere with. I'll have to bring in an expert but, if I'm right, I think this program would allow whoever installed it to mess with these things.'

'While the car was in motion?'

'If it had Bluetooth – and most modern cars do. There'd have to be a decent signal between the hacker and the car. Given where it was found, I'd say the signal would have been strong enough. Obviously if the car hit a dead spot it would stop working but the hacker would regain control as soon as it picked up Wi-Fi again.'

Clare closed her eyes, imagining Leona in a panic. Maybe the radio blaring, turned up to full volume, lights switching on and off, wipers too. What else had been going on in that car? It must have been pretty full-on to make her drive headlong into the telecoms box. Her mind was racing, trying to take in what she was hearing. 'How would something like that get into the car?'

'Could be when it was serviced, or in for repairs. A car like this has multiple electronic systems. If one of them develops a fault a warning light would come on. The driver takes it to the garage where a mechanic plugs in a laptop to access the on-board diagnostics. If there was malware in the laptop it could be set up to replicate itself in the car.'

Clare thought for a moment. 'Could anyone install it?'

'You're looking for someone with a pretty good knowledge of computers,' the examiner said. 'I'd suggest finding where the car was last repaired or serviced and take it from there.'

'Can you check for the vehicle logbook? It might be in the glove box.'

'What's left of it,' the examiner said. 'Give me ten minutes and I'll come back to you.'

Clare thanked him and asked if he'd check Harry's car for the same malware. 'I'll be sending another over as well,' she said and the examiner said he'd do his best to check them both. Then she swiped through her contacts until she found Wendy.

'How is she?'

'Doing okay,' Wendy said. 'I think she has her moments but she seems to be coping. How's the investigation going?'

'Slowly. But I need someone to look at her car. I'm going to send an officer to drive it to the vehicle examiner. They know what they're looking for so it shouldn't take long.'

'Which is?'

'Not over the phone, Wendy. I'll explain when I see you. But could you ask her where both their cars are serviced, please? I need the name of the garage.'

Wendy said she'd do this and Clare went to ask Jim to deal with Louise's car. Then she sought out Chris and Max. They were poring over laptops in the incident room and she pulled up a chair beside them.

'Something very odd.'

They moved the laptops aside and waited for her to explain.

'The vehicle examiner found some software in Leona Miller's car.' She related the conversation and Max nodded.

'I did computing at school. I remember learning about these threats. Never heard of it in a car, though.'

Chris was shaking his head. 'I don't get it. Why would someone do that? I can't see what they'd gain from it.'

'Some kid,' Max said. 'Doing it just because he can.'

'Or she,' Clare said. 'Don't assume the culprit's male.' As she said this, something stirred in the back of her mind and she heard Eilidh Campbell's voice telling her Marina Grandison attended a computer coding class. Could Coke really have involved his teenage daughter in Leona Miller's death? It seemed unlikely but men like Coke were ruthless.

'Where was the car last serviced?' Chris said.

She shook her head. 'Waiting to hear. As soon as we do, we'll pay the garage a visit.'

'Boss?'

Clare looked up to see Gillian, phone in hand. 'You got something?'

'Hotel just outside Dairsie,' Gillian said. 'They think Leona Miller had dinner there on Tuesday night. Early evening. They've a still from their car park CCTV.'

Clare rose from her seat. 'Come on,' she said to Chris. 'Let's check it out.'

—

The Dura Inn sat in lush countryside a mile outside Dairsie on a quiet country road. A board erected on the verge opposite the entrance announced the Inn was open to non-residents and fully licensed. Clare turned in through a wide gate flanked by stone pillars and crunched slowly up the gravel drive. Following signs for the car park she found a space to the rear of the hotel and they walked back round to the front door admiring the building. She thought it might be Victorian, perhaps a large country house at one time.

They stepped into a wide hallway, carpeted in dark red, the air thick with the fragrance from a vase of lilies on a polished mahogany desk. There was no sign of anyone and Clare pressed lightly on an old-fashioned reception bell. A moment later a door behind the desk opened and a young man in a dark suit appeared. His name badge read *Andrew Daw, Receptionist*. Clare flashed her ID and explained they'd had a telephone call from someone at the hotel.

'Ah, yes,' he said. 'That was Daisy. If you'd like to wait, I'll fetch her.'

A minute later a woman of about thirty-five in a dark uniform appeared. Her auburn hair was neatly scraped into a bun accentuating high cheekbones, her eyes outlined with a kohl pencil.

'Is there somewhere we could talk?' Clare said. With a glance at Andrew Daw the woman led them along the hall to a door at the end which gave onto a small office. She flicked on the light and invited them to sit on two ladderback chairs arranged in front of a desk.

'I've printed off the photos,' she said. 'I'll just fetch them.'

She reappeared a minute later with a grey envelope folder which she handed to Clare. 'There's a shot from the car park and one by reception.'

Clare opened the folder and withdrew two photo prints. The first showed a couple walking across the car park. They were both formally dressed, the woman in a dark pinafore with a light-coloured jacket over her arm. Clare thought back to the photo Simon had given them of Leona. It was definitely the same woman. The man beside her who was certainly not her husband was in a plain business suit. They appeared to be chatting but there was no physical contact between them. Looking at their clothes and their manner with each other, they might have been business colleagues having a working meal.

'They dined here?' Clare asked.

Daisy nodded. 'They come every week. Always the same. They ask for one of our booths.'

Clare raised an eyebrow.

'Little alcoves,' she said. 'Off the main dining room. Sometimes couples like a bit of privacy. It costs a bit extra but they're quite popular.'

Clare thought Daisy seemed uncomfortable and her mind went back to the post-mortem report on Leona's body. 'Was it just a meal?'

Daisy twisted a ring on her finger. 'I'm not sure how much I should say.'

'Everything you know, please,' Clare said. 'We're looking into the circumstances of the lady's death so we do need to know all about their visit here.'

Daisy's eyes widened. 'It was a crash, wasn't it? I thought she must have taken her eyes off the road for a minute.'

Clare said nothing, waiting for Daisy to continue.

'Like I say, they had dinner in one of our booths.'

'Did they order wine?'

Daisy shook her head. 'Not usually. I'd have to check the bill from Tuesday to be sure but I think she had sparkling water and he had a low alcohol beer.' She thought for a moment. 'Yes, I think that's it.' She looked from Clare to Chris. 'Do you want to know what they ate?'

'No, we don't need that. But, you have rooms here?'

Daisy flushed and gave a slight nod. 'They always booked one for the night but they never stayed.'

Clare jotted this down. It made sense. Dinner, up to the room where they'd have sex then they'd go back to their respective homes.

'How did they pay?'

'Cash,' Daisy said. 'Always cash. I think they split it fifty-fifty. I saw them a couple of times counting out notes.'

'So they came every week, had dinner, used one of the bedrooms for a few hours and left, paying cash for everything?'

Daisy nodded. 'Normally we ask for a credit card, in case there's a problem. But they've been regulars for a while now so the manager lets it go.'

Clare met Daisy's eye. 'I'd like you to think very carefully, please. Was there anything different in their manner last Tuesday? Any tensions you might not have noticed before?'

'No. They seemed the same as usual. They were always a bit careful when one of us was serving. Sometimes I'd see him holding her hand but when I came into the booth he'd drop it.'

'Was it your impression they were having a relationship?'

'Yeah. I'd say so. I reckon they were both married to other people and this was their weekly get-together. I mean you could see that from the rings.'

'Oh?'

'The wedding rings, you know? Both of them had rings. Hers was gold – like a yellow gold, yeah? But his was silvery coloured. White gold, or maybe platinum.'

Clare glanced at Chris who gave a noncommittal gesture.

'Couples usually choose matching rings,' Daisy said, and Chris nodded.

'It's true,' he said. 'Matching rings.'

197

Clare tried to think back to their chat with Simon Miller. Had he been wearing a ring? She couldn't remember.

'I'm guessing the bedroom's been cleaned by now,' she said.

'Oh yes. Cleaned and used again.'

Chris leaned forward. 'What name was on the booking?'

Daisy's brow creased as she tried to recall. 'McDonald I think – or something like that.' She shrugged. 'Probably not their real name.'

'Did you catch their first names?' Chris said.

'I think I heard her call him Eddie, or maybe Eric. But I don't think he ever used her name. I'm sure it's her, though. You can't really see from these photos but it's definitely the woman in the paper.'

Clare could feel the phone buzzing in her pocket. Was there anything else Daisy could tell them? They knew now Leona had visited the hotel every Tuesday with another man, that the couple used a bedroom for a couple of hours and paid in cash. His name might be Eddie or Eric, but how did this help them? The phone was still buzzing. She indicated the photos. 'I'd like to keep these if I may.'

Daisy shrugged. 'Sure. And if you want to see the footage I can show you. But these are the best shots.'

By the time they were out and heading for the car Clare's phone had stopped ringing and the voicemail icon was flashing. She put it to her ear and listened. Then she turned to Chris.

'Sexton Motors – know it?'

'Just out of town, past the hospital.'

She threw him the keys. 'You drive. I'll explain on the way.'

Chapter 32

'Leona Miller's car,' Clare said as Chris pulled away. 'Sexton Motors' stamp's in the service history. They've done the last three services.'

Chris pulled out into the road, turning back towards Dairsie. 'You reckon it's someone there?'

'Dunno. But I want to know who carried out that service.'

They drove along in companionable silence, Clare wondering how to go about questioning the mechanic. It was hard to know when she only had a scant understanding of what the malware could do. Probably best to play it by ear. See what he volunteered. Her thoughts turned to Robbie and she decided she'd nothing to lose by grilling Chris.

'Sara said anything about Robbie?'

She saw him tense, his fingers gripping the steering wheel a little more tightly. There was a definite pause. 'Not much.'

'Have you seen him?'

He shook his head. Glancing at Clare he said, 'She went round. Last night.'

'And?'

'No answer. She knocked on the door, called through the letterbox, tried his mobile but he wouldn't answer.'

A tight knot was forming in Clare's chest. 'Should be we concerned, Chris? He wouldn't—' she broke off not wanting to give voice to her fears.

'Nah. Sara said he was there. She heard him moving about and she's sure she saw the curtains twitch when she walked away. I think he just wants to be on his own for a bit.'

Clare thought about this and she came to a decision. 'I think I'll drop in on him.'

Chris frowned. 'You sure that's a good idea? He might think you're trying to drag him back to work.'

'Chris! That's the last thing I would do. Godsake, why does everyone think I'm some kind of monster?'

'You want me to answer that?' He glanced at her. 'Seriously, though, maybe give him another day or two.'

They were approaching the garage now and Chris signalled to turn onto the forecourt, pulling in beside a row of cars with price labels obscuring their windscreens. Clare followed the directions for the service department and they stepped into another building with a concrete floor. It was cool and draughty, the lighting harsh thanks to a bank of strip lights suspended from girders. Half a dozen cars were sitting, some with bonnets up, others with wheels off, one up on a ramp. The sound of hammering echoed round the garage, punctuating the tinny blare from a radio. Towards the back of the building a half-glass door marked Service Reception led to a portacabin-style office and they made their way towards this. A young man in dark blue overalls was on the phone and he motioned for them to come in. They entered, feeling a wall of heat from an electric radiator.

The man put his hand over the phone and said, 'Shut the door, eh?'

Clare moved further into the cabin to allow Chris to close the door and the man nodded his thanks. As he talked, she took in her surroundings. There was a key cabinet to the right of the door with rows of hooks bearing labelled keys, and a Formica table on the opposite wall, a selection of chairs scattered round it. A kettle and tray of mugs stood on the table, an open packet of Hobnobs beside it. A metal storage cabinet was the only other piece of furniture. As they waited for the man to finish his call Clare glanced out and watched as a campervan was backed carefully into a space next to the car on the ramp.

'Help you?' the man said, his phone call evidently finished.

Clare smiled and held out her warrant card. 'You serviced a car belonging to a Mrs Leona Miller.'

The man raised an eyebrow. 'Got the reg?'

She reeled it off and he moved to a computer monitor. He tapped at the keyboard and turned back to Clare. 'That's right. Last month.' And then his face fell. 'Oh, that's the woman who died, isn't it? Poor thing.' He hesitated. 'I hope you're not thinking—'

'Can you tell us who worked on the car, please?'

The man looked at Clare for a moment then back at the monitor. 'Sam,' he said, after a minute. 'Sam Glenday.'

Clare indicated the workshop. 'Is he here?'

The man shook his head. 'Annual leave. Back Monday if that helps.'

'Do you know if he's gone away?'

'Sorry, no. One of the lads might, though.' He rose from his seat and brushed past Clare, opening the door. He yelled a couple of times and one of the mechanics looked up from under a car bonnet. There was a shouted exchange and the mechanic ambled over, wiping his hands on his overalls. The pair had a brief conversation then the mechanic returned to his car bonnet.

'Doesn't look like it,' the man said, closing the door again. 'Seems he's putting in a new bathroom.'

'We'll need his address,' Clare said. 'Also, do you use—' she glanced at Chris trying to remember what the vehicle examiner had said.

'On-board diagnostics,' Chris said.

'Yeah.'

'How does it work?'

'That's Sam's department. He uses a laptop. Plugs it in and runs a program. It tells him what's wrong. Saves hours of work.'

'No one else uses it?'

'Sam's the only one trained. We wouldn't be insured if anyone else touched it.'

'So you won't be using it until Sam gets back?'

The man's face darkened. 'Why?'

'I'm afraid we'll have to take it with us.'

'You cannae do that,' the man said. 'What if we have a rush job?'

'As you said. Sam won't be back before Monday.'

'Aye but…'

'Thing is, Mr?'

'Aaron. Just Aaron's fine.'

'Thing is, Aaron,' Clare said, choosing her words carefully, 'we're investigating the possibility something went wrong with Mrs Miller's car. Now, I'm not suggesting for a minute that Sam – or anyone else – is to blame but we need to have our technical experts look at that laptop.'

Aaron picked up a pen and fiddled with it. 'The boss won't like it. You got a warrant, or whatever it is you're meant to have?'

'Not yet,' Clare said, 'but if you refuse to let us have the laptop we'll apply for one and your refusal will be noted.'

He looked down and exhaled. 'Might as well have it. But if we could have it back for Monday…' He reached past Clare to the metal cabinet and pulled open the door. Bending down he lifted out a laptop bag and handed this to Chris. 'See you look after it, mind? Worth its weight in gold.'

Clare asked Aaron for Sam's contact details and he scribbled these on a piece of paper torn from a notebook.

'Thanks,' she said, tucking the paper into her pocket. She turned to leave then remembered something. 'Can you check one more thing, please?'

Aaron's face fell as though he was desperate to be rid of them. 'Of course,' he said, his tone not matching his words.

'Do you have customers from Drumoig? A Mr and Mrs Richards?'

'Registrations?'

'Sorry.'

He moved back to the computer and clicked to search. 'There's a Miss Richardson down at Dunino. Is that who you mean?'

Clare shook her head. 'No one else?'

'Nope. Sorry.'

'No problem.' She indicated the laptop. 'We'll have this back to you as soon as we can.'

As they left the garage Clare realised the voicemail icon was flashing again. 'Must have had my phone on silent,' she muttered, clicking to listen to the message. 'Pen!' she said to Chris. 'Quickly.'

He produced a pen from his inside pocket and Clare tucked the phone in her car so she could scribble on her hand.

'Janey,' she said, giving Chris the pen back. 'She found a number in Leona Miller's phone. It's listed as *Irene* but it looks like she either calls it or receives a call from it every Tuesday around teatime.' She looked at Chris. 'Worth chasing up?'

He stood thinking for a minute. 'Why don't we pop into her work. See if anyone knows an Irene. We could show them the photos too. They might recognise the man she's with.'

'Good plan. Then we'll see if Sam the mechanic's finished his new bathroom.' She walked round to the passenger door. 'You drive. I need to call the station.'

While Chris drove Clare spoke to Jim. 'Can you run a check please on a Sam Glenday?' She reeled off the address. 'He did some work on Leona Miller's car. I'd like to know if he's come to our attention before now.'

–

Kinness Recruitment was part of a retail unit on Largo Road. There was a small car park to the rear and Chris backed into a space. Clare took the clearer of the two photos and folded it so

Leona was hidden. 'Come on,' she said, jumping out of the car. 'Let's see if anyone recognises him.'

A polished wooden door bore the company logo. Clare tried the handle, but it was locked. Chris indicated an intercom on the wall and she pressed it. A disembodied voice asked if she could help and Clare explained they were investigating the fatal accident involving Leona Miller. The door buzzed and they entered a bright office, a smiling woman at the front desk. The woman explained how shocked they all were about Leona then asked how she could help.

'Perhaps you could tell us a bit about her?'

There was a brief hesitation. 'But her death – it was an accident, wasn't it?'

'We're just tidying up loose ends,' Clare said, smoothly. 'So, you worked with her?'

'Yes.' She nodded across the office towards an empty desk. 'That's Leona's. Or, that *was* hers.'

Clare smiled. 'This must be difficult for you. Did you all get on well?'

'Mostly. It's busy here, you know? Not much time to chat.'

'Did you have nights out?'

'Just Christmas, really. Maybe the odd time through the year. And if it was someone's birthday we'd buy cakes. But mostly we just got on with our work.'

Clare looked round. 'How many of you are there?'

'Six. Well, five now. But we'll have to get someone else in. It's a busy office.' She glanced again at Leona's desk then turned back to Clare and Chris. 'There's the boss, Mr Glover, then there's Anne-Marie – she does all the accounts, personnel stuff. I suppose she's the office manager. And four of us are recruitment consultants. We match people with vacancies.'

'Is there an Irene in the office?'

The woman seemed surprised. 'No. Why do you ask?'

'No reason.' They weren't learning much here and Clare took out the photo. 'Do you recognise this man?'

Her face cleared. 'Of course. That's Mr Glover. He's the boss.'

Clare sensed Chris tense beside her but she was keen to give nothing away and she went on. 'Has he worked here long?'

'Longer than me; and I've been here ten years.'

'Does he live locally?'

'Strathkinness.'

'Family?'

'His wife, Sherry. There's a son too but he's left home now. Down south somewhere, I think.' She glanced back at the photo. 'How odd you have his photo. Where was it taken?'

Clare ignored the question. 'Is Mr Glover in?'

She looked at Clare as though waiting for an explanation. When none came she nodded. 'Would you like to see him?'

'Please.'

She lifted the phone and spoke into it then replaced the receiver. 'I'll take you through.'

Edward Glover rose to meet them as they entered his office. Clare took him in. There was no mistaking he was the man in the photo. He was tall, not unattractive but she felt instantly he wasn't someone she would trust. Perhaps it was knowing he'd been having an affair with Leona Miller. There was something so efficient, so *organised* about their Tuesday arrangement. And yet it felt cheap and tawdry. Or was she being too judgemental?

She turned her attention instead to the office. It was quite a small room but well appointed. There was a Nespresso coffee machine in one corner, a set of matching china mugs beside it. She couldn't help contrasting it with the catering facilities at Sexton Motors.

'Coffee?' he said, indicating the machine.

Clare was about to give her stock refusal then she thought it might make for a more relaxed discussion. 'That would be lovely,' she said. 'If it's not too much trouble.'

He smiled, a wide smile. 'Not at all.' He rose and moved to the coffee machine, busying himself with the capsules and water. 'Terrible thing, Leona,' he said. 'We're all very shocked.'

Clare watched him but his back was to her as he spoke. Was that deliberate? 'How long has she worked for you?'

'Oh,' he said, stopping for a moment, 'maybe six years. I could check but roughly that.'

He carried two cups over to Clare and Chris and returned to make himself a drink. Clare waited until he was sitting down again before she continued. 'You got on well?'

'Oh yes,' he said. 'She was a breath of fresh air, Leona. Always bright and cheerful.'

Clare asked a few more questions but she could see he was sticking to his story and she decided to waste no more time. She took the photo out of her bag and unfolded it. Watching him carefully she passed it across the desk. It took a few moments for him to realise what he was looking at. Then the colour drained from his face. He picked up his coffee and sipped at it. 'Where did you get this?'

Clare didn't answer immediately. She watched him trying to control his face. His hands were wrapped round the coffee cup now. Was he trying to stop them shaking? 'Where do you think we found it?' -

He sank back in his chair. 'I'm guessing it's the hotel. The Dura Inn.'

'Correct. Maybe you could explain?'

He sighed and shook his head. 'It— it was just one of those things. Leona — she pursued me, you know? She was a very strong personality. If she saw something she wanted she went out and got it. And she wanted me.' He met Clare's eye. 'She was a hard woman to say no to.'

'How long had it been going on?'

He shrugged. 'A year or so.'

'And you met regularly?'

He nodded. 'Always Tuesdays. My wife plays badminton on a Tuesday. She thinks I work late.' He hesitated. 'She doesn't have to know about this, does she?'

'It rather depends,' Clare said. 'If it's not relevant to our investigations there's no need for it to go any further.'

He seemed visibly relieved. And then he frowned. 'Wait, investigations? Surely it was just an accident.'

'That's what we aim to find out,' Clare said. 'So, can you tell me please about the last time you saw Leona?'

He took a sip of coffee then replaced the cup on the desk. 'It must have been shortly before she died,' he began. 'There's a lay-by at Guardbridge. We'd leave the office and take our cars there. Then one of us would drive to The Dura Inn. Leona drove this time. We had dinner and, well, I'm guessing you know we pay for a room. After dinner we went upstairs for a bit.'

'I'm sorry to be blunt, Mr Glover, but did you and Leona have sex on Tuesday evening?'

He flushed at the question but gave a slight nod. 'Yes,' he said. 'We had sex. Then we showered, got dressed again and went out to the car. We drove back to the lay-by. Leona was in a hurry because we'd spent longer at the Inn than usual. She was driving fast so when I heard about the accident, I assumed... Anyway, we got to the lay-by and I got into my own car. I go up the Strathkinness Road and she goes on to St Andrews.' He swallowed. 'It must have been just after that.'

'Thank you,' Clare said. 'Did you notice anything different about Leona on Tuesday? Any worries? Anything unusual in what she said or did?'

He sat thinking then shook his head. 'No, I'm sorry. She seemed the same as usual. Sparky – full of life, you know?'

Clare picked up her coffee and sipped from it. 'This is very good.'

He smiled. 'My little treat to myself.'

'Did you discuss bringing your relationship to an end?' she asked suddenly.

He seemed taken aback by the question. 'No. At least, I had no plans to end it. It was only a bit of fun. I didn't think we were doing any harm.'

Chris raised an eyebrow but said nothing.

'So, as far as you were aware,' Clare persisted, 'everything was the same as usual?'

'Yes. I don't know what happened. She must have been distracted by something.'

Clare glanced at Chris. 'I think that's covered everything, then, Mr Glover. But if you could perhaps give us a mobile number?'

He frowned at this. 'I can give you the office number.'

'A mobile's easier,' Clare said. 'And don't worry. We'll only call out of office hours if it's essential.'

He reached into his desk drawer and withdrew a small business card. Clare took it, glancing at the mobile number. From the few digits visible on her hand she could see it wasn't a match for the one Leona had stored as *Irene*. 'Do you have another mobile?' she said. 'A personal one?'

He didn't immediately answer. Then he picked up a pen and indicated the card he'd handed Clare and jotted his number down on the back. As he did so Clare checked it against the number on her hand. This time it matched.

'I'm guessing your relationship wasn't known about in the office?'

He shook his head. 'I certainly hope not. We never spoke of our arrangements. Usually I called the Inn to book a table and one of us would call the other to confirm.'

This matched with the calls Janey had found on Leona's phone. He held out the card and this time Clare tucked it in her pocket. She looked round the office, smiling at her surroundings. 'It's a lovely office. You must have worked hard to get where you are.'

He inclined his head. 'I suppose.'

'Did you study business?' She felt Chris shift in his chair, probably wondering where she was going with this.

'Computing, actually,' he said. 'Not that I do much of it now. It moves on so quickly these days.'

'I'm just glad we have our technical wizards to fix the machines for us,' Clare said. 'We wouldn't have a clue, would we, Chris?'

'Oh no,' he mumbled on cue. 'Not a clue.'

They left a clearly relieved Edward Glover and walked back to the car.

'What was all that about computers?' Chris asked.

'Leona's car. Someone fiddled with it.'

'I thought you fancied the mechanic for that?'

'He is the most likely. But we can't ignore the fact she'd been having a long-term affair with her boss. What if he'd had enough of her? Maybe he only meant to give her a fright.'

'Surely he'd just end it,' Chris said. 'Messing with her car's a bit dramatic.'

'Maybe she wouldn't take no for an answer. Maybe his wife found out and was putting pressure on him. I don't know, Chris. I admit it sounds far-fetched. But so's hacking into the car's electrics. And that program didn't get into Leona's car by itself. Somebody put it there and I'm determined to find out who.'

Chapter 33

Sam Glenday lived in a small house on Schooniehill Road, not far from Kinness Recruitment.

Chris pulled up outside and they studied the house. 'Looks like he's got the bathroom done,' he said, nodding at an old bath sitting in the front garden. 'Bet the neighbours love that.'

They climbed out of the car and walked up the path. Clare pressed the doorbell and heard it ring inside. But there was no answer. 'Check round the back,' she said to Chris and she moved to peer in the front windows. A minute later Chris reappeared. 'Had a look in the kitchen window. Can't see any sign of life.' He checked his watch. 'Maybe gone to the footie.'

'Of course,' Clare said. 'It's Saturday. He could be anywhere, really.' She began walking back to the car. 'I'll get a uniform to call round later. See if he's come back.' Her phone buzzed with a message from Jim. She read it then tucked it back in her pocket. 'He doesn't have any previous,' she said, and Chris nodded. She felt the business card in her pocket and took it out to check the mobile number. As she'd thought, it matched the one written on her hand. 'At least we know our Mr Glover is *Irene*,' she said.

'Number matches?'

'Yep.'

They stopped at the car. 'So what now?' Chris said.

She stood thinking. 'Let's get someone to run this laptop down to Tech Support. See what they can tell us.'

Gillian was despatched to the Tech Support office in Glen-rothes.

'I've phoned ahead and spoken to Diane,' Clare said. 'She knows it's priority so she'll be looking out for it.'

That done, she wandered through to her office, her head full of the morning's events. Jim had left a message from Wendy on her desk. Both the Richards' cars were serviced in Dundee, Harry's by the Peugeot dealership and Louise's by the Vauxhall garage. That fitted with Sexton Motors having no record of the Richards as customers. The message also said Louise's car had been picked up and was on its way to the vehicle examiner. And then she remembered Simon Miller. Why hadn't she checked to see if he had his own car? They'd have to check that as well. She lifted the phone and dialled his number. He answered, his voice hesitant and she was transported back to his sitting room, the day they'd spoken to him about Harry's death.

'I'm so sorry to trouble you,' she said, 'but I wondered if I could ask something.'

'Of course. Anything at all.'

'Do you have your own car, Mr Miller?'

There was a hesitation. So brief Clare almost didn't notice it. 'Yes. I do. But I don't use it much. It's mainly kept in the garage.'

'Has it been serviced recently?'

'Oh yes,' he said. 'I like to keep it in good condition.'

'Can I ask who did the service?'

'A garage in town,' he said. 'Sextons. They're very good. I can recommend them.'

Clare's mouth was dry. It wasn't unusual, a husband and wife using the same garage. In fact, it was more likely they would. But if they did find malware in Simon Miller's car, would that mean Sam Glenday was involved? 'What kind of car is it?' she asked.

'It's a Renault Clio,' he said. 'Not a new model. Not like Leona's. But it does me.'

'How old is it?'

'It's six years and five months,' he said, and she suppressed a smile at him responding so precisely. She wondered if cars of that age would have the electronic systems found in Leona's car. She hadn't a clue but she couldn't take a chance.

'Mr Miller, I don't want you to drive your car until I've had someone examine it. I'll send an officer round. If you let them have the keys we'll take it over to our experts. Just to check everything's okay with it.'

'Oh,' he said, sounding doubtful. 'What if I need it?'

'We'll have it back to you as soon as possible,' Clare said, and she went to find someone to collect Simon's car. Max caught her eye.

'Might have something,' he said.

She went over to look at his laptop.

'Coke Grandison, or Colin as he is on official documents.'

'What about him?'

'I've been onto the Land Registry and they've run a search on him and his wife, Danuta.'

'And?'

'They've a house on the Perth Road in Dundee. Nice property. Been there a few years. And, as we know, he has Granco Lettings. But there's more. Much more.'

'Go on.'

'Between him and his wife there are five different companies. Looks like they're all letting agents. I'm still looking, but the first one I checked has sixteen properties on the website, all owned by the company. The second isn't as big – only seven but it's still a lot of houses.'

Clare stared at him. 'Coke owns twenty–plus properties?'

'At least. Or rather his company does. But he and Danuta are the only company officers.'

Clare's mind was racing with this new information. 'Max, could you find out if any of the properties have garages? If so, could be that's where the van's hidden; and let's check to see if Albie Kennedy owns any flats or houses – in case Coke's put any of them in his name.'

Max made a note of this. 'How's he managed to buy so many houses?'

Clare's lips tightened. 'That's what I intend to find out.'

Chapter 34

It was almost five o'clock when the vehicle examiner phoned back. 'Okay,' he began, 'I've had a look at the murder victim's Peugeot, his wife's Vauxhall and the Renault Clio.'

Clare hardly dare breathe. 'And?'

'No malware on any of the three. I've not carried out a full examination. That'll take another day or two but definitely nothing like we found on Mrs Miller's car.'

She thanked the examiner and put down the phone. That put paid to her theory about the staff at Harry's office being targeted. Was it really just a coincidence Leona Miller and Harry Richards dying within a day of each other? She looked up to see Chris in the doorway.

'Gary's just called. He's at Sam Glenday's house. He's home now. You want to see him?'

Clare yawned. Breakfast with Tom seemed a long time ago now. She wondered how he'd spent his day. He'd said he'd cook them a meal that night. Her tummy rumbled at the prospect but she forced her thoughts back to Sam Glenday. 'Could you ask Gary to bring him in please? If he's sticky about it we'll go round but I'm wading through paperwork here.'

Chris went off to speak to Gary and a minute later he popped his head round the door again. 'On his way. Want me to prep a room?'

'Please. And see if Max would do us all some coffee. I've run out of whatever I started the day with.'

Twenty minutes later Clare and Chris led Sam Glenday to an interview room. She thought he might be in his late twenties. His blonde hair was highlighted and neatly cut, and he looked as if he was no stranger to the gym. She checked his hands and noted he wasn't wearing a wedding ring. They were marked, though. Knuckles skinned, grazes here and there and she wondered if this was the result of his recent DIY project – or had he been in a fight? She decided to record the interview and noticed Sam's eyes widen at this. Maybe he did have something to hide.

'You are entitled to have legal representation,' she said. 'I can call a solicitor for you?'

A look of panic crossed his face. 'I've done nothing wrong.'

Clare acknowledged this and began the recording, reminding Sam he could have a solicitor at any time. He confirmed he understood and the interview began.

She explained they were investigating the accident that had killed Leona Miller and he nodded. 'Terrible,' he said. 'She was a nice woman.'

Clare went on to say they'd examined Leona's car. At the mention of this he sat forward.

'There was nothing wrong with that car when it left us,' he said, his voice rising. 'I serviced it myself.'

Chris sat forward and smiled. 'Don't know how you lads do it. I'd a problem with my car and I couldn't work out what it was. Ten minutes in the garage and the mechanic had it sussed.'

This seemed to relax Sam. 'You just need to know where to look,' he said. 'Mostly it's the same things going wrong all the time.'

'Can you recall what was wrong with Mrs Miller's car?'

He was quiet for a moment, as though trying to remember. 'Problem with the fuel injection, I think,' he said eventually. 'I'd have to check the job sheet to be sure, though.'

'I'd a nightmare with mine,' Chris said. 'Is it a common fault?'

Sam shrugged. 'I dunno, really. We see a few.'

'How'd you find it?' Chris asked. 'Took me ages to work out what was wrong.'

'Got this laptop,' he said. 'Great bit of kit. Hook it up to the car's electrics and it tells you which system's faulty.'

Clare sat forward. 'Sam, I should tell you we visited Sexton Motors this afternoon and we've taken a laptop for examination.'

He stared at her. 'You've taken… the laptop? But I need it for my work.' He frowned as if trying to process this. 'How long d'you want it for? I mean, you won't find anything. If there's something wrong with that laptop it's the first I've heard of it. What are you even looking for?' He ran a hand through his hair. 'Are you accusing me of doing something to that car?'

Clare waited until he'd run out of questions then she carried on. 'I'd like to ask exactly how you diagnosed the fault on Mrs Miller's car.'

He looked at them for a moment and looked away again. 'I, erm, I plug the laptop into the car and run a program. It works through the different systems. Then it told me there was a fault with the injection system. Once I knew that I disconnected the laptop and set about finding the fault.'

Clare clasped her hands in front of her. 'Think carefully before you answer this next question.' She paused to let this sink in. 'Did you use the laptop to transfer anything at all to the car's electrics?'

He blinked a few times, as if trying to process this. 'I don't know what you mean. Like what?'

'You tell us.'

He shook his head. 'You don't get it. That laptop's there to receive information. It doesn't do anything to the car. That's my job.'

She decided it was time to be honest with Sam. 'As I said, we've had Mrs Miller's car examined. It appears a program has been introduced to the electronics system. It's a type of software known as malware. We believe this might have been a factor in Mrs Miller's accident. So I'd like to ask you once more, did you transfer anything from that laptop to Mrs Miller's car?'

'Absolutely not!' His voice was becoming raised again. 'I diagnosed the fault and fixed it. That's it!'

'Then how can you account for the malware ending up in the car?'

'I've no idea,' he said. 'Maybe she'd been fiddling with it herself. Maybe she plugged her phone in and it transferred through that. I honestly don't know. But I didn't do anything other than use the laptop as it's meant to be used.'

Clare nodded. 'Okay, Sam. Thanks for that.'

Chris said, 'Did anyone else have access to the laptop?'

'I'm the only one who's trained to use it.'

Chris regarded him. 'That's not what I asked. So cast your mind back. Could anyone else have fiddled with it, maybe if you'd gone to make a cup of tea?'

Sam made no reply. They waited and when he didn't speak Clare said, 'It's like this, Sam. If we find something on the laptop and no one else has used it we'd be forced to conclude the only person with access to it is responsible. But,' she paused to let that sink in, 'if someone else has used it, we might be able to ascertain you weren't responsible. There's no point in you taking the blame for something you'd nothing to do with.'

He seemed to be turning something over in his mind and Clare held out a warning finger to Chris not to say anything. After a minute, Sam cleared his throat.

'I don't want to lose my job,' he said.

'If we don't need to inform your employer we won't,' Clare said. 'But let me remind you: a woman has died.'

Sam flushed and his head drooped. After a moment he said, 'They sent me on this course – to learn about the diagnostics. And it was great. It's amazing stuff, what these programs do. I loved it and I came back ready to give it a go.' He smiled. 'It was great at first. All worked well. I saved the lads loads of time. Saved the customers money on the labour as well. Jobs were turned round really quickly. It's a great idea. But...' he licked his lips. 'Don't suppose I could have some water?'

Chris was despatched to fetch a cup of water and when he returned Sam carried on.

'Every now and then there would be updates and the trainers would send me PDFs to read. How the updates worked, you know?' He sipped from the water and put it down. 'I kept meaning to read them. I really did. But somehow there's never time. We start at eight in the morning and there's a lot of overtime. We work Saturdays as well. By the time I get home I'm shattered. All I want to do is to have a beer in front of Sky Sports.

'Anyway, I started to struggle. Sometimes I couldn't work the software; and the boss would get impatient. Going on about the money he'd wasted sending me on that course. Then I had an idea.'

He broke off for a minute and Clare gave him a smile. 'Go on, Sam. You're doing fine.'

He met her gaze then exhaled. 'My dad had this friend. Well, not so much a friend. More someone he knew a few years ago. I think they met at a DIY class at one of the colleges. Woodwork or something like that. Dad was into making things. Anyway, he said this man was really good with computers and he could ask him to help me out. Give me a few pointers, you know?

'So dad phoned him up and the man said he'd be happy to help. I took the laptop home one night and he came to see me. Knew all about it. Said he got all the computer magazines. I let him have a look at it and he was right. He knew exactly what he was doing. And he said to me if I ever had a problem with a car he could come to the garage and help. But he worked during the day. Anyway, the boss wouldn't let someone else fiddle with the cars. So I said I'd take the keys home if we could do it one evening.' He nodded, as if recalling. 'I think he enjoyed it, to be honest. I offered to pay him but he wouldn't have it. Cool bloke,' he added.

'How often did he help?' Clare asked.

'Dunno. Maybe seven or eight times.' He smiled. 'He was so good at it. And he helped me too. I was getting the hang of all the updates.'

Clare fixed him with her eye. 'His name please.'

He hesitated. 'I'm sure he didn't do anything wrong to the car. I wouldn't like him to get into trouble.'

'All the same,' Clare said. 'It's imperative we speak to him. And we'll need the names and addresses of the owners whose cars he's helped with.'

Sam closed his eyes. 'I'm gonna lose my job.'

'Not necessarily. If you're a good mechanic and you explain the issue with the course updates, your boss might be sympathetic.'

'I wouldn't bet on it.'

'The name, Sam.'

He sighed. 'Simon. Simon Miller.'

Chapter 35

'Get someone round to Simon Miller's house,' Clare told Jim when Sam Glenday had signed his statement and left the station. 'I've reason to believe he might have interfered with his wife's car. Don't tell him anything. Just don't let him leave. I'll be a couple of minutes behind.'

Jim put a call out on the radio while Clare fetched keys for a pool car.

'Come on,' she said to Chris. 'If he's worked out why we wanted his Renault Clio he might have legged it.'

They jumped into the car, Chris at the wheel. He switched on the siren and pulled out of the car park, the sound splitting the air. The Millers' house was less than a mile from the station and they were there within minutes. Chris pulled in behind two other police cars and they jumped out. Four officers were engaged in circling the house, calling through the letterbox and banging on the window.

'No reply,' one said as Clare approached the front door.

'Neighbours thought he was in,' another said. 'Apparently he was out for a bit of shopping this morning.'

'Which neighbour?'

The officer jerked his head towards a man weeding a garden opposite. Clare walked smartly over the road, pulling out her ID badge as she went. The man rose from his weeding, dusting soil off his hands.

'You're looking for Simon?'

'Yes. I gather you saw him earlier.'

The man nodded. 'I just said how sorry I was – about his wife, you know. He said *thank you* and we had a chat. I asked him if he was having a barbeque.'

'Why did you think that?' Clare said, cutting across him.

'He had a couple of those portable ones,' the man said. 'The kind folk take to the park. I'm guessing he doesn't have a proper one in the garden. Anyway, he said he'd been into town and bought them. Said they'd be handy for summer. I did think it was a bit odd. Not really the kind of thing you think about when you've just lost your wife.' He shrugged. 'Suppose it takes all sorts.'

'Did he say anything else?'

'No. I thought he looked a bit tired, you know? I told him to take care of himself and he said he would.'

Clare thanked him and ran back across to the house. The man was watching now and one or two other neighbours had come out to see what was happening. She motioned to the officers to go round the back of the house. 'I want the back door forced,' she said. 'No point in giving the neighbours a show. Fast as you can please.'

Chris stared at her. 'What's up?'

'I think Simon Miller might have tried to kill himself,' she said. 'We need in there now.' She looked down the garden and saw the shed. 'Check if there's anything in there we could use to force the door.'

Two officers ran to the shed which fortunately was unlocked. One emerged a minute later holding a chisel and forced it between the door and the lock. Seconds later it swung open with a loud creak.

'Open every window,' Clare called as she ran from room to room. Chris went to the front door and unlocked it, throwing it wide open. But there was no sign of Simon. A staircase in the hall led to an upper storey built into the eaves and she began climbing, taking the stairs two at a time, Chris behind her. Three doors faced them, and Chris headed for the first.

'Windows,' she called after him, then she grabbed the handle of the second door and flung it open. It was simply furnished, a single bed against one wall with a wardrobe opposite. The only window was a Velux set into the roof and she stretched up, pushing it open. Then she ran back out to the hall and faced the third door. She hesitated for a second then wrenched it open. The distinctive smell of a charcoal barbeque hit her nostrils and she ran back to the bedroom, stepping on the bed to reach the open Velux. She gulped in a few lungfuls of air then, holding her breath, ran back to the smoky room. The two portable barbeques were on the floor, in front of the hand basin. Another small Velux window was set into the roof and she opened this as wide as she could. Chris was behind her and she motioned towards the bath. It was empty of water but a fully clothed Simon Miller lay there, his eyes closed. Not wanting to breathe in the noxious fumes she continued holding her breath and motioned to Chris to take Simon's feet. Then she grasped him under the arms and, with all the strength she could muster, lifted him bodily out of the bath. Another officer was at the top of the stairs and, seeing the unconscious Simon, ran back down into the garden where they heard him radioing for an ambulance.

Her lungs bursting, Clare helped Chris heave Simon down the stairs and out to the front garden, laying him down on the paving slabs. She coughed and gasped at the fresh air until she felt her head clear. Chris was down on his hands and knees checking for a pulse.

'He's still breathing,' he said. 'How far away's the ambulance?'

'Ten minutes,' the officer called.

'He needs pure oxygen,' Clare said. 'Try the fire station. They're closer.'

'I'll call Jim,' Chris said. 'Get him to bring some over.'

The wait seemed endless; and then, finally, they heard the ambulance in the distance and a wave of relief washed over

Clare. Minutes later it screamed into the street and came to a halt just short of where Simon lay.

'He needs oxygen,' Clare said as the paramedics approached. 'CO poisoning.'

One of them ran back to the ambulance while Clare explained the situation.

'Who brought him out?' the other asked.

'Chris and I,' she said.

'You both need to be checked,' the paramedic said. 'Want to ride with us?'

She shook her head. 'We'll head for the community hospital. It's closer.'

'No driving, till you're checked,' the paramedic advised while his colleague fitted a mask over Simon's face. Within seconds he was connected to oxygen and lifted onto a trolley. They wheeled him down the path and into the waiting ambulance.

Clare watched them for a minute then she dragged her mind back to the house. 'Who's not been inside?' Two officers stepped forward. 'You two, secure the premises. Leave the windows open for the next couple of hours and call the fire station to have the house checked. Then I want a locksmith to fix the back door.' She turned to the rest of them. 'I'll ask Cupar station to send a minibus over. Take us to the community hospital. Once you've been checked you can write up your reports.' She smiled. 'And thanks for your help, guys. Good work.'

–

'Your other officers are fine,' the doctor told Clare. 'You and Chris are borderline. I'm happy to let you go as long as you won't be alone overnight.'

Clare thanked the doctor and they walked out to the car park where Sara was waiting to drive them back to the station.

'Jim says I've to take you straight home,' she said to Clare. 'And I've to make sure the DCI's there to look after you.'

'I'll be fine,' Clare said, rubbing her temple. 'A couple of paracetamol and an early night will sort me out.'

'Thought you said the DCI was away?' Chris said and Clare flashed him a look.

'Oh yeah,' she said. 'I forgot.'

'That's it,' Sara said. 'You're coming home with us tonight.'

Clare waved this away. 'Honestly Sara, I'll be fine.'

'No you won't,' she said, her voice rising. 'You've Benjy to look after and you're in no fit state to walk him. We'll stop at the cottage and pick him up then you're all coming back with us.'

She was too tired to argue. But more than anything she wanted to be at home in her own bed. 'I could call my sister,' she said.

Chris shook his head. 'Hasn't she just had a baby?'

They were at the car now and Sara held open the back door for Clare. 'Make your mind up. It's either you come home with us or you find someone to stay with you.'

She saw Chris trying not to laugh and she knew a night of Sara's concern would probably finish her off. And then Tom's face came into her head. 'Oh,' she said, climbing into the car. 'I've just remembered. I've a friend staying for the weekend.'

Chris looked at her. 'You never said.'

'Don't tell you everything.'

He climbed in beside her. 'In the middle of an investigation?'

'Just bad timing.'

He was looking at her and she met his gaze. 'What's your point, Sergeant?'

'No point. Just wondering.'

Sara started the engine and drew out of the car park. Five minutes later she pulled into the drive at Daisy Cottage. Benjy came rushing round the side of the house, followed by Tom carrying a pair of secateurs.

'Isn't that—' Chris began.

'Don't.'

'It is him, isn't it? Your ex?'

'I forgot he was coming – he asked ages ago. Anyway, he's staying the weekend,' Clare said, clicking off her seatbelt. 'His wife's away.'

'So's the DCI,' Chris said.

'And?'

He held out his hands defensively. 'Nothing. Just an observation.'

'Shut up.' She climbed out of the car, Sara ahead of her, explaining the circumstances to Tom. They had a quick conversation then Tom said, 'Sara's going to drive me to the station and I'll bring your car back.' He studied her, a worried look in his eyes. 'Are you okay, Clare? Want me to call the doctor?'

'God, will you all stop fussing! I'm perfectly fine. I had a bit of CO poisoning but I've been checked and as long as someone stays with me overnight I'll be okay. But the doctor did say nagging could be very bad for me,' she added, looking pointedly at Tom and Sara.

'I should have left the pair of you to fall in front of a bus,' Sara said, climbing back into the car. Tom gave Clare a smile and climbed in beside Sara. Minutes later they'd gone and she opened the front door, a concerned Benjy at her heels. She wandered into the house, kicking off her shoes and dropped the work bag Sara had brought with her.

'I almost feel sorry for Chris,' she said to Benjy who wagged his tail in response. Then she flopped down on the sofa and closed her eyes. It had been a very long day.

Day 6: Sunday, 9th April

Chapter 36

'Alastair phoned last night,' Tom said, as he set a mug of tea down on Clare's bedside table. 'Your DCI,' he added.

She stared at him, blinking away the tiredness. 'I know who he is, Tom. Why didn't you wake me?'

'You were dead to the world. Anyway, I told him what had happened and he said not to disturb you.'

Clare eased herself up on her elbows and glanced at the bedside clock. Ten to seven. She tried to remember what time she'd asked everyone to come in that morning and realised she hadn't. She'd been so busy dealing with Simon Miller and his house, then having to go to hospital, she'd forgotten to send out instructions for the following day. And now it was Sunday morning. 'I'd better get up,' she said, easing her legs out of bed.

'Bacon and eggs?' Tom said. 'I'm guessing you have to go in.'

She nodded. 'No option.'

'On the table in ten minutes, then.'

–

'What was Al saying?' Clare said, trying to sound casual. 'On the phone, I mean.'

Tom mopped his plate with a slice of doughy bread and butter. 'He asked how we were – Gilly and I – and he told me about his course; and we talked about you, obviously,' he added.

Clare wondered how the conversation had gone and decided she'd better call Al back in the evening. She smiled at Tom. 'This is great. It's ages since I've had a cooked breakfast.'

'My pleasure.' He looked down at Benjy sitting at his side, face upturned for any spare bits of bacon. 'I'll walk Benjy again for you,' he said. 'Then I'd better get back. Gilly's flight gets in just before five.'

'You'll meet her?'

He nodded.

'And?'

'I'll see what she says. But I like your idea of splitting my time between Glasgow and Brighton.'

'Just watch it doesn't become too much,' Clare said. 'Travel's exhausting, especially when London's involved.'

'Nothing about this is perfect. We'll just have to reach a compromise.' He looked round the room. 'You seem settled here, though. Do you think you might get married?'

She was taken aback by the directness of his question. And then Al's words came into her head. *If I did sell up it would make things more permanent.* Had he meant marriage? She realised Tom was staring at her. 'Oh I don't know,' she said. 'You know me. If in doubt.'

He reached across the table and took her hand, a gesture which surprised her. 'Don't leave it too long,' he said. 'You deserve to be happy.'

—

She drew into the car park, Tom's words ringing in her ears. Was he right? Was it time to make her relationship with Al more permanent? Maybe. Clare forced these thoughts from her head. She had two deaths and Simon Miller to deal with – if he was still alive. Only he could tell them exactly what he'd done to his wife's car and, more importantly, why. The description from the motorist who'd seen Leona driving erratically certainly suggested something was wrong with the electrics. But, if

Simon had interfered with it, were there other car owners also at risk? What had Sam the mechanic said – seven or eight cars he'd helped with? She'd have to chase him for that list of customers.

Jim was at his usual place at the front desk but there were few other officers around. 'They'll be here in the next half hour,' he said. 'I thought you'd want a later start.' He scrutinised her. 'You okay now?'

'Absolutely fine, thanks. Erm, Simon Miller?'

'Still with us. I asked Dundee to keep someone up at the hospital.' He checked his watch. 'I'll give them a call and let you know.'

She left Jim to his phone call and went through to her office, relishing the prospect of a good half hour's peace before the others arrived. Switching on her computer she sat back, considering the previous day's events. If Simon Miller was responsible for his wife's accident then maybe she'd been wrong to link the two deaths. Where did that leave the investigation into Harry Richards' murder? She was convinced Coke Grandison was behind it. Emma Halliday, Harry's former trainee, had told Kate Campbell there was something unethical about Harry's work. What had she meant by that? Kate had thought she meant the hiring and firing of trainees but was it something else? Something serious enough to get Harry killed?

Then there was the matter of Harry selling his house without his wife's knowledge. If he was in so deep with Coke Grandison why hadn't he confided in Louise? Maybe he hadn't wanted to scare her. But might there have been another reason? Had Harry planned to go abroad with someone else, taking the proceeds of his house, leaving Louise high and dry? The sooner she spoke to Emma Halliday the better.

She was still full of Tom's breakfast but decided another coffee might help her think. Wandering through to the kitchen she saw Chris and Sara coming in the side door.

'Morning, you two,' she said. 'I'm doing coffee.'

'*Dos cafés, por favor*,' Chris said, earning him a look of approval from Sara.

'You okay now, boss?' Sara said.

Clare smiled. 'Right as rain, thanks.' She glanced at Chris. 'How about you?'

'Lot of fuss about nothing.'

'You moaned all night about a headache,' Sara said.

Clare regarded him. 'Is it still sore?'

'Nah, it's fine.' He grinned. 'We ordered pizza as a treat. That sorted me out.'

'I had bacon and eggs for breakfast,' Clare countered.

'Tom's still there, then?' Chris said, his tone heavy with meaning.

'Going home today,' she said, 'after he picks his *wife* up from the airport.'

'Hmm.'

'Never mind hmm. Get that coffee down you then I want you back to checking possible lock-ups.'

Jim caught her eye as she made for her office. 'Simon Miller,' he said.

'How is he?'

'Conscious, but woozy. They're monitoring him for possible heart damage so I reckon he'll be in for a few days.'

'Can we speak to him?'

'They're going to review him again this afternoon.'

Clare nodded. 'Keep me posted.' As she reached her office door her mobile began to ring. Penny Meakin. She walked quickly, setting the cup down on her desk and swiped to take the call.

'I heard about yesterday,' Penny said. 'How are you?'

'Absolutely fine, thanks,' Clare said.

'You were checked over?'

'I was. The doctor said as long as I had someone with me overnight I'd be fine.'

'Good.' Penny's tone was brisk. 'And how is the investigation proceeding?'

Clare told her about Simon helping Sam Glenday with the on-board diagnostics. 'We think he may have installed malware allowing him to take control of his wife's car,' she said. 'But we won't know until we interview him.'

'He'd better have a solicitor,' Penny said. Clare was tempted to say she didn't need to be told that but instead she thanked Penny for reminding her.

'And your other death?'

'Not as much progress there,' Clare said. 'But I hope to speak to the victim's former trainee today. She'd mentioned unethical practices to a colleague but she hadn't been specific.' Clare then told Penny her thoughts about Coke Grandison.

'You need to be very careful there,' Penny said. 'I've authorised your warrant. It covers all Grandison's properties, businesses and vehicles. Likewise Albie Kennedy, not that I imagine he has much to his name. It should be through pretty quickly, given the seriousness of the situation. But our Mr Grandison's no fool. He'll have the best solicitor money can buy, trust me on that.'

Penny talked on for a few more minutes, reminding Clare to let her know if she had any problems. Clare put down her phone with some relief and took a long drink of coffee.

Chapter 37

'I might have something,' Bill said as Clare entered the incident room.

She drew up a chair beside him. 'Go on.'

'This white van,' he said. 'The one that was stolen. I had a couple of lads get onto the council to check their CCTV. Bit of a long shot but they spotted it.' He jabbed his laptop screen. 'It seems to go all over Dundee. Different times of day and night, last pinged a camera on Monday morning.'

'The day Harry died?'

'Yep.'

'Where?'

'Camperdown Road in Dundee.'

Clare frowned.

'North end of the city. Near the crematorium. There's a camera there,' he went on, 'so they checked it for other days. Seems to ping that camera every morning.'

'Time?'

'Seven-ish.'

'Like he's going to work?'

Bill put a hand to his chin. 'I'd say so.'

Clare sat back thinking. 'Coke lives on the Perth Road, doesn't he? What about Albie Kennedy?'

'Turriff Place. Just off Camperdown Road.'

'That makes sense,' Clare said, 'if Albie's in the habit of using the van.' She stared at the data on screen. 'He runs Marina to school, doesn't he?'

Bill nodded. 'Aye. But in the Beamer.'

'Okay. Let's say he picks up the van about seven. That's too early for the school run so where would he be going?'

'There's an industrial estate less than a mile away.'

'Let me guess – Coke has a unit there?'

Bill nodded. 'I'd say Albie drives over to the estate, sees what needs doing, then he heads up to the Perth Road to pick up Marina. Coke doesn't want his little girl arriving in a manky white van so he lets Albie use the Beamer for the school run. But anything dodgy – well it's a lot cheaper to replace a white van than a fancy BMW.'

Clare thought for a moment. 'Who's been tailing Coke and Albie?'

'Dundee lads. Keeping an eye, round the clock.'

'Anything?'

Bill shook his head. 'They checked in an hour ago. Albie went to the pub last night but he's not been out of the house today. Coke and his wife went shopping then to a restaurant for a meal. Apart from that they've been at home.'

'Map,' Clare said. 'We need a map.'

Bill opened up a new window on his laptop and typed *Dundee* into Google, zooming in on the area where the van passed the camera. 'Right. This is Turriff Place,' he said, indicating a residential street. 'It's a dead end so the van must be stored somewhere between Albie's house and the camera at the end of Camperdown Road.'

'Any lock-ups in the area?'

'I'll check with the local cops. Bound to be something. Getting access might be a problem, though.'

'We'll worry about that when we've found them,' Clare said, rising from her seat. 'Let me know as soon as you can.' She moved to the door then turned back. 'Good work, Bill.'

He smiled. 'We'll get there.'

—

Clare was about to have her lunch when Sam Glenday phoned.

'I went into the garage,' he said. 'No one there on a Sunday. Got you that list.'

'The cars Simon Miller worked on?'

'Yeah. Want me to read them out?'

'Please.' Clare reached for her notepad and began writing down customer details for the eight cars Simon had helped with. She noted Leona Miller's name, but it was the last one on the list that took her aback. 'Sorry, Sam, could you repeat the last one?'

He read it out again and Clare scribbled it down. Then she underlined the name. 'When was this?' she said, trying to keep her voice level. 'That last one?'

'About five weeks ago.'

'Okay,' she said. 'I don't want you to mention this to anyone else in the garage. Got it?'

'Erm, sure. Suits me. Does that mean you won't investigate it?'

'No,' Clare said. 'You will definitely be hearing from me.'

She sat staring at the list for a minute, drumming her pen on the desk. Then she tucked it into her pocket and picked up her bag. Chris was chatting to Jim as she walked quickly through the front office. He ran to catch up with her.

'We going somewhere?'

'I am. You're staying to help Bill track down those lock-ups.'

'You want to tell me where you're going?'

'Nope.' The automatic door to the main entrance slid back and she marched out to the car park, the afternoon air cool against her cheeks. She noticed Chris was standing just outside the entrance, watching her. She ignored him and gunned the car, pulling out of the car park and into the street.

Five minutes took her to a quiet road near the outskirts of town. She jumped out of the car and walked up the path of a semi-detached house. The curtains on the front room were drawn and there was no sign of life. A dark blue car was in the drive, the registration the last Sam Glenday had given her, and she fought down the anger she felt. She gave two sharp rings on the doorbell and leaned forward to hear if there was any sound within. After a few seconds she rang again. The third time she thought she heard a noise from inside and stood back to wait. Seconds later the door opened a little, and a familiar face peered out.

Clare's heart melted at the expression on the face. 'Can I come in?' she said, her voice as gentle as she could manage. 'Please?'

Chapter 38

She was shocked at Robbie's appearance. His T-shirt was stained and he obviously hadn't shaved for days. He looked as though he hadn't showered either. But it was his pale, drawn face, his hollow eyes that made the anger she felt towards Sam Glenday and Simon Miller melt into sympathy for her young officer. She had no way of knowing if Simon had installed malware on Robbie's car, but she realised now he must have been struggling with his mental health for some time. If things had been going wrong with his car might he have thought he was imagining it – becoming paranoid as he watched it appear to take on a life of its own? It could just have tipped him over the edge.

'Shall I make us some tea?' she said, indicating the kitchen.

Robbie raised a hand in protest but she waved this away. 'I could do with a cup,' and she made for the kitchen before he could stop her. She'd only been in his house once before and remembered now he'd just put in a new kitchen. The units were a lovely pale blue shade with light oak varnished worktops, all the appliances hidden behind false doors. It was sleek and lovely and, on another day, it might have made Clare think about her own kitchen back at Daisy Cottage. Might even have tempted her to send for some brochures. But the sink piled high with dirty dishes put all these thoughts from her mind. She stopped involuntarily, taken aback by the scene before her. Then she looked round and found a cream-coloured kettle. She took this to the sink and swivelling the tap away from the dishes she filled it. Then she took off her jacket, hanging it on a hook alongside a striped apron and turned back to the sink. She ran the water until it was hot and set about clearing the dishes.

Robbie appeared in the door, leaning against the jamb. 'I'm sorry,' he said, waving a hand towards the sink. Clare flashed him a smile but he wouldn't meet her eye. 'You must think me—'

'I don't think anything at all,' she said, picking up a scourer and attacking the plates, 'except I wish I'd come to see you sooner.' She smiled again. 'Soon have this lot washed then we'll have a cuppa.'

Dishes done, they took their drinks through to the sitting room. Robbie stood, initially, as if unwilling to sit. Clare chatted about the new kitchen and what a nice part of town it was. 'Why not sit?' she said, eventually. 'I'll get a crick in my neck, looking up at you.'

He hovered for a moment then eased himself down on a chair opposite, still refusing to meet Clare's eyes.

She pressed on. 'Robbie, I realise now you've been feeling unwell for some time. I'm so sorry I didn't pick up on it.'

He waved this away, but Clare went on.

'As your manager I have a duty of care and I've failed in that. So I'd like to help if I can.'

He looked at her and shook his head. 'It's stupid.'

She waited for a moment to see if he would say anything else. 'What's stupid?'

'Me,' he mumbled, his voice low. 'It's stupid being like this.' He clasped his hands round the mug and Clare noticed they were shaking.

She sat forward in her seat. 'Robbie, listen to me: what you're experiencing, what you're feeling, well it's an illness, just like a broken leg, or a dose of the flu. It's an illness and it is not your fault. You must believe that. And…' she hesitated, anxious to choose the right words, '…those slip-ups at work, they're all part of being ill. You are not to blame here.'

His grip on the mug tightened, his knuckles growing white. 'That poor man.'

'Harry Richards?' Clare said. 'Put that right out of your head. From what I've gathered, he was involved with some very dodgy people. Even if you had taken the stalking report further, I doubt it would have prevented Harry's murder.'

He shrugged but said nothing.

'Have you seen your GP?'

He nodded. 'Pills,' he said. 'Sertraline.'

Clare recognised the name. 'Are they helping at all?'

'Not really. She said it might take a few weeks.'

'Fair enough,' Clare said. 'Here's hoping they kick in a bit quicker. In the meantime,' she said, 'listen to me please. I am not here to check up on you and I'm not here to hassle you into coming back to work. There are two things I need to speak to you about. The first relates to your health and the second is an operational matter. Obviously, you're signed off sick so I can't speak to you about work; but this matter concerns you person- ally and I'd like to ask about it. If you're not happy, though, we can do it another time.' She watched him carefully as he considered this, hoping she'd judged her approach correctly. It wasn't just about finding out what Simon Miller had done. Having seen how ill Robbie was she wanted more than ever to help, perhaps to allay his fears if his car had been doing odd things.

He ran his tongue round his lips. 'Okay.'

'Thanks, Rob. I appreciate it.' She paused to make sure he was listening. 'I understand you had your car serviced a few weeks ago.'

A look of surprise crossed his face. 'How did you know that?'

'Was it Sexton Motors?' Clare said, avoiding his question.

'Yeah. But how do you know?'

Clare was quiet for a moment as she ordered her thoughts. She had to remember Robbie was a potential victim here rather than an officer. There was a limit to how much she could tell him. 'How's the car been since the service?'

His brow creased. 'I don't know what you mean, boss.'

'Any problems? Anything playing up?'

He looked at her, as if wondering where she was going with this. 'No,' he said. 'They do a good job. I've gone to them for years.'

'What about the lights and wipers, radio – they all work as they should?'

'Well, yeah. I mean sometimes the radio loses signal, just on some stations. But everything else's fine.' He met her eye. 'Why are you asking? Is there a problem at Sextons?'

'There may be… a problem with the electrics in your car,' Clare said, choosing her words carefully. 'I'd like someone to look at it before you drive it again. Is that okay?'

He was staring at her as if waiting for more information and when none came he said, 'I suppose. Not like I've anywhere to go.'

Clare smiled. 'Thanks. I'll get it done as soon as possible. Might have it checked over by a vehicle examiner. Just to be on the safe side.' She hoped she'd judged her tone correctly. The last thing she wanted to do was add to Robbie's worries.

He seemed satisfied with this and when he'd fetched the car keys she went on. 'The other thing I need to ask is whether you feel work has affected your mental health – contributed to how you are just now.'

He took a moment before replying. 'Not really. I've been a bit down for a while. Relationship stuff, you know. Makes it hard to focus sometimes.' He flicked a glance at Clare then away again.

She remembered Sara saying something about Robbie's bank account. It had sounded like he'd been the victim of fraud but he didn't seem keen to volunteer any information. 'No money worries?' she prompted, hoping this might make him feel he could open up.

'No. That's all okay, thanks.'

'Nothing else worrying you?'

But he was no longer looking at her. He'd closed up again. She sat studying him and, when it seemed he had no more to say, she said, 'I hope you would come to me if you were worried about anything. There are things I can do to help.'

'Sure,' he said, his eyes on the floor.

'There's one more thing, then,' she said. 'And I'd like you to think about this very carefully. It's probably the most important thing you could do.'

He looked up, his interest sparked.

'You know all those deductions you guys moan about coming off your pay every month?'

He forced a smile. 'Yeah.'

'Well, some of it goes to The Police Treatment Centre.'

He stared at her. 'That place in Auchterarder?'

'That's one of them, yes.'

He shook his head. 'That's for guys needing physio, folk with injuries.'

'They offer all kinds of treatment, including psychological wellbeing. I'm going to recommend you apply for a two-week residential. Get away from here – right away. There are people you can talk to. They can give you coping strategies. Honestly, it's a wonderful place.' She hesitated. 'I'm not suggesting what you're experiencing can be dealt with by two weeks away but it would be a start. You'll wait months – years maybe – for counselling on the NHS. In the meantime, you're contributing through your salary every month and by doing that you help keep the centre running. Now it's time for the police to help you.'

He was quiet for a moment. 'I'd never get a place. There's probably a huge waiting list.'

'You leave that to me,' Clare said. 'I can be very persuasive when I like.' She drained her cup then rose to her feet. 'And besides, the Super's desperate to keep me sweet. Might as well make the most of it.' She picked up Robbie's cup. 'I'll just wash these and leave you in peace. And I'll send you a link to the application form so you can have a look.'

He saw her to the door. 'Er, thanks,' he said, 'for coming.'

She clapped him on the back. 'I'll keep in touch. Just take it easy. And fill that form in. The sooner the better.'

Clare walked back to the car feeling a lump in her throat. Had she handled him correctly? Only time would tell. Glancing back she saw he'd closed the door. She climbed into the car and drove down the street until Robbie's house was out of sight. Unexpectedly she could feel tears welling up and she pulled into the kerb, switching off the engine. Poor Robbie. He'd always been so cheery and dependable. Seeing him like this...

She dabbed at the corner of her eye with a finger and fought back the temptation to cry. Instead, she blew her nose and tried to focus on Simon Miller and the malware. Had he installed the same program on Robbie's car? With luck they'd be able to interview him today. She made a mental note to ask Jim to check with the hospital. Then she turned the key in the ignition and headed back to the station.

Chapter 39

'Bill's got a list of lock-ups from the Dundee guys,' Chris said. 'They're checking tenants and owners now.'

Clare put down her bag and took off her jacket. 'Anything else?'

'Yeah. That Emma Halliday woman has been in touch with Janey. Seems she'll be home,' he checked his watch, 'about now. She's happy for us to swing by.'

Clare frowned. 'Where does she live?'

'Balmullo.'

Clare nodded. She knew the village. 'Let me just grab some lunch, send a couple of emails then we'll head over.'

They were on their way within half an hour, Clare driving.

'You gonna tell me where you've been?'

She glanced at him, feigning ignorance. 'When?'

'You know when. This morning.'

'I'd a bit of personal business,' she lied.

'On a Sunday?'

'And your point is?' Her tone was sharp.

'Nothing. Just wondering if you're keeping me out of the loop for some reason. Wouldn't be the first time.'

'Nope. Nothing like that. Anyway, job for you when we get back,' she said.

'Why do I think I won't like it?'

'Because you won't. But it has to be done.'

'Go on.'

'I've a list of cars to be checked for malware. I'd like you to liaise with the vehicle examiner to make appointments for the drivers. I want all of them checked ASAP.'

She'd made up her mind to leave Robbie's car off the list and take it over herself. Avoid any unnecessary embarrassment for him.

'Can't you get uniform to do that?'

'Yes I could but, in case you hadn't noticed, I'm investigating two deaths, one of which is a gruesome gangland-type murder and I'm a bit pressed for officers.'

He said nothing to this and they drove on in silence, Clare ignoring Chris's pointed looks.

Emma Halliday's house was at the top end of Pitcairn Drive. It was an attractive street, each house a little different from its neighbour. Clare drove slowly along, mindful of groups of children out on bikes and scooters. Some of them stood and stared at the car as it drove past. One small girl in a yellow dress waved and Chris waved back.

Although they had the house number there was little doubt about which was Emma's. A VW Golf Estate was parked in front of the garage, the tailgate standing open to the street. Around the car the detritus of a week spent in the outdoors was scattered. A mountain bike was propped up against the front wall of the house with two substantial-looking climbing ropes next to it. A sleeping bag and a larger orange bag which Clare guessed contained a tent were on the ground beside them and a large IKEA carrier bag held what seemed to be the remains of Emma's food store for the week.

Clare took it all in with something approaching horror. 'I feel a bit guilty descending on her when she's just arrived home.'

'Ach these outdoor types are pretty resilient,' Chris said.

'And you'd know, how?'

As they studied the scene a woman in patterned leggings and a vest top came out of the house and scooped up the climbing ropes. She was tanned and freckled, her corn-coloured hair tied loosely back and Clare thought she looked like an advert for outdoor living. Suddenly she felt very dull and lazy by comparison. 'Come on,' she said walking towards the house. 'Let's see what she can tell us.'

They approached the front door and Chris bent to pick up the IKEA bag, carrying it to the house. Clare touched the bell lightly and a voice called out she'd just be a minute. As they waited a few of the children who'd been playing on their bikes came to a halt and stared at them. A minute later Emma appeared and smiled.

'You must be Janey,' she said to Clare.

'Actually, I'm DI Clare Mackay and this is DS Chris West.'

Emma reached for the IKEA bag. 'Thanks,' she said. 'Feel free to grab something else.'

Feeling guilty for interrupting her unpacking, they helped Emma carry the rest of her stuff into the house.

'Just dump it in the hall,' she said. 'I'll sort it later.' She closed the tailgate of the car and locked it then she led them back into the house. 'Coffee?'

Clare waved this away. 'You're obviously busy so we won't keep you.'

Emma laughed. 'This lot? Nah. I'll do it over the next few nights after work. No rush. Only the metal gear needs sorting today.'

'Oh?' Clare was intrigued. Emma seemed happy to chat and Clare was keen to put her at ease, given they were about to question her on the ethics of her former employer.

'Yeah, I've been up to Cape Wrath, climbing. The sea cliffs are stunning. But the salt gets onto the gear so I soak it out in a bucket. Stops it corroding.'

'Every day's a school day,' Chris said, and Emma laughed.

She led them into a bright room with a comfortable-looking navy sofa. There were bookcases either side of a gas fire, the tops scattered with candles, framed photos and a selection of birthday cards.

'It's your birthday?' Clare said.

'Last week.' She indicated the sofa. 'Please have a seat. Sure I can't get you a coffee?'

Clare ignored what she knew would be Chris's best puppy dog eyes and shook her head. 'We're fine, thanks. But go ahead if you'd like one.'

Emma picked up a water bottle from the top of the bookcase. 'This is fine,' she said. 'I had a huge pot of coffee to keep me awake for the drive home. Better not have any more.' She took a long drink from the bottle then put it back on the bookcase. 'How can I help? Your colleague Janey said you wanted to talk about Harry. You know I don't work for him any more, right?'

Clare and Chris exchanged glances. Emma clearly hadn't heard.

'Emma,' Clare began, 'I'm guessing you've not heard. Sadly, Harry died on Monday.'

Her eyes widened. 'Harry? Harry's dead?' The colour drained from her face and she reached for the water bottle again. 'Seriously?'

Clare nodded. 'I'm afraid so. And we are treating his death as murder.'

Emma put the bottle down and for a moment seemed lost for words. 'Oh my God,' she said finally. 'Who'd want to hurt Harry? He was a real sweetie. It wasn't an accident?'

'Definitely not.'

She sat back, shaking her head. 'How's Louise? Is she okay?'

'Yes. We have an officer with her. She's shocked, obviously, but coping.'

'Can... Can I contact her?'

'I don't see any harm in that,' Clare said. 'I'm sure she'd appreciate it.' She glanced at Chris. 'We were hoping you might be able to give us some information.'

'Of course. Anything at all.'

'I gather you had some concerns about how Harry conducted his business.'

Emma's brow creased and Clare sensed she had gone into professional mode.

'A member of staff overheard you suggesting something was unethical,' Clare said. 'I can tell you we have a warrant to access client contact details but it doesn't extend to their dealings with Harry. So I won't ask you to divulge anything that might breach client privilege. But we do need to know if your concerns could be linked to his murder.'

Emma sat thinking for a minute or two. 'Sorry,' she said. 'I just need to work out what I can tell you.'

Clare smiled. 'I appreciate that. Maybe it would help if I asked some questions?'

Emma's face cleared. 'Yes,' she said. 'That might be best.'

'Let's start with Harry's clients, then,' Clare said. 'I gather he did property conveyancing and compensation claims. Is that correct?'

'Yes.'

'Anything else?'

She shook her head. 'No that's it.'

Clare thought about Harry's work and she guessed, if rules had been broken, it was more likely with the compensation claims. 'The practices that concerned you – were they related to compensation cases?'

'No.'

'Oh.' Clare was surprised. 'They were to do with property, then?'

There was a pause and Emma said, 'I believe so.'

'And was the problem with sellers or buyers?'

Again Emma hesitated. 'Sellers.'

'Harry was helping clients to sell their houses, yes?'

'Correct.'

'And you believe he wasn't acting ethically?'

'The conveyancing – it was done properly. The sales all went through no problem.'

247

They were getting nowhere here. Clare tried again. 'Can you explain, perhaps without naming any clients or any property details, what the problem was?'

Emma nodded. 'I think I can. I must emphasise most of the work Harry did was absolutely fine. But there were some cases – more and more by the time I left – well, let's say I had concerns about them.'

'In what way?'

'The selling price. Some of the properties were sold well below market value.'

'Is that unusual?' Clare asked. 'Maybe for a quick sale?'

'Not to that extent. In some cases houses and flats were sold for a quarter of the valuation.'

Clare stared at her. 'Why would anyone do that?' Something was niggling away at her but it wouldn't come and she forced it to the back of her mind.

'I really don't know and I don't know why Harry agreed to handle the sales,' Emma said. 'We have a duty, you see. Things we have to look out for – like if the sellers are using a solicitor miles away from where they stay. That's a red flag. Then there's the selling price. As you say, some are after a quick sale but this was ridiculous. And often the properties weren't even on the open market. The sellers told us they had a buyer lined up and Harry did the conveyancing.' She shook her head. 'Definitely not best practice.'

'Did you speak to him about it?'

'I did.'

'And?'

'He said there were special circumstances. These clients either had difficult properties to sell or they wanted to avoid the marketing expense.' She hesitated. 'I considered going to the Law Society for advice. But I was afraid if I did there'd be no going back. I knew I was leaving soon anyway. I'd had a job offer from my present employer and it didn't seem worth rocking the boat.' She looked at Clare, her eyes troubled. 'Do you think it's anything to do with what happened to Harry?'

'It's too early to say,' Clare said. 'Can you recall details of any of the properties?'

'No. And I doubt I'd be allowed to tell you anyway. You'd have to speak to whoever takes over the practice. Probably need a warrant to cover that, to be honest.'

Clare asked a few more questions about the other staff but she learned little more. Emma had got on well with both Kate and Simon and she wasn't aware of any other problems Harry might have had. 'There's one last thing,' Clare said, reaching into her bag. She withdrew a photo of Coke Grandison. 'Did you ever see this man at the office?'

Emma's face darkened. 'I did. Not often but I do remember him being there once. Another time I thought I saw him sitting in a car outside the office. But I can't be sure about that.'

'Do you know what Harry's relationship with him was?' Clare asked.

'I didn't, to be honest. I did wonder if it was to do with his compensation cases. I asked Harry once who he was but he said I was better off not knowing.'

Chris sat forward. 'What did you think he meant by that?'

'I suppose I thought he might be a bit rough. The kind of guy you don't mess with. It was just an impression, though. I really don't know.' She took the photo and stared at it. 'I never did learn his name.' She handed it back to Clare. 'Who is he?'

Clare paused for a moment then she shot a glance at Chris. Was there any harm in telling Emma Coke's name? He was a local businessman, photo in the papers every few weeks. It wasn't like his identity was a secret. 'Colin Grandison,' she said. 'Better known as Coke.'

Emma's eyes widened. 'Grandison?' she said. 'That's Colin Grandison?'

Clare looked at her. 'How do you know him, Emma?'

She sat back, her eyes flitting from left to right as she considered something. 'Tell me again the terms of the warrant you've been granted.'

Clare glanced at Chris. 'It gives us access to client names and addresses but no details of their business with the firm.'

Emma nodded slowly. 'So it wouldn't matter if I discussed someone who was *not* a client?'

Clare exhaled. 'I'm no legal expert but I'd have thought not.'

'Then I can tell you this much: a good many of Harry's clients sold their properties to a Colin Grandison. His exact address escapes me for now but I think it was the west end of Dundee somewhere.'

Clare felt the familiar nervousness in her stomach, the sense they might just be getting somewhere and she was anxious not to blow it. 'Can I ask if the clients who sold their properties to Mr Grandison were among those that caused you professional concern?'

Emma met Clare's eye for five, maybe ten seconds. Then she spoke again, slowly and deliberately. 'Under the terms of your warrant, I would have to answer *no comment.*'

Chapter 40

Chris drove back to the station while Clare leafed through her notepad, going over everything Emma had said. There was still something niggling at her and then she remembered. She took out her phone and dialled Tom's number, clicking her tongue in irritation when it went to voicemail. Chris glanced at her but she ignored him and waited for the beep. She left a message asking Tom to call her about the flat he'd mentioned. Then she tucked her phone back in her pocket.

'You want to catch me up?' Chris said.

'Remember Tom was here?'

'I do.'

'He was up on business but he also wanted to look at a flat. He's thinking of investing in property and he'd spotted one that'd been sold pretty cheaply. It hadn't gone on the open market – private deal.'

'And you're thinking…'

'It could just be a coincidence but if I can get the address from Tom we can check it out. If that kind of info's available on the Land Registry website we might not need another warrant.'

As they neared the Guardbridge roundabout her phone began to ring and she snatched it up then frowned when she saw it wasn't Tom.

'Bill?'

'I think we might have the vehicle location,' Bill said. 'Not confirmed but I'd say there's a good chance.'

'Get on the radio,' Clare said. 'I want every available officer back in the station.' Then she turned to Chris. 'Forget what

I said about those vehicles. We might be getting somewhere. And not a word about Emma knowing Coke to anyone.'

At the station she went straight to her office and closed the door. Then she called Penny Meakin to update her.

'I plan to speak to the solicitor appointed to deal with Harry's affairs tomorrow,' Clare told her. 'I'm hoping he'll confirm Harry's clients sold properties to Coke for well under market value. In the meantime, I don't plan to share this with the team.'

Penny agreed and Clare went on to tell her they might have found the white van. Then she took a deep breath and told Penny what she proposed. After a short silence Penny said she would dial into the briefing Clare had called.

Within half an hour the incident room was packed, a mix of uniform and plain-clothes officers squeezed onto every desk and chair, some standing at the back. A laptop was set up at the front of the room for Penny to appear via Zoom which Clare had to admit made her more nervous than usual.

Once Penny was online Clare called the briefing to order. 'Thanks everyone.' She glanced at Penny's face on the screen and turned back to the room, trying to forget she was there. 'Four days before Harry Richards died, Coke Grandison reported a white van missing. We've reason to believe this van was used by Harry's killers and we may now have a location.' She paused to make sure they were attending. 'It's a lock-up behind the shops on Camperdown Road in Dundee, pretty close to Albie Kennedy's house. On studying the footage we think the van has joined the road from the other side. That fits with it approaching from some old garages behind the row of shops.'

'How regularly has the van passed the cameras?' Penny asked.

'At least once a day,' Clare said, 'the last hit being on Monday.' She turned back to the room. 'The driver in the footage resembles Albie Kennedy, although it's hard to be sure. But it's too much of a coincidence, the van being in daily use then nothing since the day Harry died. My guess is whoever killed Harry – Albie and A N Other – used the van to clean themselves up, possibly burned their clothing somewhere then they've driven to the lock-up to store the van until the fuss dies down.'

'Why wouldn't they just torch the van?' Nita asked.

'It's a good question,' Clare said. 'Maybe it's too new – or maybe he thinks, because he's reported it stolen, we won't link him to Harry's murder. That way he gets rid of Harry *and* he gets to keep the van.'

Clare hesitated for a moment. 'I'd like to hit Coke and Albie's houses and Coke's business premises at the same time as we enter the lock-up.'

'Are we not jumping the gun, searching Coke's house?' Janey asked.

Clare smiled. 'It's a fair point. But if there is anything that ties Coke to Harry's death, and he learns we've found the van, he'll get rid of it. It is risky, but I think it's worth hitting all four together.'

Penny was silent, as if weighing this. 'On balance I'd prefer you to wait until you have something more concrete. If you go storming in without sufficient evidence you could lose the whole case.'

'I appreciate that,' Clare said, choosing her words carefully. 'But the more we investigate the more chance there is Coke will know we're onto him. He'll already be on his guard, given we're investigating Harry's murder.'

'Fair point,' Penny said. 'When do you propose carrying out the searches?'

'Tonight, assuming the warrant's through in time.'

'Just the four properties, then?'

Clare was quiet as she considered all the flats and houses Coke's letting agency had on its books. 'I think so, for now.'

'You have enough officers?' Penny asked.

Clare did a quick mental calculation. 'Barely,' she said. 'I could do with another ten or twenty. Coke's Perth Road house looks pretty big.'

'You do know the fuss someone like Coke will make if you're wrong?' Penny said.

'I do. But I think it's a chance worth taking.'

Penny nodded. 'Will you want armed response out?'

Clare considered this. 'On balance, I think not. Coke's all about respectability these days. He's more likely to run legal rings round us than pull a weapon.'

'All the same, I want everyone in Kevlar vests,' Penny said. She was quiet for a moment and Clare wondered if the connection had frozen. 'Leave it with me,' she said. 'I'll chase up the warrant and drum you up some extra officers.'

Clare set about allocating officers to roles. 'Assuming the warrant comes through we'll hit the premises at 3:30 a.m. I'll need an enforcer at each location and let's have some big lads at Albie's in case he kicks off. I don't want any officers injured but I don't want Coke or Albie claiming we've been heavy handed either. Okay?' They all indicated they understood and Clare checked her watch. 'Off home now for a few hours. Back here at midnight, unless you hear to the contrary.'

Clare spent an hour in her office going through the plans for the night and answering a few emails that couldn't wait. Then she logged off and went out to her car. She'd called ahead to ask Moira if she'd have Benjy overnight and Moira had been only too happy to help. *As long as you need*, she'd said. *That poor man. I really hope you catch his killer.*

By the time she reached home Moira had collected Benjy. Tom had gone too, leaving a bottle of wine with a thank-you card, and the house was strangely quiet. She tried calling Al's phone but it went to voicemail. She tried again this time leaving a message telling him she'd be on an operation that evening and would call again when she could.

'And good luck with your course,' she added. She glanced at the clock. Better get a few hours' sleep. It was shaping up to be a long night.

Chapter 41

The station was as busy as Clare had ever seen it when she entered around eleven.

'More on the way,' Jim said. 'Should be here by half past.'

She smiled, heartened by the sight of so many officers. But the solidarity of colleagues coming together couldn't take away from the seriousness of what was planned. The warrant had come in a couple of hours earlier and she sent a quick message to thank Penny for expediting it. Chris and Max had produced location plans for the properties and divided the officers into four teams.

'Good work, lads,' Clare said and she moved to the front of the room. 'Let's make a start then. First of all, thanks to you all for coming out tonight, especially our colleagues from other stations.' There was a murmur acknowledging this and she went on. 'The object of tonight's operation is to enter and search premises belonging to Colin – or Coke – Grandison and Albert Kennedy. A search warrant has been granted but I do not propose to arrest either Coke or Albie unless the search turns up something incriminating. Also, I hope to enter three of the four properties in Dundee without the use of force. These are Coke's house on the Perth Road, Albie Kennedy's house in Turriff Place and Coke's business premises, Granco Lettings, in the Dryburgh industrial estate. The fourth property is a lock-up off Camperdown Road. I have reason to believe this may be the location of a vehicle involved in the murder of solicitor Harry Richards.'

'Is Coke in the frame for Harry's murder?' an officer from Dundee asked.

'Possibly. I won't put it any stronger than that. I suspect the killing was done either by Albie Kennedy or an associate of his, or possibly both. But I believe Coke may have ordered it. At the moment I don't know why or even if he did but finding that van is crucial.

'I want officers in place at all four properties for 3 a.m. We move in at three thirty on my signal. Coke and Albie's houses and the lock-up will be entered simultaneously. We'll then seek the keys for Granco Lettings and ask Coke to accompany officers so he can disable the alarm.'

'Want us to take the big red key?' another officer asked. 'Just in case?'

'Make sure you have one at each location,' Clare said. 'But I want to avoid forced entry to the houses if possible. Coke knows how to work the system so give him every opportunity to comply.'

A uniformed PC Clare didn't recognise raised his hand. 'What are we looking for?'

'Anything that might suggest moneylending: notebooks, addresses, computers, laptops and phones. Also, any documents relating to house purchases. Make sure you've a good supply of evidence bags.' She indicated the screen where Chris had put up a plan of Coke's Perth Road house. 'There's a front entrance,' she said tapping the screen, 'a garage to the side and a back gate leading to a lane behind the house so all that needs covered. I don't anticipate Coke or Danuta – that's his wife – I don't anticipate either of them making a run for it. He's far more likely to call a shit-hot solicitor. But I want officers on the street as well in case he does try to slip out.' She nodded at Max. 'I want you at Coke's house.' Then she turned to Chris. 'Next image please.' He clicked and a photo of a small flat-roofed building appeared on screen.

'Coke's main business premises, Granco Lettings,' she said. 'Chris and his team will take that. Unfortunately the place'll be knee-deep in paperwork thanks to the nature of the business. Hopefully a lot will be on computer but I want all papers and computers seized as potential evidence and a thorough search of the premises; and make sure you check store rooms as well, especially if they're locked. I doubt he'll have kept anything relating to Harry's death but we have to be thorough.'

She motioned to Chris to move on and, again, the image on screen changed to show a two-storey end-terrace house. 'Albie Kennedy's. Bill and Janey, I'd like your team to take this one. Same applies. Back and front doors, vehicles, paperwork etc. But be particularly careful. He's a big lad with a history of violence.'

Janey smiled. 'It'll be a pleasure,' and Bill nodded in agreement.

'Finally,' Clare said as the image changed again, 'the lock-up behind the shops on Camperdown Road. I'll be there with the other team and that will be forced. I'm not waiting for keys. We'll have a locksmith out to make good the door if necessary and SOCO are standing by if the van is there. My team, you'll need high-powered torches as well.' She glanced towards Chris and Max. 'Have I missed anything?'

They looked at each other and shook their heads. 'Pretty much all sorted.'

'Right, then,' Clare said. 'Get some food inside you. It's going to be a long night. Ready to set off at two.'

—

They set out just after two, a convoy of unmarked cars and minibuses. Clare drove, Nita beside her, Sara and Benny, a plain-clothes officer from Dundee, in the back. It was strange not having Chris or Max in the car but it was vital she divided her best officers between the four locations. The other three chatted on, Nita throwing the odd remark Clare's way but her head was full of the operation. Had she covered everything? What if they found nothing?

They were crossing the Tay Road Bridge now, high above the water at the Fife side. She never tired of the view and it was even more dramatic at night, the lights of Dundee glittering in the distance. But tonight she saw none of it, her eyes firmly fixed on the road ahead, her mind running over the carefully planned operation. They wouldn't get a second chance with Coke. She knew that. They had to find that van.

By two forty-five they were all in place, officers hunkered down awaiting Clare's signal, cars parked broadside across the road ends in case Coke or Albie decided to make a run for it. The minutes ticked by agonisingly slowly and she was glad at least it wasn't a cold night. Suddenly a siren split the night air as a fire engine raced along nearby Macalpine Road and Clare checked her watch for the tenth time. At three twenty-five she authorised the officers to move into position. One by one the team leaders confirmed they were in place. And then her watch clicked to three thirty and she gave the order.

She stood, radio clamped to her ear as Nita and Benny attacked the lock-up door with a crowbar. Then she heard Max informing whoever had answered Coke's door that he'd a warrant to search the premises. There was a murmur of conversation but it sounded as if there was no resistance. The shouting from Albie Kennedy's house could be heard by Clare and her team above the sound of the crowbar and she hoped Bill and Janey would handle him okay. As Janey's voice came across the radio informing them Albie had been arrested for assaulting an officer, the lock-up door gave with a creak that rent the night air.

'Anyone hurt?' Clare said into the radio.

'Nothing major,' she said. 'Bill took a kick to the leg and Albie punched Gillian but both fine.'

'Have them checked over before they go off duty,' Clare said and she left them to their search.

The lock-up door hung at an odd angle and she had to bend to see inside. Nita was swinging a high-powered torch around but Clare didn't have to go any closer to see it was completely empty.

They turned to her, disappointment on every face and her heart fell to her boots.

'Strong smell of bleach,' Benny said, and Clare nodded.

'I'll get SOCO out anyway,' she said. 'If they've bleached the place the van must have been here to begin with. There might still be something they can detect.' She went back to the car to make the call, thinking of the officers going through Coke and Albie's houses now, no doubt filling dozens of evidence bags. But without the van there was no prospect of charging either man with Harry's murder.

The radio buzzed and she heard Max's voice.

'Go ahead.'

'Chris is taking Coke down to the Granco offices now,' he said.

'Any trouble?'

'No. He's called his solicitor and says he'll sue us all but he's co-operative enough.' Max hesitated. 'Any luck at the lock-up?'

'Nope.'

'Sorry, boss.'

'Thanks, Max. I'll leave you to your search.'

They drove back to St Andrews in silence, Clare having said that Nita, Sara and Benny might as well call it a night. 'There's plenty of troops at the other three locations. Get yourselves home.'

Sara lingered for a minute. 'I think,' she began, 'I think it was worth a shot, boss. And I'm sure we'll get him. And Albie. Might just take a bit longer.'

Clare forced a smile. 'Thanks, Sara. Appreciate it. Now get off home. In for midday tomorrow.'

Left alone in the station she took in the front office, eerie in the night-time silence. She'd never been completely alone in the building. She looked round at it. Her station. Her domain. And right at that moment she'd gladly swap it for a one-way ticket to pretty much anywhere. The voicemail icon on her phone was flashing. A message from Tom, probably giving her the address of the flat he'd looked at. She hovered over the icon to play the message then clicked instead to call Penny Meakin.

Day 7: Monday, 10th April

Chapter 42

Albie Kennedy had spent the night in a cell down at Methil station and Clare had asked for him to be brought up mid-morning. She'd had an uncomfortable conversation with Penny Meakin who'd informed her Coke had put in an official complaint about his treatment. Max's expression darkened when he heard about the complaint.

'It was all done by the book,' he said.

Clare waved this away. 'You don't have to convince me.'

'Funny thing, though…'

'Yeah?'

'The wife – Danuta. I got the distinct impression there was some tension between her and Coke.'

Clare perched on a nearby desk. 'How so?'

He stood thinking for a moment, his brow creased. 'How she was. I expected her anger to be directed towards us – coming into her house, middle of the night, taking it to bits. But she was fine with us. It was Coke she ripped into. They went through to the kitchen ahead of us and I heard her saying something like '*Is this the life you want for our daughter?*"

'How did he react?'

'Told her to shut her fucking mouth.'

Clare raised an eyebrow. 'Anything else?'

Max thought for a moment. 'Coke went to get keys for his unit on the industrial estate and before he went he put a finger on her lips. *Don't be saying anything stupid now, love*, he said. Danuta scowled after him and muttered something about him not scaring her.'

262

Clare nodded slowly. 'Interesting. I wonder if that's a way in for us.'

'I thought so,' Max said. 'So I slipped her one of my cards. Said to call us anytime.'

'Did she take it?'

'Yep. Stared at it for a minute then she heard Coke coming back and she tucked it in her dressing gown pocket. Then we left with Coke.'

'I wonder if we should bring her in.'

Max shook his head. 'Not as long as Coke's running free. But maybe if we get enough to see him remanded...'

Clare considered this and turned her attention back to the day ahead. 'Get much at the unit?'

Max indicated a pile of evidence bags. 'Couple of laptops and enough paperwork to keep us busy till the end of time. Plus a box of mobile phones.'

'Burners?'

'That type, certainly. All still in the packaging. He said he bought a job lot to be used for his next charity event. Said sometimes people didn't like giving their personal numbers so he hands these phones out.'

The mention of charity made Clare groan inwardly. She'd already seen the headlines on several news websites:

Bungled Police Raid at Charity Champ's Home

and

Heart-of-Gold Grandison's Home Searched

Evidently Coke had connections in the media as well. No doubt the evening papers would be full of it. Jim was fending off reporters desperate for a quote and Penny had asked for hourly updates on the evidence gathered.

'It's not only a media disaster,' she'd said, her tone icy, 'but you've probably made sure we'll never find the evidence we need. Whoever has that van will be getting rid of it right now.'

Coke's solicitor, a large distinguished-looking man in a striped suit, had said to news reporters his client would be seeking damages for the hurt and upset caused in what he had called *a wholly unjustified raid on the home of a local hero.*

Clare had to admit it was a PR disaster. Max kept bringing her mugs of coffee, and a Wagon Wheel had somehow ended up on her desk. They were all dancing round her, avoiding the fact the operation had been a complete failure.

Eventually Chris had drawn the short straw and braved her office. 'You gonna hang out here all day?' he said, breaking off a bit of her Wagon Wheel and popping it in his mouth.

She shrugged. 'You got a better idea?'

'Yeah. Howsabout interviewing Albie Kennedy? He's on his way up and he might just slip up. He's not as sharp as Coke.'

She inclined her head. 'Suppose.'

'Good. And for the love of God paint a smile on. You've a face like a skelped arse.'

'Lovely. That finishing school you went to was worth every penny.'

'It's the lowest form of wit, *Inspectora.*'

'Whatever. Gimme a shout when he's here. And he'd better have a solicitor too. Unless of course Jim can't get one,' her tone distinctly hopeful.

'All in hand. Coke's organised one.'

She shook her head. 'I can hardly wait.'

Half an hour later Chris popped his head round the door to let her know Albie and his solicitor were ready for them. 'He's an absolute beaut,' he added.

'Albie?'

'The solicitor.'

Clare rolled her eyes and followed him to the incident room. He and Max had organised a set of CCTV photos showing

Albie and the white van in different locations, including Camperdown Road. 'Let's hope he's wrong-footed when we show him these,' she said, heading for the interview room.

Perhaps it was the cramped surroundings of the interview room but Clare was surprised at how large Albie was. His closely cropped hair only served to emphasise his huge head. He wore a small earring, a diamond or a cheaper stone – it was impossible to tell – but it seemed at odds with his appearance. He was brawny, his bulk spilling over the plastic chair, a pair of beefy arms folded across his chest. Clare took him in, suspecting he'd bought his Motörhead T-shirt a size too small to emphasise his biceps. His eyes bored into her with a steely contempt and she did her best to hold his gaze. She began the interview by saying Albie had been arrested for assaulting a police officer. At this point the solicitor, a young man with good hair and a smooth manner sat forward.

'Mr Kennedy deeply regrets his actions last night. He has been experiencing some sleep problems of late, including sleep walking. When the officers banged on his door he was disorientated and did not initially realise who they were. He believed he was in danger and lashed out to protect himself. Mr Kennedy is deeply sorry for any stress or injuries caused to the officers.' He smiled at Albie who nodded, his expression unchanged. 'I'm sure a caution would be sufficient under the circumstances.'

The solicitor clicked his pen off and put it back in his jacket pocket, a gesture, Clare guessed, designed to signal the interview was at an end. She ignored this and addressed Albie.

'The officers who visited your house last night clearly identified themselves and showed their warrant cards. Three of those were in police uniforms. It seems odd you didn't know who they were.'

He sat unmoving, his eyes still trained on Clare. 'Like my brief says. I was disorientated. Just a mistake.'

'As you know,' the solicitor interrupted, 'Mr Kennedy has an unblemished record. He has assured me there will be no repeat of last night's events.'

Clare regarded him then she passed a file across the desk. 'I am showing Mr Kennedy photos AF1 through to AF5. These are stills taken from CCTV at various locations. Do you agree the photos show you in the van, Albie?'

He glanced down then back to Clare again. 'Nope.'

Clare spread the photos out on the desk. 'This,' she said, 'was taken from the CCTV on the Tay Road Bridge. The image of the driver is almost identical to a similar photo showing you in a BMW vehicle owned by Mr Colin Grandison.'

Albie shrugged. 'Do a bit of driving for Coke.'

'You agree that's you in the BMW?'

'Suppose.'

'And the white van?'

'Dunno.'

'These images could be of any male with similar hair and sunglasses,' the solicitor said. 'I don't see they relate to my client at all.'

Clare moved another image in front of the solicitor. 'This is your client two weeks ago walking along Camperdown Road in Dundee at ten to seven in the morning. Note the light-coloured T-shirt. And this,' she moved another photo to the front, 'is a man of the same appearance driving a white van shortly afterwards on the same road. I believe the white van was kept in a lock-up behind the shops on Camperdown Road and your client walked there each day to pick it up.'

Albie's expression had formed into a smirk now.

He knows we didn't find the van, Clare thought. *He must have realised we'd make the connection and he's shifted it somewhere else. But where?*

'I must tell you the lock-up is now the subject of a forensic examination by our Scene of Crime Officers,' she said.

'Knock yourself out,' Albie said.

Clare decided to change tack. 'Where were you on Monday, 3rd April?'

Albie's eyes widened in mock surprise. 'Depends.'

'Let's try afternoon, say, between three and six.'

'Usually pick up Coke's daughter. She goes to a posh school over this way.'

'Not on a Monday you don't,' Clare said.

There was a flicker of something in Albie's eyes. 'Done your homework.'

'Just answer the question.'

'Can't remember.'

'Mr Kennedy is a busy man,' the solicitor said. 'I don't think it's reasonable to expect him to remember every detail one week later.'

'Did you cross the Tay Road Bridge in a white van last Monday afternoon?' Clare persisted. 'One week ago today.'

'Not that I recall.'

She tried for another ten minutes but Albie stuck to his story and in the end she had to end the interview. 'You'll receive a caution for the assault on two officers last night,' she said.

'Whatever.'

As they left the interview room she was suddenly conscious of his breath on her neck and she whirled round. He was close – uncomfortably close – and he was grinning at her. His solicitor was a couple of paces behind, eyes fixed on his phone. Albie's breath was warm in her face, a mixture of stale cigarettes and beer and she drew back involuntarily.

'Nice little dog you've got,' he said, his voice low and she stared at him. 'Shame if something happened to it.'

She flinched and looked to see if anyone had overheard but Chris was talking to Jim, explaining about the caution.

Then he gave her a wink, his eyes never leaving hers. The solicitor had caught up with them now and she left them with Chris and Jim. She went straight to the kitchen and switched on the kettle, clutching her hands together to stop them shaking. How dare he! How dare he threaten Benjy. How did he even know she had a dog? An uneasy feeling was gathering in the pit of her stomach and suddenly she knew she was going to throw up. She ran out of the kitchen past Max who had come to fetch his lunch from the fridge. She only just made it to the toilet in time, clasping the seat as she retched and heaved until there was nothing left. Her face burned and she felt a pulse beating against a tight band round her head. Benjy. Her lovely dog who she'd somehow inherited following her first case in St Andrews. Benjy who drove her mad but who she loved more than anything else in her life. She would do anything for that dog. How dare this revolting muscle-bound thug threaten him.

She spat a couple of times in an attempt to clean her mouth and grabbed a handful of toilet paper, dabbing at her lips. Then she pulled herself to her feet and pressed the flush. She emerged from the cubicle to find Sara, her face full of concern.

'Boss?'

She shook her head. 'I'm fine, Sara. Just a tummy upset.'

Sara looked unconvinced. 'Sure?'

'Yeah. But thanks. I'll just have a quiet five minutes in my office.'

Sara fetched a glass of water and followed her through. 'You're sure there's nothing else I can do?'

Clare shook her head. 'No, but thanks.'

The PC left her, closing the door quietly and Clare lay back in her chair, rubbing her temples. Her head was thumping now but she knew if she took paracetamol it would make her sick again. She sipped at the water, enjoying the coolness as it slipped down her throat.

And then her phone rang, causing a spasm of pain in her head. She glanced at the display and swiped to take the call.

Chapter 43

'Did he say why he wants to see us?' Chris asked, as he swung the car up onto Ninewells Avenue, the sweeping road that led to the large teaching hospital in Dundee.

'Only that he needs to speak to us before we see Simon,' Clare said.

'Maybe standard in attempted suicides. Probably wants to warn us not to go in heavy handed.'

'We'll see.'

Neither of them spoke as Chris turned the car at the round-about, slowing for the fifteen miles an hour sign. He glanced at Clare a couple of times and when she didn't look back he said, 'Sure you're okay?'

'I said, didn't I?'

'And it was just a tummy upset?'

She sighed. 'If you must know it was Albie Kennedy.'

'Clare,' he said, 'we'll nail him. It was just one of those interviews. We'll find the evidence.'

She shook her head. 'It's not that.'

'Then what?'

She hesitated. 'He said I had a nice little dog. Said it'd be a pity if something happened to him.'

'You what?' Chris's fingers whitened on the steering wheel. 'That absolute bastard.' He was quiet for a moment. 'It's all talk, though. Guys like him – they're full of hot air. You do know that, Clare?'

'But how did he know I had a dog?' she said. 'How? I mean it wouldn't be the first time I've been followed home – had to do a quick left turn into a side road when someone was behind me. But I'm only ever with Benjy when I'm off duty. How did he know, Chris? How?'

'Just bad luck,' Chris said. 'One of those things. Remember he comes through for Coke's daughter twice a day. He could easily have passed you out walking Benjy – on a day off, yeah?'

She didn't answer.

'Or he could have been chancing his arm. Lots of folk have dogs. He was probably fishing. Hoping for a reaction.' He reached out and squeezed her arm. 'Forget him.'

'Suppose.' She glanced down at her notepad as Chris drew into a parking space. 'Gawd I hate the Acute Medical Unit. It's always rammed.'

'You never know. Monday afternoon. Might be quieter.'

They made their way through the hospital, down to the unit which was as busy as they'd ever seen it. After a few minutes a nurse approached to ask if she could help.

'We're looking for Dr Alston,' Clare explained.

The nurse looked round, scanning the beds. 'I think he's with a patient just now but I'll tell him you're here.'

They found a corner out of the way of the staff who were rushing back and forth between bays and side rooms. A porter went past wheeling a white-faced woman in a chair while a man in blue scrubs stood writing up notes, the phone ringing incessantly.

'Must be hellish working here,' Chris muttered.

'I bet the days pass quickly, though.'

'DI Mackay?'

Clare spun round to see a tired looking man in a pale blue open necked shirt, a stethoscope tucked into his top pocket.

She nodded and introduced Chris. 'You wanted to speak to us?'

'About Simon Miller, yes. Let's find somewhere quiet to talk.'

He led them to a small room and flicked a sign on the door to show it was engaged. When they had sat he took a seat opposite. 'As you probably know Simon presented at A&E with acute carbon monoxide poisoning. He was treated with pure oxygen and is recovering. We're still monitoring him but we hope he'll be well enough to go home in the next day or two. He'll need psychiatric follow-up but, physically we should be able to discharge him soon.'

'We do need to question him,' Clare said. 'Is he fit enough for that?'

'Yes. Initially he was confused which was to be expected. But he seems much clearer now. There's nothing to suppose any statement he gave you would be unreliable, medically speaking. But there is something else I need to discuss with you.'

They waited and the doctor went on. 'Simon has a pattern of injuries suggesting he's been assaulted repeatedly, over a long period of time.'

Clare stared at him. 'What kind of assaults?'

'Physical but not sexual. He has what we would call defensive injuries which have occurred at different times over the past few years. Perhaps longer. There is a fracture of the ulna,' he said. 'Healed now but possibly in the last twelve months. He also has two cracked ribs and a perforated eardrum. There is some fairly recent bruising and some perhaps a week or two old.'

'You say defensive,' Clare said slowly trying to make sense of this.

'I'm afraid so. These injuries suggest regular assaults. In fact they are the kind of injuries we see on victims of domestic abuse. The ulna, for instance, is one of the forearm bones. It's typically fractured when the victim puts an arm up to shield their head. And the eardrum suggests a severe blow to the side of the head.'

Clare frowned and the doctor said, 'Men aren't immune from abuse. We do see far more women but it's not unheard of for a man to be subject to this kind of treatment.'

Chris was frowning. 'But who would do that?'

'As to that,' the doctor said, 'you'll have to ask him yourself. He won't talk to us about it.'

'Has he been to A&E with these injuries?' Clare asked.

The doctor shook his head. 'Sadly, no. If he had, we might have been able to help.'

Clare sat taking this in. 'Is there anything else we should know before we see him?'

'No. But, whatever you plan to question him about, I'd go easy. His injuries are not just physical.'

Simon was in a side room, close to the nurses' station. Clare tapped on the door and pushed it open slowly. He was lying down, his head turned away and he looked round as they entered. It took him a moment to recognise them then he made an effort to sit up.

'Hello, Simon,' Clare said, pulling a chair up to the bed. 'How are you?'

He flicked a glance at Clare then away again. 'Oh, you know.'

'They're treating you all right?'

He nodded. 'They're wonderful. I'm just sorry...'

Clare gave him a moment. 'Would you mind if we asked you some questions?'

He took a breath in and out. 'If you like.'

'Thank you. And, if you need a break, just let us know.' She smiled. 'Can you think back to Saturday please?' her voice as gentle as she could make it. 'You went into the bathroom, yes?'

'Yes.'

'With the barbeques.'

'Yes.'

'Did you want to die, Simon?'

He looked down at the honeycomb blanket on the bed, his fingers worrying it. 'I suppose.'

Clare glanced at Chris. 'Simon, I must warn you we would like to question you about your wife's death. I must also tell you we've spoken to a car mechanic by the name of Sam Glenday.

So, before we go any further, I am going to caution you formally and I'll be recording this interview. You are entitled to have a solicitor present and I can arrange for one to attend before we ask you anything else.'

His eyes widened and for a few moments he didn't speak. 'I don't want a solicitor.'

'Are you sure? It would be better if you had one.'

He shook his head. 'No need. Please, ask me whatever you like.'

Clare delivered the formal caution and Simon acknowledged this. 'Can you tell us why you wanted to die?' she said.

He opened his mouth then stopped, as though he couldn't find the right words. 'If you've spoken to Sam you must know.'

'I'd like you to tell us.'

'Because of Leona. What I did.'

They waited.

'Her car,' he said. 'I put this program into it and it let me mess with the electrics.'

'How did you do this?'

'You mustn't blame Sam,' he said. 'He knew nothing about it. He was struggling with the software and these things are easy for me. I've always liked computers. I was happy to help. And I had this program. Had it for a while before Sam phoned me.'

'Where did you find it?'

'Some website. Dark web,' he added. 'I downloaded it ages ago. I wasn't sure why but I was interested in what it could do. Then Sam asked if I could help with the on-board diagnostics. I told Leona and she said if I was helping Sam he should do something for us in return. Her car was playing up so I suggested we let him have a look at it.' He shook his head. 'It was as easy as that.'

Clare took a moment, choosing her words. 'To be clear, you suggested Sam should service your wife's car so you could install the malware on it?'

'Yes,' he said, his voice small.

'Why did you do that?'

He swallowed and ran his tongue round his lips. 'I wanted to do... something.'

'Something?' Clare said.

He looked down. 'Something to hurt her.' His voice was faint and Clare saw his face was growing red.

'Why did you want to hurt her?'

Again, he said nothing and they waited. Finally he spoke again. 'They told you, didn't they? The doctors.'

'About your injuries?' Clare said. 'Yes, they did. How did you come by them?'

The room was absolutely silent. Clare was aware of the bustle going on in the busy ward outside but there, in that side room, with this shell of a man lying in the bed, it was as if the world had stopped for a moment. 'You must think I'm pathetic,' he said, at last. 'She certainly did.' There was a bitter edge to his voice now. 'She said a proper man wouldn't put up with it. But I couldn't,' he said, shaking his head. 'I couldn't hit her back.' He raised his eyes to meet Clare's. 'I've never hit anyone in my life, let alone a woman.'

Chris shifted in his seat, but Clare made a slight movement with her hand and he eased himself back again.

'I annoyed her,' Simon said. 'I was always saying the wrong thing. Doing the wrong thing. Sometimes I'd rehearse what I was going to say when she came through the door. I'd have her tea ready, kettle on. Put the lamps on to make the room cheerful. But I always managed to do something wrong. She'd be tired, you know? Her work, it was busy. She'd be tired and I'd annoy her. I'd try to make it up to her, tell her I was sorry but that seemed to rile her even more. I couldn't do right for doing wrong.'

'So she hit you?' Clare asked.

He said nothing for a moment then nodded. 'She'd just see red and she couldn't control herself. Afterwards – it was as if it had never happened. She'd ask if I wanted a cup of tea, what we should watch on TV. She was like a different person. I think,' he said, 'I think it was her way of saying sorry. Trying to make up for it.'

'You couldn't leave?' Clare said.

He stared at her, as if she'd said something ridiculous. 'Where would I go? It's not like there are shelters for battered men. And even if there were, how could I admit my own wife was hitting me? Who would believe me? Besides, that house is my home. I'd put a lot of work into it. Why should I be the one to leave?'

Clare regarded him. 'So you installed the malware on your wife's car?'

'Yes.'

'And what did you do after that?'

He cleared his throat and spoke again. 'Nothing to start with. I think just knowing I had it was a help. Knowing I could mess with her car – if I wanted to.' He smiled, as if recalling this. 'She went out on Tuesday nights, you know. Straight from work. Told me it was night classes but she never wanted to talk about what she was doing. She'd get angry if I even asked. But I knew – I knew she was with someone else.'

'You suspected your wife was having an affair?'

'Yes.' His voice was barely above a whisper. 'But there was nothing I could do. Except – I kept thinking about the malware. Thinking how I could use it. But I didn't have the courage.' He paused for a moment. 'Last Tuesday I sent her a text. Usually she grabbed a sandwich on Tuesday nights – or so she told me. So I texted saying I'd have something ready for her when she came home and what time did her class finish. I thought maybe she'd be pleased.' He let his gaze fall and his grip on the blanket tightened. 'She messaged back straight away, telling me not to be stupid – said I was disturbing her in the middle of the class.' He tailed off and it seemed as if he might not go on. Clare let the silence fall and rest there for a minute, and her patience was rewarded.

'And then,' he said, 'I – I don't know what came over me.' He lifted his gaze and met Clare's eyes. 'I just felt this surge

275

of anger. From nowhere. I was so furious with her.' His hands were shaking now and he let go of the blanket, gripping one hand with the other. 'I've no idea where it came from. I went to the computer and opened up the program. The car wasn't moving of course but I knew what time she usually drove home. So I bided my time. And when I reckoned she'd be in the car I started messing with it.' A smile played on his lips. 'It's easy enough. Child's play, if you know what you're doing. I turned the radio up to full volume then down again. Made the lights go on and off – windscreen wipers, everything I could think of. I turned the heating up then put the aircon on.' He looked at them both. 'You probably won't understand this but it felt so good to be in control for a change. Okay, it was only a car journey but if it meant I'd taken the shine off her evening then it was worth it. Even if she was in a temper when she came home. Only, she never did...'

'You realise—' Clare began.

'That I caused her accident? More than likely.'

'We have a witness who saw her driving erratically,' Clare said.

He nodded. 'I didn't mean for her to die. I just wanted her to know what it was like to not be in control for once.'

Clare regarded him, took in his grey pallor and thought how he'd aged in just a few days. 'Are you all right to continue, Simon?'

'Yes,' he said. 'I'd rather get it over with.'

She studied him for a moment, assuring herself she wasn't pushing him too far. 'And is that why you decided to end your life?' she asked. 'With the barbeques in the bathroom?'

'I couldn't live with what I'd done,' he said. 'I hated Leona for the way she treated me. But I loved her too. And she didn't deserve to die. Not like that.'

Clare waited to see if he was going to say any more then she said, 'Just to be clear, you admit hacking into your wife's car last Tuesday night to interfere with the electrics, an action which probably caused her to crash?'

He hesitated. 'Yes.' He looked at Clare. 'Will I go to prison?'

'Let's not look too far ahead,' she said. 'There will be charges but I would strongly advise you to offer your injuries in mitigation.' She smiled. 'You don't need me to tell you a good solicitor is essential.'

He nodded. 'There's something else I should tell you.'

Chapter 44

Max carried a tray of coffees into Clare's office and set it down on the desk. He handed them out and pulled up a chair.

'What was the other thing?' he asked. 'After he told you he'd messed with Leona's car?'

Clare sighed. 'It's quite sad, really.'

Chris slurped his coffee. 'It's fraud.'

'I know, but you saw how he was. Why he did it.'

Max was staring at them. 'Would one of you like to—'

'Sorry,' Clare said. 'I'll try to explain. This program he installed on the cars – this malware – it let him mess about with the electrics but he also realised if the driver plugged in their phone and unlocked it he could access it.'

'And everything on it,' Chris added.

Max's face cleared. 'Oh I get it. If the driver was logged into something like Amazon.'

'Exactly. Then he found he could change the settings on the driver's email account and divert emails to the Trash folder. That way he could buy stuff and the driver would know nothing about it. Some of them had two-factor authentication set up so he didn't bother with those, but a lot didn't.'

'What sort of stuff did he buy?'

Clare shook her head. 'Nothing valuable; and nothing that needed a delivery address, to avoid the transactions being traced. He said he only wanted to see if anyone noticed. He'd buy an eBook or an electronic voucher for five or ten pounds. Then he'd access the Trash folder and forward the emails to a disposable address; and if the person had internet banking set up on their phone he could access that too.'

'But the amounts he took were really small,' Chris said. 'He reckoned with folk paying for so many things by card they wouldn't notice.' He looked at Clare. 'I certainly wouldn't spot the odd five quid transaction. Would you?'

'Probably not.'

'How much did he steal?' Max asked.

'A couple of hundred, overall,' Clare said.

Max stared. 'All that for a couple of hundred quid?'

'Yep. I'm not even sure he spent any of it.'

'Then why do it? What did he get out of it?'

Clare ran a hand through her hair. 'I'm no psychologist, guys, but I think it was to do with control. He couldn't control things at home and I think this kind of made up for it, in an odd sort of way.' She sipped at her coffee then put it down. 'We'll definitely need a psychiatric report before we talk about any charges.'

'What are you thinking?' Max asked.

She considered this. 'It's hard to know where to start.'

'Has to be murder,' Chris said. 'His actions killed Leona.'

Clare frowned. 'I'm not so sure. It's such an unusual case. I'm more inclined to go for culpable homicide. It might be hard to prove he intended to kill her. It's not like he hacked into the brakes or steering.' She drummed her fingers on the desk. 'If we went for murder, a jury could find him innocent, especially if his defence leads with the abuse he suffered.'

'Safer to go for culpable homicide then,' Max said.

Chris didn't look convinced. 'What about the car hacking?'

'Crikey, I dunno.' Clare shook her head. 'Breaching the Computer Misuse Act, maybe? And then there's accessing those drivers' phones.'

'Fraud?' Chris suggested. 'Or embezzlement?'

She nodded. 'Something like that. But we can't do anything until he's been properly assessed. He may not even be fit to plead.'

Chris shook his head. 'I reckon he knew exactly what he was doing. I say we charge him. It's up to his defence to plead the abuse in mitigation.'

Clare yawned. 'Suppose.' She checked her watch. 'I'm going to type this up then look in at Harry's office. Hopefully see the solicitor who's dealing with his clients. There are some property sales I'd like to ask him about.'

–

Kate Campbell's face sank as Clare entered the office. 'It's absolute chaos,' she said. 'Derek's doing all the conveyancing but there's Simon's work as well and the phone...' As if on cue it began to ring and she gave Clare an apologetic smile.

Clare waited a minute or two but when Kate stood, phone tucked behind her ear and pulled open a filing cabinet she decided to leave her to it. She waved her thanks and turned to go. The door to Harry's office was ajar and she moved to tap on it.

Derek Peterson was installed behind Harry's desk, two piles of papers in front of him. He was younger than Clare expected, possibly late twenties, tidily dressed in a sober suit and dark tie. He rose to greet her and offered her a seat.

'I'm working my way through the upcoming property sales,' he said. 'Trying to deal with the most urgent ones first. As you can imagine, it's not easy stepping into another solicitor's caseload.'

Clare nodded. 'I remember what it was like when I bought my house.'

He smiled politely at this. 'I... er don't suppose there's any news?' he asked. 'About Harry?'

'We are making progress,' Clare said. 'But it's too early to say any more.'

He sat back in his chair and appraised her. 'Ah,' he said, 'the stock response.'

'I'm afraid so.' She looked round the room, taking in the coffee machine, the oil painting on the wall, the rich cream blinds angled to give both light and privacy, and she thought how starkly it contrasted with the utility of her own office. She turned back to him, about to mention her conversation with Emma Halliday when she noticed a panel set into the wall.

He turned, following her gaze then rose and pulled the panel open to reveal a wall safe with a keypad. 'I don't have the combination.'

Clare's brow creased. 'Is that usual? For a solicitor, I mean?'

He looked at it. 'I wouldn't say so. Much of what we do is online now, locked drawers for the paper stuff.'

She looked towards the door. 'I wonder if Kate…'

'I've asked. She doesn't know it.'

Clare took out her phone and swiped through contacts until she found Louise Richards' number. The call was answered quickly and she explained about the safe.

'Sorry,' Louise said. 'I've no idea. I mean I knew Harry had a safe but I assumed the others would know the combination. Maybe Simon…'

Clare's mind worked quickly. It might be a random combination. Maybe he stored it in his phone. Or maybe… 'What about significant dates?' she asked Louise. 'Can you give me family dates of birth? That sort of thing?' She reached across the desk and picked up a pen. Derek pushed a notepad towards her and Clare began jotting down dates as Louise reeled them off. Then she thanked her and ended the call.

'Let's hope it's not one of those that locks after three attempts,' she said, moving round the desk.

'One moment.' Derek rose and stepped between Clare and the safe. 'The terms of your warrant. They may not cover the contents.'

Clare swore under her breath. He was right. If they breached the terms of the warrant the contents of the safe might be deemed inadmissible in court. And she didn't want to risk doing anything that would let Coke Grandison off the hook.

'What about this,' Derek said. 'I'll attempt to open the safe with the numbers you give me and I'll examine the contents. If I deem they fall within the terms of your warrant I will allow you to view them.'

'And if not?'

He regarded her for a moment, as if choosing his words. 'Let's just say if I believe the contents will assist your enquiries then I might make some – some *suggestions* as to how a future warrant could be drawn up. Without prejudice, of course,' he added.

'Of course.' Clare smiled and handed him the list of dates she'd scribbled down.

It seemed fitting somehow that the combination was the date of Harry and Louise's wedding. The door swung open and she craned her neck to see over Derek's shoulder. He turned back. 'I think it would be best if you waited in the reception area. I'll be as quick as I can.'

Kate offered to make Clare a cup of tea but she waved this away, hoping Derek wouldn't take too long. 'I don't want to keep you from your work.'

Kate resumed tapping at her computer keyboard then she stopped. 'I wanted to ask – Simon – how is he?'

Clare hesitated. What *could* she say about Simon? It would be a shock to Kate when the truth came out, but now definitely wasn't the time. 'I really can't say.'

'Is it true? He tried to...'

Clare sighed. 'All I can tell you is I think he's recovering.'

Kate looked at her for a moment. 'If you do see him again, will you... will you give him my love? He's a very dear man.'

Clare felt an unexpected lump in her throat and she swallowed. Then Derek appeared in the doorway.

'If you'd like to come through...'

She followed him back to the office and her eyes went immediately to the desk. He'd pushed back the documents he'd been working on and she saw a sheaf of papers held together by a treasury tag.

'I must say,' he began, 'that these papers do not fall within the scope of your warrant. They contain information relating to clients' transactions. Normally, I would seek their permission before allowing you to see them. But, in this case there are two reasons I think you should have sight of them. Firstly, I don't believe sharing them with you will be disadvantageous, harmful or otherwise damaging to Harry's clients; and secondly, there is a statement signed by Harry which implicates himself and others in criminal activity.'

Suddenly Clare's mouth was dry. Was this what they'd been waiting for? Something that would lead them to Coke Grandison? Or Albie Kennedy? 'Perhaps I should see the statement.'

Derek removed the top sheet and handed it to Clare, turning the desk lamp round so it shone on the paper. She took it, bent her head and started to read.

> I, Harold James Richards, being of sound mind and body hereby wish to set out actions I have taken over the past few months. I believe these actions do not constitute best practice and they make it plain I have fallen short of the duty I owed to my clients. Further, I believe my clients have been victims of criminal activity. I hope this statement will help the police to bring charges against those involved.
>
> On 2nd September last year I agreed, against my better judgement, to transfer title of a house for an elderly couple, Sidney and Janet Whitehurst, for a sum far below the market value. At the time I mistakenly believed there were good reasons for the low selling price. Mr and Mrs Whitehurst assured me they wanted to sell to a cousin who had agreed they would be allowed to remain in the property for the rest of their lives, rent-free. They were most insistent and, in the end, I consented to act for them. The purchaser was a Mrs Danuta Grandison.

I had met Mr Grandison at a charity fundraising event but did not initially make the connection. Mr Grandison then visited me at my office. He told me, in his view, I was guilty of malpractice but if I helped him with one more house purchase he wouldn't mention it.

I soon realised he had me trapped as more and more property sales came my way, the purchaser always Mr or Mrs Grandison, but it was some months before I realised what was behind the sales.

Mr Grandison is an illegal moneylender. I did not know this to begin with but I am convinced of it now. I can find no evidence he has a licence for this practice. He lends money to those in difficulty on impossible terms; and when they cannot keep up the repayments he offers to buy their houses at a pitifully low value in return for cancelling the debt. Sadly, many of his clients felt they had no option but to agree.

It was unethical of me to proceed with these sales and I deeply regret my part in this. All I can do now is to provide a list of the people whose houses Mr and Mrs Grandison own in the hope the former owners will be willing to corroborate this statement.

Finally, may I express my profound regret for my part in these property sales.

The document was signed, dated and witnessed by Kate and Simon.

'I will ask Kate about it,' Derek said when Clare had read it through, 'but I imagine she and Simon were asked to witness Harry's signature without sight of the actual document. No doubt they saw him sign and date it then they also signed to confirm they'd witnessed his signature.' He smiled. 'Perfectly legal.'

Clare read it over again to make sure she understood, then she indicated the other sheets, still bound by the treasury tag. 'And these?'

'Full details of every purchase. Names and addresses of sellers and buyers, market value of the properties and the purchase prices. As you'll see, most of the houses were sold for less than a quarter of the market value.' He shook his head. 'He was foolish to become involved in this.' He tapped the sheets. 'I suppose he thought this was his insurance policy. Sadly…'

'May I see?' Clare said. She held out her hand and he passed the sheets across the desk. She leafed through, glancing at the contents, shaking her head. One address rang a bell. A flat in the south-west of town. She took out her phone and played the voicemail from Tom. She listened and saw it was the flat he'd mentioned. Sold for less than half the market value, according to Harry's notes. No wonder Tom had wanted to see the property for himself. An image of Coke Grandison came into her head and she felt anger building within her. 'I need to take these,' she said and he nodded.

'If I can have a receipt.'

She spent a few more minutes looking through the papers then she secured them again with the treasury tag. 'I must ask you not to mention this to Kate – or anyone else,' she said. 'I doubt Mr Grandison knew this document existed. I'd like to keep it that way until we have enough evidence to arrest him.'

She asked for a piece of paper and wrote out a receipt for the documents.

'There's this as well,' Derek added, tapping a small smartphone Clare had assumed was his own.

'Oh?' She couldn't keep the surprise out of her voice. *Not your usual burner*, she thought. 'Have you managed to access it?'

'I have. Same code as the office safe. I'll write it down.'

'And?'

'There's a video file,' he said. 'I think it will help.'

Clare looked at him for a moment but he seemed disinclined to say more so she took the phone, added it to the receipt and rose to leave.

'Good luck with the investigation,' he said. 'I have my own thoughts about Harry's conduct but he didn't deserve this. I hope you manage to bring the culprits to justice.'

Chapter 45

By some miracle Jim found a charger that fitted the phone.

'I knew this box of stuff would come in handy,' he said, tucking it below his desk again.

Clare thanked him and took the cable into her office where Chris and Max were waiting. She plugged it into the phone, connected it to her computer and set about downloading the video file. It took a minute for the file to transfer then she clicked to open it.

She had seen Harry twice over the past week. Once in the blood-soaked car, his head thrown back to reveal the gaping wound in his neck, and again at the mortuary where his face had been cleaned up, the white gown pulled up round his neck to hide the horror of his death. But this was a living, breathing Harry that filled the screen.

They watched, fascinated as he stated his name and that he wished to put on record that he'd fallen short of protecting his clients' best interests. The account he gave corroborated the written statement and he went on to name the clients listed in the documents from the safe. After a few minutes the video ended. They sat processing this then Chris broke the silence.

'That's all very well but will it stand up in court? It's not like he can be cross-examined.'

'I'd have to check,' Clare said, 'but I think it is admissible. I think it falls under *Hearsay Evidence*. It's down to the judge but in cases of mental incapacity or, as we have here, death of a witness, the judge can agree to a signed statement or video evidence being shown to the jury.'

'So we've got him?' Max said. 'Grandison.'

Clare shook her head. 'It's a dead man's word against his. The prosecution has to prove their case beyond reasonable doubt. That,' she tapped the computer monitor, 'and these papers — it's not enough.'

They were quiet for a minute then Max said, 'What about the properties?'

'What about them?'

'Is it worth chatting to the people he bought from? That document said he'd allowed them to stay rent-free after they sold?'

Clare considered this. 'I'm not sure. I doubt there was a formal agreement. I bet Coke either turfed them out or started demanding rent.'

'But some of the sales were quite recent,' Chris said. 'Maybe he's not had time to get the tenants out. Could be worth speaking to them. They might be willing to give us a statement.'

'Good point. Okay,' she said. 'I'll send a couple of guys round to speak to the current tenants.'

'Maybe we should check if any of them have garages,' Max said.

She stared at him then a smile spread over her face. 'Max, you absolute genius.'

'You never say that to me,' Chris said.

'Might be a reason for that.' Clare drew the keyboard across the desk and clicked to open up Google. 'Give me the first one.'

Chris read out the address and she typed it into the search bar. She clicked on the map and dragged the little yellow figure over to show street view, then scrolled along until she came to the house in question. 'Dammit. No garage. Next one?'

They worked through the list of houses, most of which seemed to be ex-council properties, none with garages.

'Gotterstone Drive,' Chris said. 'Only another two after this.'

'Where's that?' Clare typed the address in.

'Dundee. Just off the Arbroath Road.' Again, Clare dragged the little yellow figure over and the map changed to a view of the street. 'Okay,' she said, scrolling along. Then she stopped and jabbed the screen. 'Is that or is that not a garage, gents?'

'*Si*,' Chris said in his best Spanish accent. '*Es un garaje!*'

'Let's not get ahead of ourselves,' Clare said. 'It might be empty.'

'Might not,' Chris said, rising. 'Want to head over there now?'

'See if Dundee can do it,' she said. 'Save us a trip. No point in haring over there if it's empty. But get someone sensible, mind. I don't want them tramping over it in their size tens.'

—

'Garage is locked,' Bill said. 'New tenant doesn't know where the key is.'

Clare put the phone on speaker and set it down on her desk. 'I bet I know where it is,' she said. 'One of Coke's boys'll have it.'

'Want us to break in?'

She thought for a moment. The search warrant allowed them access to all the Grandisons' properties, including those owned by Granco; and she could always call a locksmith out to fix it. 'Do it.'

'You want to hang on while we open it? We've a crowbar in the car.'

'Go on, then.' She waited, not quite catching the muffled conversation between Janey and Bill. Then she heard a metallic groan as they attacked the garage door.

'It's here!' Bill said. 'White Transit van.' He reeled off the registration and Clare checked it against the white van they'd caught on the Tay Road Bridge CCTV.

'That's the one,' she said. 'Bill, I don't want you to go anywhere near it. But can you stay until SOCO arrive?'

'Will do. Strong smell of bleach in this one as well, though.'

'We'll just have to hope he missed a bit.' She was about to end the call when she heard another voice. Bill was speaking now and she wondered who the other voice belonged to. A minute later he was back. 'I've got the tenant here, boss. Says she saw the van arriving.'

Clare was suddenly alert. 'Yeah?'

'Pretty late one evening last week. She can't remember which night. She was taking the dog out for a last pee when she realised the garage door was open. She thought maybe somebody had broken in. Then a big lad appeared. Told her it was the landlord's van and nothing to worry about. She said he'd a couple of black bags, knotted at the neck.'

'The blood-soaked clothes, I bet,' Clare said. 'Can she give you a description?'

'Already has. Big fella – really big. Motörhead T-shirt and she noticed a sparkly earring.'

'Albie,' Clare said. 'Got to be. Anything else?'

'Yep. He got into a black BMW. It was waiting for him, engine idling. Another fella in the driver's seat.'

'Could she describe the driver?'

'Nah. Too dark to see.'

'What about the bin bags?'

'In the boot.'

'Can you bring her across please, Bill? I'd like to see if she picks Albie out from a selection of photos.'

'Will do. As soon as SOCO get here.'

–

It was another two hours before Bill and Janey arrived with Carol Thorne in tow. She was slim, with short brown hair, dressed in a black jumper and leggings. Her eyes roamed round the station, as if she was taking it all in. A good sign, Clare thought. An observant witness who could pick Albie out of a selection of photos would go a long way towards helping their case; and if SOCO found traces of Harry's blood in the van...

She introduced herself and led Carol to an interview room where Chris had prepared a selection of photos, including one of Albie.

Carol hesitated over Albie's photo for a few seconds then set it aside to leaf through the others. Then she tapped it with her finger. 'That's him,' she said.

'How sure are you?'

'Hundred per cent. The dog was pulling towards him, sniffing, you know? And he said he wasn't good with dogs and could I take him away.' She smiled. 'Funny, big lad like that being afraid of a little dog.'

'What kind of dog do you have?' Clare asked, keeping the conversation light.

'Bichon Frise,' Carol said. 'Tiny wee thing to be scared of.'

Clare was about to say she had a dog as well then Albie Kennedy's words came into her head and she thought better of it. Instead, she said, 'How long have you lived there?'

'Coming up for a month. I was lucky to get it. It's a nice house.'

'How did you find it?'

'Just luck. I was checking the letting agency every day and saw this one pretty much as soon as it went up. I called them, viewed it and said I'd take it.' She smiled. 'It's lovely.'

'Any idea who was there before you?'

'Yeah. Nice couple. They'd gone by the time I viewed the house but they popped by one night, leaving a forwarding address in case there was any mail.'

'Do you have it?'

'The address?' Carol reached into her pocket and took out her mobile phone. 'Hold on.' She scrolled for a minute then held it out so Clare could copy the details.

'Thanks so much for your time,' Clare said. 'I'll arrange for someone to take you back home.' Then she stopped and said, 'Can I ask you please not to mention this to anyone? That includes the letting agency and the previous tenants.'

Carol raised an eyebrow. 'I suppose.'

'It's very important,' Clare stressed. 'No one at all.'

Carol agreed to this and Gillian was despatched to drive her back to Dundee.

'What now?' Chris said, trailing after Clare to her office.

'Now,' she said, 'we wait to hear from SOCO.'

'What about Coke's BMW? If those bin bags Albie put in the boot had blood-soaked clothing in them there might be traces in the car.'

Clare mulled this over. 'I'd like to seize the car but after the search fiasco I daren't risk it. Not yet.' She paused to order her thoughts. 'I think we'll see what the previous owners have to say for themselves.'

Chapter 46

Rose and Joe Hogg lived in a holiday park just off the main road in Leuchars.

'I didn't even know this was here,' Clare said, as they drove slowly in through the park gates.

'Nor me.'

They stepped out of the car and Chris glanced over to a large area of grass just outside the park. 'Nice, though.'

'Come on,' Clare said. 'We're running out of day.' She began walking quickly along the narrow road that ran between the homes, checking numbers as she went. 'I think it's that one over there,' she said, indicating one on the bend of the road.

Chris followed her, looking left and right. 'Reminds me of a holiday we had with my mum and dad,' he said. 'Scarborough.'

'I think this is residential,' Clare said. 'Maybe the kind for older folk.'

'Like you, you mean?'

'I'll tell you what's nice about getting older,' she said as they approached the Hoggs' house.

'Astound me.'

'I'm a lot nearer getting my pension than you, sonny.'

'Hah! We'll never reach pension age,' he said. 'They'll keep adding a few years on until you have to be a hundred to get anything.'

'You're probably right. Eyup, I think that's them sitting outside.'

An older couple were sitting on green plastic garden chairs. The woman was dressed in a grey tracksuit, her silver hair streaked with lilac. She was knitting something with navy blue wool. The man wore combat trousers and a brown pullover. He had a pen in one hand, a folded newspaper in the other and Clare thought he might be doing a crossword. He looked up as they approached and his eyes narrowed. Rose looked up too and she stopped knitting, pulling the stitches down her needles. They both seemed wary and Clare hurried to take out her warrant card. A look of relief crossed Joe Hogg's face and he rose to greet them.

Clare introduced herself and Chris, and Rose resumed her knitting.

'I'll just finish this row then I'll make us a cup of tea,' she said.

Clare was about to refuse when Chris got in first.

'That would be lovely. I'm parched.'

Clare glanced at him and she turned back to Rose. 'Only if it's no trouble.'

Rose finished her knitting and put it in a canvas bag then she stood and indicated the door. 'Let's go inside. It's getting a bit airy now.' She led them into a surprisingly light room. The décor was neutral and Clare thought it lacked the personal touch.

'We're just renting,' Rose explained. 'Our own stuff's in storage. Just until we find somewhere we can afford.' The kettle came to the boil and she moved to warm a teapot. 'Tea okay?' she asked. 'We do have coffee but it's just instant.'

'Tea's perfect,' Clare said. She watched Rose busying herself for a minute. 'How long have you been here?'

Rose's back stiffened and she didn't immediately reply. Joe moved to join her and took a carton of milk out of a small fridge.

'A few weeks,' Rose said, eventually, still with her back to them. She carried the teapot over to a gateleg table and put it down. 'Sugar?'

Clare shook her head. 'Neither of us.'

Joe brought over the milk and a packet of chocolate digestives and they sat opposite Clare and Chris. 'So,' he said, glancing at his wife, 'what's this about?'

Clare studied them – their faces lined with worry. They must have been through hell with Coke Grandison, perhaps even thinking they'd done something illegal, and her heart went out to them. 'I gather you sold your house recently,' she said, trying to make it easy for them.

They nodded but said nothing. Clare noticed Joe took his wife's hand.

'To a Mrs Danuta Grandison,' Clare said. 'Is that correct?'

'Mind me asking why you want to know?' Joe said.

'Of course. I must emphasise you're not in any trouble. We're just trying to find out a bit more about the house sale.'

Rose seemed relieved at this, but Joe's expression didn't change.

'What do you want to know?'

'The solicitor you used,' Clare said. 'Had you used him before?'

Rose looked at her husband, as if trying to communicate something but he was looking at Clare.

'No. We had one recommended to us.'

'Who recommended him?'

Joe picked up his mug and drank from it. 'Not sure I remember,' he said. 'Erm, help yourselves to biscuits.'

Clare ignored this. 'Was it a Mr Grandison who suggested you use Harry Richards to sell your house?'

'Tell them,' Rose burst in suddenly. 'Tell them, Joe. I'm sick of pretending nothing's wrong.'

He stared at his wife, eyes full of meaning. 'Nothing to tell,' a warning tone in his voice. 'Is there?'

Rose was looking at him, her eyes filled with tears.

'Perhaps it might be easier if I tell you what we think happened.'

The couple exchanged glances but said nothing.

'I think,' Clare said, 'you borrowed some money from Mr Grandison and the interest on the loan was more than you could afford. When you realised this Mr Grandison offered you a way out − sell your house to him and the debt would be cleared. But the selling price was far lower than it should have been.'

'He didn't give us any option,' Rose said, dabbing her eyes.

'Rosie?' Joe's voice was low. 'We can't.'

'Yes we can,' she said with a sudden flash of temper. 'It's done now. The sale was all legal so why shouldn't we tell the officers what happened?'

'You know what he said,' Joe hissed.

'I don't care any more. He's taken our home. It's time something was done about him.' She turned back to Clare. 'Joe lost his job, you see? Made redundant. Then the car failed its MOT, the bills were going up and we just couldn't make ends meet.'

'How did you find out Mr Grandison was lending money?'

'Someone from Joe's work told him. Said he knew this man. He'd made enough money for himself and his family and he was happy to help other people out.' She flicked a glance at Joe. 'He made it sound so easy, didn't he?'

Joe nodded but still didn't speak.

'The money,' Rose said. 'It was an absolute Godsend.'

'Until the interest started going up,' Joe added, prompted out of his silence. 'No matter how much we paid it still kept going up. I even went to the bank to ask about a loan but with us both out of work they wouldn't look at it.'

Clare could feel the anger rising in her. The same story as Aleks Petrova. Coke Grandison pretending to come to their rescue out of the goodness of his heart. And once they'd taken his money, he had them right where he wanted them. At least Aleks had found the money to pay Coke off. But how many others were there like the Hoggs?

'Who was this man?' Clare asked Joe. 'The one from your work.'

Joe didn't meet her eye. 'Can't remember. He was only temporary. Not sure I ever knew his name.'

Clare raised an eyebrow but Joe seemed disinclined to say more and she turned back to Rose. 'And your house?'

They made no reply to this, even Rose apparently unwilling to speak.

'Did Mr Grandison threaten you?' Clare asked. 'Did he warn you not to speak about the house sale to anyone?'

Rose was crying now and Joe put an arm round her. 'Yes,' he said eventually, his voice a whisper. 'He didn't exactly say what he'd do if we told anyone. But he didn't have to. So, unless you're actually taping this without us knowing, we won't give a statement. I don't want to come home and find this place has gone up in flames. Or worse.'

Clare looked at them, worry written all over their faces. 'I can't go into details,' she said, 'but we are building a case against Mr Grandison. Your testimony would really help with that.'

Joe rose from his seat. 'Sorry,' he said. 'You'll have to build your case without us. It's just too risky.'

—

They drove back in silence, Chris only speaking as they neared St Andrews. 'Tell you what I was thinking.'

'Yeah?'

'Coke's business.'

'Granco?'

'Yeah, that. They own a lot of properties.'

'So?'

'We only found eight or nine that Harry sold. Might he have other solicitors in his pocket? Played the same trick on them as he did with Harry?'

Clare slowed as they approached the roundabout on the outskirts of town. 'He might. Not sure how we find them, though, given how many properties are sold every year.'

'But we do know the ones he owns were probably bought for well below market value,' Chris said. 'If we take a list of Granco's properties we can check them against the Land Registry, or even Zoopla. See how much they sold for. What's more, it shows previous sale prices so if a house went for, say, a couple of hundred thousand five years ago then for thirty thousand last year that's the one we look at.'

'Good idea,' Clare said. 'Could you get on with that when we get back?'

His face fell. 'I wasn't actually volunteering.'

'Yeah but you'll be great at it.' She signalled right and turned up City Road. 'Tell you something else we've overlooked.'

'If it means more work for me, I'm not sure I want to know.'

'Harry sold his own house, right?'

'Yeah. To that holiday company.'

'Derek Peterson — the solicitor who's taken over Harry's caseload — reckons the money was transferred to an offshore account.'

'I suppose you want me to look into that as well?'

Clare slowed as the lights at a pedestrian crossing turned red. She sat drumming her fingers on the steering wheel watching a clutch of students wandering languidly across the road. The lights went to amber and she pulled away. 'No. You concentrate on the house sales. I'll get Max onto Harry's money.'

Jim had left a message on Clare's desk which she read while eating the remains of her lunch.

> SOCO at the van. It's definitely been bleached but Raymond says they'll work through the night to see if they can isolate any DNA or blood.

She put the note down and finished the rest of her sandwich. What if they did find Harry's blood in the van? Coke had reported it stolen several days before Harry died. He could claim whoever stole the van killed Harry then drove around until they found an unlocked garage to hide it in. Maybe even claim they knew Coke owned the property and somehow got into the garage to dump the van, framing Coke in the process. *He's a slippery sucker*, she said to herself. And even if Coke or Albie's

DNA was in the van they'd simply argue they'd used it before it was stolen. No, it wouldn't be enough. But it was something.

She glanced at her watch. Almost six. Time to call it a day. She switched off her computer and bent to pick up her work bag when her phone began to ring again.

Moira. What on earth did she want? She swiped to take the call and Moira began speaking straight away.

'Oh Clare,' she said, her voice unnaturally high. 'I'm so sorry. It's Benjy. There's been an accident.'

Chapter 47

There was a queue at the vet's reception desk and at least four dogs in the waiting room, jumping and barking at each other. Clare whirled round and saw Moira standing opposite the desk, her white face tear stained.

'Oh Clare,' she said, rushing towards her and grabbing her hands. 'I'm so so sorry.'

Clare waved this away. 'Don't be daft. Where's Benjy now?'

'He's in surgery. They think it's his cruciate ligament.'

Clare felt sick. She didn't know what that meant. 'Is it serious?'

Moira tried to smile. 'It'll be okay,' she said. 'It's a common injury. They can repair it. He'll just be immobile for a few weeks.'

Clare could feel tears pricking her eyes. 'Really?' Her voice was thick. 'He won't have to be—'

Moira pulled her into a hug. 'Oh no,' she said. 'They think he was lucky.' She indicated a door further down the corridor. 'There's a room we can wait in. They'll come and get us when there's news.'

Clare followed her to a small room where a woman was sitting with an empty cat basket. She nodded to the woman who smiled back. Then they sat down and Moira began to explain what had happened.

'He was on the lead,' she said. 'We were just finishing our walk. About fifty yards from Daisy Cottage. It came out of nowhere.'

'What was it?'

'Some kind of car. I heard it in the distance so I moved over to the side of the road. Then it sounded like it was speeding up so I looked back and saw it heading straight for us. It was like he'd lost control and I thought he was going to hit us. So I jumped onto the verge and pulled the lead but I wasn't quick enough and the car caught Benjy on the back leg, just as he was scampering up after me. The sound he made.'

Clare's hand went to her mouth. 'Was he very distressed?'

Moira shook her head. 'He was so brave. Whimpered a bit but he lay still, licking my hand. Luckily I had my phone so I covered him with my jacket and called the vet. I didn't want to move him. They came pretty quickly and brought him here.'

Clare squeezed Moira's arm. 'I'm sorry this happened. You were so kind to deal with it.'

'Don't be silly,' she said. 'I love Benjy as if he was my own dog. And he will be okay, Clare. They're very good here.'

Clare sank back in her seat, her eyes trained on the door for any sign of the vet. 'What about the car?' she said, suddenly. She'd been so focused on Benjy she'd forgotten to ask. 'Did the driver stop?'

'He did not! I was busy dealing with Benjy or I'd have taken his number.'

'It was a man?'

'I can't be sure. To be honest it's all a bit of a blur. All I know is the car was black.'

'Black?' Clare repeated. 'Can you remember anything else? Was it a 4x4? Or a small car?'

Moira shook her head. 'Not small. Like a big saloon car, you know? Long, rather than high; and black. That's all I saw. But I did wonder if the driver was drunk, or on drugs. It was almost like he was trying to hit us.'

—

It was another two hours before Clare left the vet's surgery. Benjy was sedated and expected to make a good recovery.

'He'll have to stay off it as much as possible,' the vet had said. 'We've put a rigid dressing on it for the next few days. But you'll have to keep him pretty immobile, probably for a couple of months.'

Clare had no idea how she would do it, but that was tomorrow's problem. Benjy was staying the night at the surgery and she'd already called Chris to say she'd need some time off tomorrow to collect him. He'd been concerned and offered to come over.

'We'll bring you some food,' he said. 'Sara's made a huge shepherd's pie. I think she's trying to kill me.'

She hadn't laughed at the joke but had thanked him politely. 'All I want to do is go home and have a glass of wine.'

'Have some food, though,' Chris had said and she'd promised she would.

The house was in darkness by the time she turned her key in the lock. The silence without Benjy was almost painful and she stayed there, her back against the door, imagining his whimper as the car hit him. The ache in her chest seemed to come up into her throat and she gulped and choked suddenly as sobs overtook her. The strain of the day closed in now and she could still feel Albie Kennedy's breath, hot on her neck as he stood behind her. She opened her mouth and roared with rage. She roared and wept, sinking to her knees until she could cry no more. She had no idea how long she lay curled up in the hall but eventually she found the strength to stand up again. Flicking lights on as she went, she made straight for the kitchen and took a bottle of red from the wine rack, pouring herself a large glass. She drank half of it in one go, relishing the shock as the tannins hit her taste buds. Then she topped her glass up and opened the fridge. But the lump in her throat made eating impossible and, despite her promise to Chris, she closed the door again and carried her glass through to the sitting room.

The house was cool now, the central heating having gone off and she wished with all her heart that Al – her DCI – had been there. He'd have taken her in his arms and told her everything would be okay. That Benjy would be all right, that they'd manage his recovery between them. He'd have lit the fire, run her a bath and somehow he'd have persuaded her to eat something. She looked at her phone. She should call him. Tell him about Benjy. He'd want to know. But what could he do? He was nearly fifty miles away with a week's course to run – and it was only Monday. Could she take leave? In the middle of an investigation? It was unthinkable, especially with the shortage of DCIs. And she didn't want to give Penny Meakin an excuse to think any worse of her, after the Coke and Albie debacle.

Albie.

'You bastard,' she said, tightening her grip on the wine glass. 'I'll nail you if it's the last bloody thing I do.'

Day 8: Tuesday, 11th April

Chapter 48

The station was buzzing when she arrived, but all eyes turned to look as she walked towards her office. Jim came forward, his face softened with concern.

'How is the wee fella?' he asked.

Clare thought she hadn't any tears left but, with Jim's kindness, she felt them welling up again. 'He's going to be fine,' she said, her voice hoarse. 'He'll need a few months to get over it but—' She broke off. 'I'll just...'

She escaped to her office and closed the door behind her; and then she saw her desk and gave way to silent sobs, fearful they would hear her outside. A vase of cream roses stood in the centre of the desk, a gift card beside them. There was a box of Milk Tray chocolates and pride of place had been given to a full, unopened pack of Wagon Wheels. There was also something wrapped in a green paper towel which she guessed would be one of Zoe's cakes. Suddenly her stomach reminded her she'd not eaten since the call about Benjy. Taking a tissue from a box on the desk she dabbed at her eyes and blew her nose. It was time to brave the kitchen.

Max and Chris were hovering outside her office door, Sara further down the corridor. They regarded her warily, as if unsure what to say.

'You look a right state,' Chris said, eventually, the concern on his face belying the light-hearted nature of his words.

'I'll never look as bad as you, though,' she said heading for the kitchen. 'Any bread? I'm starving.'

Over tea and toast Chris explained they'd found three more properties on Granco's books. 'Sold well below market value,' he said. 'I've got addresses for the sellers. Bill, Janey and I will get round them today.'

Clare bit into her toast and chewed it. 'If Coke's warned them off as well it might be difficult to get a statement.'

Chris nodded. 'Yeah but we're gradually building a case against him.'

'To be honest,' Clare said, 'I'd rather nail him for Harry's murder.'

'And we will,' he said. 'Softly, softly, catchy Cokey.'

She raised an eyebrow at this but he looked quite pleased with himself. 'What about Harry's money?' she asked Max.

'Bit more luck there,' he said. 'We've traced the offshore account.'

'So Louise might get her hands on it?'

'Should do. Might take a bit of time but hopefully.'

'Glad to hear it,' Clare said. 'She might even be able to buy the house back.' She picked up her tea. 'You've no idea how good this tastes.' Then she set the mug down. 'Anything else?'

'SOCO called this morning before you arrived,' Chris said. 'They've found traces of blood in the van and they're going to prioritise it. We might know later today if it's Harry's.'

Clare sat back considering all this. 'Problem is, even if we do find Harry's blood in the van, it doesn't prove Coke or Albie killed him. Remember Coke reported the van missing – what was it – four days before we think Harry died? He'll simply claim Harry was killed by whoever stole the van.'

'We do have Carol Thorne's statement,' Max said. 'She ID'd Albie, remember?'

Clare was quiet for a moment. 'It's not enough,' she said. 'We might just have to settle for the moneylending – if we can tie it in with the house sales.'

Max shook his head. 'Not right, is it?'

'No argument there. Oh,' she said, 'thank you for all this.' She indicated the flowers and other things. 'You're a right shower at times but this was lovely. Especially the Wagon Wheels.'

Chris sighed heavily. 'You'll never know what that cost me.'

Clare found herself smiling for the first time in days. 'Go on. Spill.'

'Sara said if I didn't go and get you my Wagon Wheels there and then the wedding was off.'

'She did.' Max laughed. 'She made him go straight to where he hid them and we all followed. Best laugh I've had all week.'

'So?' Clare said, her interest piqued. 'Where were they?'

Max glanced at Chris who shrugged. 'You know the paper for the printer?'

'In the store room, yes. Oh, wait – one of those boxes?'

'Yep. The bottom one,' Max said. 'He'd taken the paper out and put the Wagon Wheels in there. Really clever place.'

Chris acknowledged this. 'I try.'

'Hah, so no more hiding the biscuits for you,' Clare said.

'Don't you believe it.'

'You'll never find another place as good as that.'

'Already done.'

'Go on then,' Clare said. 'Tell us.'

'Not on your life, *Inspectora*. Not on your life.' He looked at the packet on Clare's desk, doing his best puppy dog eyes. 'I wouldn't say no to one now, actually.'

'Not on your life, *Sargento*. Not on your life.'

–

Bill, Janey and Chris had gone over to Dundee to interview the people who'd sold their houses to Coke, and Clare was catching up on paperwork in her office when the door opened. She looked up and saw the DCI standing there.

'Al!'

He came into the room and she rose to greet him. 'The lad phoned me,' he said.

'Chris?'

'Yeah.' He closed the door with his foot and moved to take her in his arms. 'He knew you wouldn't want to disturb me but he thought I'd want to know.'

She stood there, relief flooding through her. Then she drew back. 'He shouldn't have done that.'

'He shouldn't have had to,' he said. 'You should have told me yourself.'

She shook her head. 'Your course.'

'To hell with the course,' he said. 'Benjy could have died and you're in the middle of a major inquiry. Anyway, half the work was in setting it up. I'm not involved in today's sessions and I'll do the rest of mine by Zoom. If I can get back for the last day on Friday, great. If not, it won't be the end of the world.'

'Oh Al,' she said. 'You've no idea how glad I am to see you. Come on. I'll make you a cup of tea and fill you in.'

Over tea and more toast – Clare couldn't believe how hungry she was – she told him about Benjy's accident and Albie Kennedy's veiled threat. 'I'm going to nail him, Al,' she said.

'Just remember not to do it in anger. Otherwise you're likely to make mistakes. Take your time and make sure it's watertight.'

She was about to reply when her phone buzzed with a message from the vet. 'Benjy's ready to come home,' she said, reaching for her jacket.

'I'll get him,' he said. 'You stay and catch up on the case.'

She scraped back her chair and drained the rest of her mug. 'Not a chance. Come on.'

–

Benjy was a sorry sight, a rigid bandage right up his back leg and Clare thought she might start crying again. The DCI squeezed her hand then he went to scoop the little dog up and carry him to the car. His tail wagged when he saw them and Clare took his face in her hands and nuzzled into his neck.

'We can lend you a cage,' the vet said, 'if you don't have one. It's important he moves as little as possible for the next few days. And we'll see him back here next Monday to put a more flexible bandage on.'

Al carried Benjy and Clare took the cage. She elected to sit in the back with him while Al drove and they were soon on their way to Daisy Cottage. Once indoors, Clare set about constructing the cage.

'I've an old duvet upstairs,' she said. 'I'll pop a cover on and use that to make it a bit comfier for him.'

'Any chew toys?'

'Yeah. I've a stash somewhere. I'll find a new one. Might keep him busy for a bit.' She looked at Benjy lying down now and her heart melted all over again.

They settled him in the cage with a new chew toy but he was soon asleep.

'Maybe all the drugs,' Al said. 'Or the shock catching up with him.' He checked his watch. 'You get back. I've got this.'

'I'm not sure,' she said.

'Honestly. Go and get some work done. You might need to take some time off in the next few weeks so get on while you can.'

She hesitated then the decision was made for her when her phone began to ring.

Jim.

She swiped to take the call.

'Sorry,' he said, 'but I think you should get back here. Something's come up.'

Chapter 49

'She's in Interview Room Two,' Jim said. 'Solicitor's with her.'

'What did she say?' Clare asked, shrugging off her jacket.

'Asked for Max. Said she had some information about her husband.'

Clare looked round the office. 'Chris here?'

Jim shook his head. 'Over in Dundee. But Max is waiting in the incident room. I'll give him a shout.'

'Just give me five minutes then we'll see her.'

A little over five minutes later Clare and Max entered the interview room and she took her first look at Danuta Grandison. She was much younger than her husband, and glamorous with it. Her blonde hair, thick and lustrous, was held back in a clip, her sun-tanned face expertly made up. She was casually dressed in pale green jeans and a crisp white blouse, a linen jacket slung over the chair behind her. An older woman in a dark suit sat next to her, a leather notebook on the desk. She smiled at Clare and introduced herself and Danuta.

'I am Ella Freeman, Mrs Grandison's solicitor.'

Clare thanked them for coming. 'I understand you have some information,' she said, smiling at Danuta.

Danuta looked at her solicitor who said, 'Mrs Grandison would like to make it clear she was completely unaware of any wrongdoing. She was not involved in anything relating to the purchase of properties arranged by her husband, Mr Colin Grandison. Mrs Grandison was gifted certain properties by her husband but, other than allowing them to be placed in her name, she had nothing to do with the purchases. Should Mr

Grandison or anyone else suggest otherwise we will defend such accusations robustly.'

Clare studied Danuta. She seemed composed, quite untroubled by her surroundings. 'Can I ask, Mrs Grandison, why you've come forward today?'

Danuta flicked a glance at Max then she met Clare's gaze without flinching. Clare thought she was considering her response and she waited.

'Enough's enough,' Danuta said, finally.

'What do you mean by that?'

'Coke,' she said. 'That stuff on Sunday night. I'm sick of him bringing trouble to our door, me and Marina. I reckon he's heading for a fall and I don't want to be dragged down with him.'

'And you have information you believe might contribute to – his fall?'

She leaned forward and put her arms on the desk. 'I can give you Coke's head on a platter. But I want him put away. If he hears I've talked...'

'We can protect you, Mrs Grandison.'

She laughed. 'From Coke? I doubt it. No, Inspector. You have to make sure you nail him. I want Coke out of the way and...' she glanced at Ella, '...I want immunity.'

Clare regarded her. 'That would depend on what you've done.'

Danuta raised a slender eyebrow and she sat back again. 'Like Ella said – I've done nothing.'

'In that case, you won't face any charges. But I can't give you a guarantee until I hear what you have to say.'

Danuta glanced at Ella who gave a slight nod then she turned back to Clare. 'Coke – he has this rental agency. Granco. He buys up property and lets it out.'

'How does he fund the purchases?'

'Various bits of business,' she said. 'He gets things done, you know? And people pay him.'

'What sort of things?'

She smiled and shook her head. 'A lot I don't know. I just know there's always money. Anyway, some of it goes on the properties. But he lends money as well.'

'You're saying your husband, Colin Grandison, is a moneylender.'

'Yeah. Coke lends folk money.'

'Does he have a licence?'

'It's not that kind of moneylending.'

'Who does he lend to?'

'Folk in trouble. Anyone who needs a bit of cash to tide them over. I don't have names. Coke keeps a note but I dunno where. Anyway, he charges interest – a lot of interest. The way he works it, they never pay it all back. Doesn't matter how much they pay he always ups the interest so they still owe him; and that's when he offers them a solution.'

'What kind of solution?'

'Depends. Some of them have houses, you know? Or flats. He offers to buy them. Sometimes he throws in a bit of cash as well. *I'll take this off your hands and give you ten grand for your trouble*, he says. Often as not they're so desperate they have to agree. He tells them they can stay in the house till they get sorted. But then suddenly he needs it, says he has a tenant lined up and they have to get out. By that time the sale's gone through – nothing they can do.'

Ella leaned forward. 'We'd like to reiterate Mrs Grandison took no part in either the moneylending or in any negotiations regarding house purchases.'

'Noted.' Clare nodded at Danuta. 'Go on, please.'

'Thing is,' she said, 'these houses – he pays a fraction of what they're worth. He's not only lending money at ridiculous rates, he's cheating them out of their homes as well.'

'You knew this was going on?' Clare said.

Danuta shrugged. 'Suppose I turned a blind eye at first.'

'What changed your mind?'

She took a moment to answer. 'That solicitor.'

Clare felt her mouth go dry and she swallowed. 'Which solicitor?'

'The one that died. Harry Richards.'

'What about him?'

Danuta glanced at Ella who inclined her head. 'He was the one who did Coke's property deals,' she said. 'Some of them, at least. All went fine for a few months then one night I hear Coke on the phone to Albie.'

'That's Albert Kennedy?' Clare said.

'Yeah, him. Big thug. Anyway, Coke's on the phone and he didn't know I was listening. And I heard him saying that Harry wanted out. Harry had told him the house he'd just sold would be the last one. Obviously I couldn't hear Albie's side of the conversation but Coke said, "*I don't trust him, Albie. If he does a runner and leaves,*" then Coke listened for a bit. Finally he said, "*Let's make sure we shut him up for good. Get Jonjo to help. He owes me.*"'

'Jonjo?' Clare asked.

'One of Coke's boys. Jonjo Matheson. Lives up the Hilltown. Not above a bit of violence when it's needed.'

'When was this?' Clare asked.

''Bout a week before Harry died. Couple of days later I heard Coke on the phone again. This time he was saying he'd reported the van stolen, and to keep it out of sight until Monday. He'd arrange to meet Harry at the usual place. Albie and Jonjo were to come in the van.'

'Do you know when they planned to meet?'

Danuta smiled. 'I can do better than that,' she said. She reached down and picked up a Lulu Guinness handbag and undid the clasp. Then she opened a zipped compartment and withdrew a small memory stick. 'This is all you need,' she said, holding it up.

Clare looked at it. 'What's on it?'

'Everywhere Coke's vehicles have been for the past month.'

'You tracked him?'

'Yup. He's been at the capers, you see – and not for the first time. Some wee scrubber up in Forfar. But I could never prove it. Anyway, this time I'd had enough so I went online and found these trackers. Tiny, they are. I bought four. One for each of his cars and one for that white van. Easy enough to slip them into the boot. Just where you get into the lights, you know? He never knew they were there. I saw all his trips up and down to Forfar, but I also saw him going over to Fife. And on that Monday – the day that Harry guy died – the Audi and the van were all at Tentsmuir Forest. When I saw the report of Harry's death in the paper, I knew. Knew it was Coke.'

Clare took the memory stick from her, weighing it in her hand. Would it be admissible in court? It was illegal to track someone without their consent but maybe… She flicked a glance at Ella who seemed to follow Clare's thinking.

'Mrs Grandison is a named driver on the insurance policies for all three cars and, as a director of Granco Lettings, she jointly owns the Transit van with her husband. She's been rightly concerned about vehicle theft recently and was within her rights to place a tracker in all four vehicles in case they were stolen. The information that came to light regarding the whereabouts of the vehicles on the day Harry Richards died was quite coincidental and something we both felt should be brought to your attention.'

Clare couldn't help but admire Ella's ability to put a spin on something that was borderline illegal. She acknowledged this and turned back to Danuta. 'Thank you, Mrs Grandison.'

Danuta shrugged. 'There's more.'

'Oh?'

She reached down and Clare realised she had a carrier bag as well. 'I kept his shoes, you know? From that day.'

'The shoes he was wearing the day Harry died?' Clare asked. 'Why did you do that?'

'Saw this documentary,' Danuta said. 'How different places have different soil. I knew Coke wouldn't be anywhere near

315

the business end of a knife. You won't catch him with blood on his shiny suit; but if he'd been there, in that forest, there might be stuff on his shoes. I thought maybe you could use them as evidence.'

Clare glanced at Max who raised an eyebrow in return. 'Didn't he miss the shoes?'

'Yeah, but he's got loads. I just said the cleaning lady probably put them in the wrong cupboard. Told him they'd turn up. He never mentioned it again.'

Clare nodded. 'We'll fetch an evidence bag for them once we're finished here.' She scanned her notes, trying to think if there was anything else she wanted to ask. Was there enough here to convict Coke and Albie? With Carol Thorne's evidence and, hopefully, Harry's blood in the white van, they might just do it. She ended the interview and smiled. 'I'm a bit concerned for you, Mrs Grandison. If anyone saw you coming here they might get word back to your husband. Is there somewhere you could stay for a bit? Just until we have him under lock and key.'

'No need,' Danuta said. 'I've left Coke. I've known for years this day would come. So I've been salting his money away. Call it an insurance policy. I've a new mobile phone he doesn't know about and Ella's booked me into a small hotel just until I sort myself out.'

Clare was surprised. 'But your daughter?'

Danuta's face softened. 'I know,' she said. 'I sent her a WhatsApp saying I'd be away for a few days. She's seventeen now. She'll be fine. Coke wouldn't harm a hair on her head. Once you lads have Coke in custody I'll work out what we're going to do. I don't want to get in the way of her exams. She's a bright girl.'

There didn't seem to be any more to say and Clare indicated they were finished.

Ella clicked off her pen and picked up her briefcase. 'Perhaps you'd be good enough to let me know when Mr Grandison is in custody?'

'Of course.' Clare smiled at the solicitor then she turned back to Danuta. 'We will need you to testify against your husband, assuming he pleads not guilty. Are you willing to do that?'

She shrugged. 'Sure. If you have Coke, Albie and Jonjo in custody the rest will melt away. They don't frighten me.'

'All the same,' Clare took a card from her pocket, 'phone me day or night if you're worried. Put my number into your new phone now. Just in case you need it.'

Danuta took the card and studied it. 'Sure, why not.' She took out a very new looking smartphone and added Clare's number to the contacts. Then she smiled and picked up her jacket. 'Ready?' she said to Ella who nodded in response.

They watched her go, Clare shaking her head. 'Coolest customer I've ever met,' she said and Max agreed. As Danuta left, Chris came in the side door.

'Think I might be getting somewhere,' he said.

Clare laughed. 'So are we, Chris. You've just missed the show of a lifetime.'

Chapter 50

'His name's Gerry Dolan,' Chris said. 'His parents bought their council house years ago and he inherited it when they died. Then, usual story: debts – borrowed from Coke – you know the rest. Coke forced him to sell the house stupidly cheap.'

'And he's willing to go on the record?' Clare asked.

'He is. Doc told him he has terminal cancer so he wants to do something about it before he dies. Says he doesn't care if Coke comes after him now.'

'Maybe that other couple will give a statement as well,' Max said. 'If Coke's remanded in custody.'

'I'd bet a whole load of them will go on the record, if Coke's put away,' Chris said. 'Clare, let's charge them.'

She reached for her phone. 'I'll just check with Raymond.'

'I was just about to phone you,' Raymond said, when he picked up the call.

'Anything?'

'Your victim's blood is in that white van.'

'Definitely?'

'No doubt about it. They'd done a pretty good job of cleaning it but, as you know, it's hard to get rid of absolutely everything.'

'Brilliant. Thanks so much. I'm going to send you another vehicle, Raymond. Black BMW, just as soon as I get my hands on it. We think there may have been bags of bloodstained clothing in the boot.'

She put down her phone and relayed the conversation to Chris and Max.

'So?' Max said.

'I think it's enough,' she said, reaching for the phone. 'I'm going to speak to the Super.'

Penny listened and asked a few questions. Then she said, 'Pick them up. Cars as well. Just make sure you nail them this time.'

Jim put out a call for as many officers as possible to return to the station. Within half an hour the incident room was packed and Clare set about dividing them into teams.

'No element of surprise this time,' she said. 'Check their addresses, usual haunts and I want the keys for every vehicle, especially that black BMW; and if you can't find the keys, get it on the back of a truck.'

Within minutes they had left and she returned to her office to await news. She took the chance to call the DCI and he confirmed Benjy was currently in his crate watching dog training on TV. 'He's fascinated by it,' he said. 'You never know – some of it might rub off.'

Then the calls started coming in. They picked up Jonjo Matheson first.

'Arsey little fucker,' one of the cops said down the radio, 'but we've got him in the van now.'

The waiting was endless. She didn't want to stray too far from her phone so she sat in her office, trying to work through a backlog of emails. Jim kept her supplied with cups of tea and Zoe popped in occasionally to offer more cake.

'Rotten about your dog,' she said, putting another slice of carrot cake down on Clare's desk. 'I'd kill the bastard if it was me.'

Clare laughed. 'I'm tempted, Zoe.'

Albie Kennedy was next. 'No real bother,' Max said. 'Mild as milk, telling us he'll be out by bedtime.'

But there was no word from Chris who was leading the team to arrest Coke Grandison. Clare ploughed on through the emails and finally she saw Chris's number flash up on her phone.

'Got him?' she asked before he could speak.

'Sorry. Tried everywhere.'

She sat thinking for a minute, an uneasy feeling developing in her stomach. 'Give me five minutes.'

She dialled the number for Danuta Grandison's solicitor. It went to voicemail so she hung up and dialled again. This time the call was answered. 'That hotel,' she said when Ella answered. 'I need to know where it is.'

Ella hesitated then Clare said, 'Mr Grandison has gone missing. Do you understand? I need to make sure Danuta is safe.'

'Oh my God,' Ella said. 'Hold on.' Clare waited, then she heard Ella's voice again. 'It's Kinfauns View. Just outside Perth.' Clare thanked her and went back to Chris. 'Get yourselves up to the Kinfauns View hotel – just outside Perth. He might have gone after his wife. I'll get in touch with Perth. They're nearer than you,' and she swiped to find the number for the duty inspector at Perth.

'You want armed response out?' the inspector asked.

She considered this for a moment. Was it really necessary? Then she recalled the gaping wound in Harry Richards' neck and how vital Danuta's evidence was. 'Definitely. Can you organise from there?'

'No problem. Leave it with me.'

—

An hour later her phone began to ring. Drew Walsh, the Armed Response Unit commander. She snatched it up.

'Drew?'

'Nothing doing,' he said. 'Neither of them's here. She checked in right enough but the staff haven't seen her for a couple of hours.'

Her phone began to buzz again. An unfamiliar number. Her mind immediately went to Benjy. Had he taken a turn for the

320

worse? 'Drew can I call you back? I've another call coming in.' Without waiting for a reply she swiped to take the call.

'DI Mackay.'

No one spoke in reply. She could hear a noise in the background. A humming, like an engine. Then she heard a voice and it took her a moment to realise it was Danuta. She was about to call her name in case she'd pocket dialled but something stopped her.

'What the hell are we crossing the Friarton for?' Danuta's voice said.

And then Clare realised what was happening. Danuta was in the car with Coke. He must have followed her to the police station in St Andrews. Maybe he knew her solicitor's car. Then he'd followed them on to the hotel and bided his time until Danuta came out to the garden for some air. She could see it now. Coke wasn't as big or as muscly as Albie Kennedy but he was wiry and, she guessed, deceptively strong. Danuta, for all her outward confidence would have been no match for him. Not if Coke knew they were onto him. Desperate men...

She snatched up the phone, her hand over the microphone to prevent any sound, and went quickly to her office door, motioning to Jim to follow her to the incident room. Janey and Nita were there, poring over a laptop screen and Clare put her finger to her lips. She turned the phone to speaker and indicated the map on the wall. Peering at it she found what she was looking for – the Friarton Bridge that crossed the River Tay just outside Perth. Covering the phone's microphone again she said, 'Coke's snatched Danuta. They're crossing the Friarton, I'd guess, heading south.'

'I asked you where we're going,' Danuta's voice came again. 'You'll see.'

There was a pause then Danuta said, 'Where'd you get this old heap from anyway? I didn't know you'd a Fiesta. What the hell possessed you to buy a red one? It's not exactly subtle.'

'She's in a red Ford Fiesta,' Clare said to Jim. 'Heading south off the Friarton.'

He nodded and went to radio this out to all units.

'Just the job, sweetheart,' Coke's voice said. 'Don't want to be using a nice new car where this is going.'

'Oh yeah?'

Clare could hear the mock bravado in Danuta's voice and she hoped Danuta realised how helpful she was being.

'Where's that then?'

'Nowhere you'll be worrying about,' he said. 'Not for long, anyway.'

Clare's heart was thumping, imagining this nightmare journey. 'Hang on, Danuta,' she murmured. 'We'll find you.'

'Chrissake, Coke. You were nearly on the hard shoulder there!'

'Hard shoulder,' Clare said. 'She's on the motorway.'

'M90,' Janey said. 'But which direction?'

'Look,' Danuta's voice came again, 'go off at Bridge of Earn and let me out. Then go! You've enough money salted away. Get out of the country. Just let me out here.'

'No chance, darling,' Coke's voice said. 'I couldn't go without saying a proper goodbye.'

Janey was tracing their journey on the map. 'Going south. If he's gone past the Bridge of Earn turnoff, the next one is... junction seven — Milnathort.'

'That's about ten miles,' Nita said. 'Won't take them long. I'll see if Jim can get an unmarked car to the junction.'

'It'll be tight,' Janey said. 'If they're travelling at sixty they'll be ten minutes, tops.'

'Car's on its way,' Jim called. 'I've asked for cars at the next couple of junctions as well.'

'I just hope her phone has enough charge,' Clare said.

'You going to tell me what you mean?' Danuta said. 'What's a proper goodbye? Fucksake, Coke — where we going?'

He laughed. A harsh, mirthless laugh 'I'm going to introduce you to my new pal,' he said.

'Oh yeah?' Danuta again. 'Who's that then? I'm not sure I want to meet any more of your pals after what they did to that solicitor.'

'And the moral of that tale,' Coke said, 'is don't fall out with your Uncle Coke.'

Clare checked her watch. 'I reckon they're four minutes from the junction.' She glanced across at Jim, his ear clamped to a radio. 'Six minutes,' he mouthed.

'Tell them to step on it.'

'What's this pal's name? You gonna tell me?' Danuta said.

Clare had to admire her cool. She was playing a blinder.

There was silence in the car then Coke's voice said, 'Let's just call him Ronnie.'

'Ronnie who?'

'Doesn't matter. Just Ronnie.'

'Okay,' Danuta said. 'What's he like, this Ronnie?'

'Oh he's full of charm,' Coke said. 'He's going to love you, sweetheart. He'll probably flatter you. Or do I mean flatten?'

There was a silence broken by a rhythmical ticking and a change in the car engine noise.

'That's an indicator,' Clare said. 'Dammit, they're at the junction already. Our car won't make it in time.'

Nita was tapping away at a laptop. 'Might have something, boss.'

'Go on.'

'I put Ron, Ronnie, Ronald and Milnathort into Google. It's come up with a scrapyard. *Ronnie Tough, Scrapmerchant.* Outskirts of Milnathort. If that's where they're heading they'll be there in a few minutes.'

Clare felt bile rise in her throat. 'Oh God,' she said. 'He's going to have her crushed in the car. Address, Nita?'

Nita reeled off the address and Jim indicated he was on it, ordering every available car and officer to the scrapyard.

'I'm getting out.' Danuta's voice was shrill now.

'Do that and I'll mow you down before you've got ten yards. You sit tight, lady!'

'No, I'm getting out.'

There was a squeak and it sounded as if the car had come to a halt. They heard what sounded like a slap, then another and a muffled cry from Danuta. The car engine hummed again, the only other sound Danuta's sobs.

'Three minutes to the scrapyard,' Jim called. 'Two cars heading there now.'

'Make sure they know it's a red Fiesta,' Clare called back, forgetting to put her hand over the microphone.

They heard the brakes squeak again.

'You got a bloody phone there? Who've you called, you bitch?'

There was the sound of a scuffle then a rushing noise that Clare thought might be wind.

And then the phone went dead.

'Dammit,' she said. 'He's either switched it off or he's chucked it out the window.'

They sat there, helplessly, waiting for news over the radio, Clare checking her watch every ten seconds. She heard Jim speaking to someone out in the front office and went to see who it was. Gary, one of the uniform PCs was standing with Albie Kennedy and she went to see why he was out of the interview room. Nita and Janey followed, their interest piqued.

'Just taking Mr Kennedy to the toilet,' Gary said. 'This way.'

But Albie stopped in his tracks when he saw Clare, a leer spreading across his face. 'Thought I might see you again, doll-face.' He lowered his voice. 'Tell me, how's that dog of yours getting on? Heard he'd a bit of an accident.'

It took Clare less than a second to decide between discretion and valour. Out of the corner of her eye she saw Jim put out a restraining hand, but he was too late. She drew back her fist and smacked Albie right in the mouth. He staggered back, lifting his hand to his face. Then he held his hand out and saw the blood.

His expression changed to one of glee and he wiped the blood off with his sleeve.

'You're finished,' he said. 'Assaulting a prisoner in front of—' He looked round at Jim, Gary, Nita and Janey. Zoe had been standing by her desk putting on her coat and now she stood open-mouthed, staring at them. 'Five witnesses, I make it,' Albie said. 'We'll see what my solicitor says when he gets here.'

Janey was first to speak. 'Never saw a thing.'

'Nor me,' Nita said, moving to stand beside Clare.

'I blame myself,' Jim said. 'I meant to clean up that wet patch on the floor. I'll get a mop now.'

Albie raised an eyebrow. 'I see,' he said, dabbing at his mouth again. 'So that's how it is, eh?' He looked across at Zoe. 'What about you, curly? You're a civvy. Not one o' them. You saw her batter me, didn't you?'

Zoe stared at him for a moment, unblinking. Then she turned back to Jim. 'Sorry,' she said. 'Probably my water bottle. I never noticed it leaking.'

Jim gave her a smile. 'Not to worry. Soon have it cleaned up.'

'And you, son?' Albie turned to Gary.

He faced Albie square on. 'Nearly slipped on it myself. Be good to get it mopped up. So, we going to this toilet or what?'

'Go with them,' Clare said to Jim. 'I want everything he says witnessed.' Then she went to her office and closed the door.

She sank down, head in her hands. How could she have been so stupid? Albie would tell his solicitor and even if the others backed her up it would mean a shedload of trouble for them all. 'You idiot, Clare,' she said out loud. There was a tap on the door and Janey and Nita came in. She looked up at them, her face a picture of misery. 'Guys, I am so sorry. Absolutely unforgivable.'

They came in and shut the door. 'Av a dog myself,' Janey said. 'Wee labradoodle. If anyone harmed a hair on his head I'd do a lot more than smack them.'

'We're sticking to our story,' Nita said. 'As it happens there was a wet patch on the floor earlier. I saw Zoe wipe it with a couple of paper towels. Chances are she missed a bit. Gary's going to say he saw Albie slip and, when he got up, he claimed you'd hit him – because of the crack he made about your dog. Said he'd get you into trouble, hopefully suspended.'

'We're all behind you,' Janey said. 'Not one of us blames you for a second.'

Clare shook her head. 'All these lies.'

'Look at it this way,' Janey said. 'You know he was responsible for what happened to Benjy. But you'll never prove it. No witnesses. It's tit for tat. He hit you, you hit him back. Anyway,' she rose from her seat, 'it's done now and we're sticking to that story. If you bottle it we'll all get in trouble for lying. So you with us?'

Clare took in their faces, Nita's so serious, Janey's puce with anger and she nodded slowly. 'I can't thank you guys enough,' she said.

'First round's on you,' Nita said. 'Soon as we get this case sorted.'

'Deal.'

The door opened again and Jim burst in. 'Got them both,' he said. 'Danuta's safe. She's been knocked about a bit but she's on her way to hospital with a police escort. Coke made a run for it but they got him. Ronnie the Scrappy's coming in too. Hopefully he'll give a statement. Otherwise they're threatening him with conspiracy to murder.'

Clare leaned back in her chair and rubbed her head. 'I'll tell you what, guys, if I have to live through many more days like this, I'll be lucky to see my next birthday.'

Chapter 51

Jim spoke to Chris and Max when they returned to the station and they agreed to interview both Coke and Albie.

'Best you stay out of it, slugger,' Chris said and Clare suppressed a smile.

'And Jim's filled out an accident report,' Max added. 'For Albie's fall, you know?'

This time Clare really did smile.

'They've all signed it,' he said. 'Given a copy to his solicitor.'

'Did he say anything?'

'Apparently he told the solicitor you'd hit him but they'd closed ranks. Jim said he'd never heard anything so ridiculous in his life and that Albie had been overheard promising to *drop the Inspector in the shit.*'

She stared at Max. 'I don't believe Jim swore.'

'You'll have to take our word for it,' Chris said.

There was a tap on the door and Jim poked his head in. 'That's Albie ready for interview,' he said. 'Coke's solicitor should be here in half an hour. And they've picked up the BMW. SOCO are going over it now.'

The three of them left Clare alone with her thoughts. Her mind went back to the moment she'd let Albie have it and she shook her head. 'Stupid Clare,' she muttered. 'Stupid.' Thinking of Albie reminded her of Benjy and she picked up the phone to call home.

'He's been out in the garden on a blanket,' Al told her.

'You've not let him walk about?'

'Only to have a pee. The vet said that would be okay. He's still a bit quiet so it's not been hard to keep him lying down.' He hesitated. 'Dare I ask how it's going?'

'Not sure yet. I'll know more when I'm home, hopefully a couple of hours.'

'I'll have some food ready.'

'Thanks, Al.' She set her phone down and tried to put thoughts of Benjy out of her head. Then she remembered the memory stick Danuta had given her. She'd have to send it straight to Tech Support to get them to analyse the data on it. But she couldn't resist plugging it into her computer for a quick look. It took her a few minutes to work out which tracker related to each of Coke's vehicles. The BMW was easy enough with its daily trips to and from Marina's school. Knowing the location of the lock-up near Albie's house helped her work out which was the white van. A third vehicle was hardly driven at all, mostly at weekends and she decided it must be the Triumph. That only left the Audi. She looked at the data for this and the white van. It was all there. The Audi had arrived at Tentsmuir around three thirty on the Monday afternoon, the white van five minutes later. The vehicles stayed about an hour then left Tentsmuir within a few minutes of each other. So there it was. Harry Richards had been killed around four on the Monday afternoon. The blood-soaked scene in his car came into her head again and she closed down the files and wrote an evidence label for the stick.

–

'We've charged Coke with abduction,' Chris said. 'Money laundering charges to come once we've gathered more evidence. Hopefully enough for conspiracy to murder as well. He'll be up in court in the morning and the abduction charge will be enough to see him remanded in custody.'

'What about the other two?' Clare asked.

'Albie and Jonjo?' Chris shook his head. 'Both *no comment* to everything, but we've arrested them on suspicion of murder. SOCO have teams at their houses now. You never know. They might get something. If not, my guess is their solicitors will advise them to turn on each other. Coke might even claim Albie went rogue to save himself – who knows? If Harry's blood turns up in that BMW though I say we charge Albie with murder.'

'Agreed,' Clare said. 'I'm not sure if we'll ever know who sat in the front seat with Harry and who cut his throat from behind. But they both deserve to go down for it.' She smiled at them. 'Well done, guys. You must be whacked. Get off home.'

'You too,' Chris said. 'You've not got any better looking as the day's gone on!'

'I'd smack you one as well,' she said, 'but I'm too damn tired.'

'Pace yourself,' Chris said, rising and heading for the door. 'You don't want to bruise your knuckles!'

–

Clare heard Benjy barking as she put her key in the door. 'This must be the first time he's not coming running to greet me,' she said, stooping to open the crate door to ruffle him behind the ears.

'It's certainly going to be a long two months,' the DCI said.

'That long?'

He nodded. 'Need to make sure it's properly healed.'

'Suppose.' She yawned. 'God I'm tired. It seems a long time since this morning.' She sniffed. 'Something smells great.'

'Lamb curry. I'm just making chapatis.'

'Fab.' She slid down and sat on the floor next to Benjy's cage, rubbing his neck. He twisted his head round so he could lick her hand and suddenly she was glad she'd hit Albie Kennedy. 'I did it for you,' she whispered to Benjy and he gave a small *wuff* of approval.

Day 9: Wednesday, 12th April

Chapter 52

'That BMW,' Raymond said.

Clare put down her bag to open her office door and kicked it inside, shutting the door behind her. Then she switched her phone to speaker and put it on the desk. 'Yeah?'

'Positive ID for Harry Richards' blood.'

'Yes!'

'We were lucky. Just two spots, but it's enough. Will you charge him – the big lad?'

'Albie Kennedy? You bet I will. Anything at his house?'

'Nothing yet. But we've taken his shoes away to cross match with the ones Mrs Grandison handed in. Same for the other lad – Jonjo?'

'Jonjo Matheson. If we could place all three at the scene that would be ideal.'

'Don't get your hopes up,' he said. 'In any case, they could easily claim they'd visited the forest for a walk. It's a popular beauty spot.'

'Yes, that's true. But we've lots of little bits of evidence against Coke and Albie. Individually they don't amount to much but, taken together, I think it'll be enough. And the team is working on Jonjo's contacts. There's bound to be someone who'll be glad to see him out of the way. He's dangerous, that one.'

She thanked Raymond for working so fast and fired up her computer, watching in dismay as her Inbox loaded. Disinclined to tackle it she wandered through to the incident room. Bill was tapping away at a laptop and looked up as she came in.

'Morning, boss. How's the wee dog?'

She smiled. 'He's doing okay, thanks. Starting to perk up which is going to be a problem, given we're meant to keep him off that leg. But it's a good problem to have.'

He nodded. 'I'm glad. Erm, potentially more good news.'

'Oh yeah?'

'Word's gone out that Jonjo Matheson's been lifted and one or two heads have popped up. One definitely speaking to the bold boy mouthing off in the pub on Tuesday night. Apparently saying he *did a solicitor over in Fife* and splashing the cash around. Seems he wasn't making any secret of it. He likes it to be known he's a hard man.'

'Really?'

'Yeah. Dundee lads are still chapping doors but I'd be surprised if we don't find a few more witnesses. There's even word Kenny Deuchars might give a statement in return for changing his permitted address. Fresh start and all that.'

'Excellent. I've just heard Harry's blood was found in the BMW as well so it looks as if we might nail all three.'

'Even Coke?'

Clare inclined her head. 'Probably not on Harry's murder, although I'm going to push for conspiracy to commit. But the abduction – well, he'll serve a minimum of four years for that. Could be a lot longer. Plus I'll throw attempted murder in as well. I've no doubt he'd have knocked Danuta unconscious then had the car crushed. And Ronnie the Scrappy will give us a statement, unless he wants us going through his yard with a fine-toothed comb.'

Bill nodded. 'Sounds good.' He sat back in his chair. 'Bit of a week all round, this case.'

'Yep. Not one we'll forget in a hurry.'

'What about your paralegal – the one who caused his wife's crash?'

'Still in hospital,' Clare said. 'Last I heard they plan to transfer him to a psychiatric unit for a full assessment.'

'Bizarre case,' Bill said.

'No argument there.'

Chris and Max came in together as she was leaving the incident room. They asked about Benjy then said they'd make a start on the paperwork.

'I hear Danuta's getting out of hospital later today,' Max said. 'Want us to take her statement?'

'Actually Max, that would be great. And could you two go round all the people who sold their houses to Coke, please? They might be more inclined to go on the record, now he's under lock and key.'

She left them to it and wandered back to her office. The strain of the past few days had caught up with her and, even though she'd gone to bed early, she'd slept with one ear open for Benjy. Al was off again today but she knew he could do with going back to Tullieallan to oversee the last two days of his course. She thought about this for a minute then picked up the phone and dialled Penny's number.

'I hear you had a good result,' Penny said. 'Pretty near thing with the wife, though.'

'Yes,' Clare admitted. 'That wasn't ideal. But at least it gives us something concrete to charge Coke Grandison with.' She went on to explain the various charges and Penny agreed.

'It's good work,' she said, 'particularly without a DCI to help. I'm very impressed.'

Clare thanked her and Penny went on.

'I heard your dog had an accident. How is he?'

She explained about Benjy's injury and Penny listened. Then she said, 'I'd a German Shepherd who ruptured his cruciate ligament. But it healed beautifully. Bit of a job keeping him occupied at the time, though.' She paused for a moment. 'You'll be needing some time off, yes?'

'A couple of days would be very helpful.'

'Take the rest of the week. If you can sort something out for the dog over the weekend we'll see you back on Monday.'

Clare thanked Penny and was about to end the call when Penny spoke again.

'Just make sure there are no more… *water spills* in the station, yes?'

Clare wasn't sure but she thought she detected a note of amusement in Penny's tone.

'Definitely not,' she said. 'It won't happen again.'

She picked up a pen and began to doodle on her notepad, her mind running over the events of the past few days. There was enough evidence to charge Albie and Jonjo with murder and she was pretty sure the Fiscal would go for it. They'd likely turn on each other but their advocates could fight it out in court. She decided to leave it to Chris and Max to prefer the charges. The less she saw of Albie the better. Then she remembered her promise to Danuta's solicitor and she sent a quick message, letting her know Coke was in custody and that Danuta would be released from hospital in a few hours.

> Unfortunately the family home's still being searched. Perhaps Danuta and her daughter could go to a hotel. Maybe one nearer Marina's school?

Ella replied immediately thanking her, saying she would arrange accommodation for the pair. *Better to be out of Dundee just now*, she'd added and Clare couldn't help but agree.

She glanced at her Inbox, studying the emails and decided they could wait until next week and she switched on her out-of-office message.

'I've a couple of calls to make,' she told Chris and Max, 'then I'm on leave until next Monday.'

'All right for some,' Chris grumbled, but she saw he was smiling and clapped him on the back.

'Keep an eye on him, Max,' she said and made for the door before Chris could protest.

She climbed into her car and stifled a yawn. The sun was out and she lowered the visor to screen her eyes. Then she started the engine and drew out of the car park.

Fifteen minutes took her to the Drumoig estate. Louise Richards was kneeling down in front of a narrow border attacking it with a hand fork. She looked up when Clare slammed the car door. A look of alarm turned to relief and she rose, dusting off her knees.

'Time for a coffee?'

'That would be lovely.'

She led Clare in and through to the kitchen. Clare couldn't help but notice the black bin liners in the hall, knotted at the neck, and her mind went back to Albie Kennedy loading the bags of bloody clothing into the back of the BMW.

Louise followed her look. 'Harry's things,' she said. 'Well some of them, at least.' She shook her head. 'There's such a lot to go through. But they're no use to him now. The Salvation Army is coming to collect them this afternoon. At least they'll be put to good use.'

Clare smiled. 'That's a kind thing to do.'

Louise spooned coffee into the cafetiere and filled it from the steaming tap. Then she carried this over to the table and set it down. 'Cake?'

Clare was about to refuse then Louise said, 'Please do take a slice. I made it when your colleague was here – Wendy. She was such a nice woman. But she's gone now and there's only me to eat it.'

'Always glad to help out,' Clare said, taking a slice. She waited until Louise had sat down. 'This'll get out soon – the papers will be full of it so I'd rather you heard it from me.'

Louise stared at her. 'What? What is it?'

Clare began to explain about Harry's arrangement with Coke Grandison and Louise's face darkened.

'I know that man,' she said. 'He came here once and I told Harry I didn't want him here again. Do you think it was... him?'

'We think Harry was killed on his orders but he probably had other people to do it.'

Louise sighed. 'And those poor people? The ones whose houses Harry helped sell? What about them?'

'I'm not sure,' Clare said. 'I think they'd have to consult their solicitors. It's pretty awful but I'm not sure it's something we could prosecute.'

Louise was quiet for a moment then she looked round the room. 'I suppose I'll have to get out of here as well.'

Clare smiled. 'There, I think we may have some better news. We've found an offshore account that seems to have the money from the house sale. I'm guessing Harry thought it would fund your lives abroad. You do realise he planned for you both to leave and not return?'

Louise nodded. 'I suppose it was his way of trying to escape these people. If only we'd gone a couple of weeks earlier.'

Clare let that hang in the air. 'It's possible the company Harry sold to may allow you to buy the house back for the same price. Assuming you want to stay.'

Louise's brow creased. 'I'm not sure I do. Not after what's happened. The stalking and everything. Maybe it's time for a change. Fresh start. I've a sister in Dorset, you know? She's coming up next week. I might ask her to look for something down there. I've always liked it.'

'I've never been,' Clare said.

'Oh you should go. It's a lovely part of the world.'

They chatted on for a few more minutes then Clare put down her cup. 'I'd better get on,' she said. 'But you still have my card, yes? Call me if there's anything else I can do.'

Louise rose and took hold of Clare's hand. 'This has been the most dreadful time,' she said. 'My absolute worst nightmare. But you and your colleagues – I can't thank you enough.'

Clare squeezed her hand, then she turned and walked out of the Richards' house for the last time.

She opened the gate, disturbing a flock of noisy sparrows who'd been busy in the hedge and they flew up and across the garden. All round there were signs of spring turning to early summer. A rhododendron across the road was in full bloom and there was a warmth in the air that told Clare summer wasn't far away. The car had been sitting in the sun and she wound down the windows to enjoy the breeze. She drove slowly back to the junction and turned towards St Andrews.

–

Robbie was sitting outside his house on a garden bench, reading a newspaper. He looked up as she approached, his eyes wary. But he rose to greet her, nodding at the open door.

'Think I'd rather sit in the sun,' she said. 'If that's all right?'

He waited for her to sit then he perched next to her, the folded newspaper in his hands.

'This isn't an official visit,' she said. 'I'm just here to see how you are.' She smiled. 'It's good to see you out in the fresh air.'

He shrugged. 'Doc said I was to get out every day. I'm going for a walk soon but I could do you a tea if you like?'

Clare shook her head. 'I'm full of coffee and cake.' Then she said, 'Have you thought about my offer? The Police Treatment Centre?'

He flushed and dropped his gaze, twisting the newspaper in his hands. 'It doesn't seem right, taking up a place.'

'Robbie, why do you think they offer a psychological well-being programme?'

He didn't answer but shook his head.

'This is exactly what it's for – officers suffering from the stress of the job; and I'll tell you something else too – if we don't use it we'll lose it. So I'm recommending you apply and, if you do, I'll ask the Super to back you.' She looked at him, forcing him to meet her eye. 'What do you say?'

'Fine, then,' he said eventually. 'If you think I should.'

'Good. I'm glad that's settled. There is one more thing I have to tell you, but it's strictly confidential, yeah?'

His eyes narrowed. 'Um, okay.'

She started to explain about Simon Miller hacking the cars. 'You remember we had your car examined? Well, there was malware found on it. Simon also told us he used the malware to steal small amounts from the drivers he'd hacked. Minor transactions folk wouldn't notice. Now I'm not asking if this happened to you but if you had been worrying about things you ended up paying for and couldn't remember ordering, chances are it was Simon's work.'

It was as if the sun had come out from behind a cloud. Robbie's face cleared and he began nodding. 'Yes!' he said. 'That did happen. I thought I was going mad. But it was him all the time?'

'It was. He's undergoing psychiatric assessment but that's confidential as well. I'm not sure if you'll get the money back but—'

'I don't care about the money. I'm just relieved I'm not losing my mind.' He was smiling now and she suddenly realised it had been weeks since she'd seen him smile. 'Thanks, boss.'

She left him soon after, stopping in the car only to tap out an email to Penny asking if she'd be kind enough to support Robbie's application to the treatment centre. Then she turned the car towards the Craigtoun Road and headed for Daisy Cottage.

She found Al sitting on a blanket in the back garden, Benjy lying beside him enjoying the sun. 'I'm off for the rest of the week,' she said. 'So you can head back to Tullieallan tonight or in the morning. Whatever's easiest.'

He reached for her hand and pulled her gently down beside them. Benjy shifted his position so he was next to her, his tail thumping against the blanket. She kicked off her shoes and flexed her feet. 'God, but I'm tired.'

He drew her towards him and kissed the side of her head. 'Fancy a drink?'

She waved this away. 'Let's just enjoy the sun.' She shifted down the blanket and lay back gazing up at the sky, one hand idly scratching Benjy's tummy. For a few minutes they didn't speak, then she said, 'Did you mean it about selling your house?'

He propped himself up on his elbows. 'I did,' he said. 'Have you thought about it?'

A propeller plane buzzed across the sky and she followed its progress until it dipped down behind the trees beyond the cottage garden, the buzzing growing faint. 'I have,' she said, when it was out of sight. 'And I think it's a lovely idea.' She turned her gaze to meet his and she saw he was smiling.

'Really?'

'Really.'

He bent and kissed her on the lips, allowing his to linger on hers for a moment. Then he drew back. 'I'll call the estate agent this afternoon.'

She smiled at him. 'Do that. But stay here for a while. I think this might be one of those perfect moments.'

Suddenly Benjy leapt up and began to bark as the doorbell rang. Clare sat up quickly and held onto him before he could tear round the side of the house. 'It's only the postie, you stupid dog!'

Al got to his feet and went to answer the door. 'Benjy Mackay,' he said, as he went. 'Moment Killer!'

They laughed at this and she watched him go to meet the postie, listening to their voices as they passed the time of day. Benjy had relaxed now and she nuzzled into the little dog's neck enjoying the warmth of his body against hers. She eased herself back down on the rug and thought — just at that moment — there was nowhere else she would rather be.

Fifteen months later

FAO: Scottish media outlets
EMBARGO: Immediate

SCOTTISH SOLICITOR TO HELP VICTIMS OF ROGUE MONEYLENDER

HOUSE owners who were forced to sell their properties at knock-down prices to pay off debts to a convicted moneylender have been offered a ray of hope from a leading Scottish solicitor.

Emma Halliday, of Jepson McHardy in Dundee, has offered to represent victims of Colin Grandison in getting the full market value of their homes back from his assets.

Fraud specialists from Police Scotland are investigating Mr Grandison's finances and are confident a seven-figure sum will be available for Ms Halliday's action.

If successful it would be the first group action of its kind in Scotland and may pave the way for similar cases to be brought in the future.

And Ms Halliday, who has branded Grandison 'unscrupulous' says she's aiming to help those victims get their lives back on track.

'These people have been exploited in the worst possible way,' she said, 'having their homes, their sanctuaries taken by this unscrupulous man. I aim to help them recover what should never have been lost in the first place.'

Steve McHardy, Senior Partner at Jepson McHardy said, 'I'm extremely proud of Emma for taking this principled stance and we will support her in this endeavour in any way we can.'

Acknowledgements

As ever, I'm indebted to a growing band of wonderful folk whose willingness to help is so much appreciated.

In choosing a solicitor for my victim I faced tricky questions of warrants, client privilege and so much more. I was therefore grateful to Katie MacLeod, Trainee Solicitor and Euan Duncan, Partner, both of MacRoberts LLP, to Adam Bennett and to *The Beagle*, all of whom were so helpful. Andy Allan talked me through the technical aspects of a post-mortem while, on a lighter note, Iain Todd and Roy Darragh were a bit too keen to school me in golfing matters. Roger Mitchell kept me right on electricity substations while Chris Martin fielded endlessly complicated questions about vehicle electronic systems. Finally, the incomparable Jonathan Whitelaw helped me draft what I hope was a credible press release. Thank you all for your time and expertise. Any errors in these matters are mine, alone.

To my wonderful agent, Hannah Weatherill, thank you for all you've done – I'll miss you so much. My special thanks go also to Diane, Elizabeth and Natalie at Northbank for their ongoing help and support. I really do have the best agents in the business.

My publishers Canelo continue to do a wonderful job with every book. In particular my grateful thanks go to Iain, Alicia, Sian, to the whole SMP team and especially to Fran whose wicked sense of humour I'll miss so much. Even though Louise chose having a baby over working on my book (the very idea!) her wise words and editing skills have stuck with me, and it's been a privilege to work with Katy Loftus in the final stages of this book.

Beyond the writing, my sincere thanks go to Deborah Blake for her incredible editing, to Chloe Johnson for her most detailed proofreading and to James Macey for this stunning cover.

Finally, to Zeus the dog, for sitting patiently while I tussled with this novel, delaying his walks disgracefully. Extra biscuits for you, Zeus!

Do you love crime fiction and are always on the lookout for brilliant authors?

Canelo Crime is home to some of the most exciting novels around. Thousands of readers are already enjoying our compulsive stories. Are you ready to find your new favourite writer?

Find out more and sign up to our newsletter at canelocrime.com